NUCLEAR ROCKET PROPULSION

McGRAW-HILL SERIES IN MISSILE AND SPACE
TECHNOLOGY

H. GUYFORD STEVER, *Consulting Editor*

Bussard and DeLauer · NUCLEAR ROCKET PROPULSION

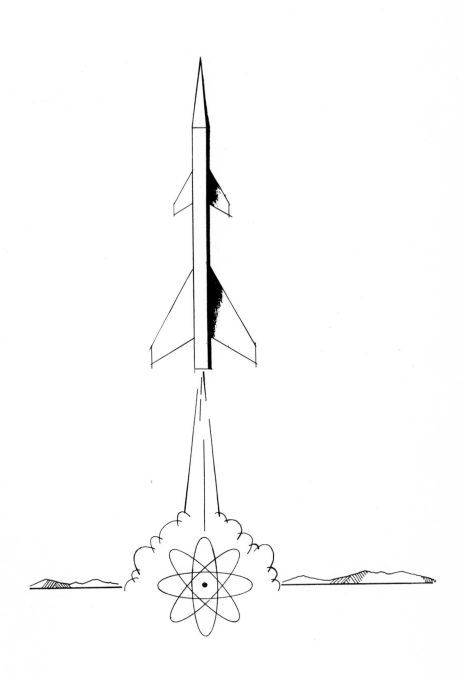

nuclear rocket propulsion

R. W. BUSSARD and R. D. DeLAUER
Los Alamos Scientific Laboratory
University of California

McGraw-Hill Book Company, Inc.
New York   Toronto   London   1958

NUCLEAR ROCKET PROPULSION

Library of Congress Catalog Card Number 57-14687

THE MAPLE PRESS COMPANY, YORK, PA.

FOREWORD

The remarkable progress which has been made during the last decade in the practical applications of nuclear power has made it inevitable that the extraordinary characteristics of this new source of energy be examined as possible power sources for rockets of both long range and large load-carrying capacity. The Los Alamos Scientific Laboratory has been engaged for some time in research and exploration in this intriguing field, in which Messrs. Bussard and DeLauer have been most active participants. Their text, "Nuclear Rocket Propulsion," necessarily describes this new and growing area of research in its relative infancy.

Although nuclear rocketry is no exception to the general dependence of nuclear matters upon almost every field of physical science and engineering, the authors have provided the reader with all the currently available and unclassified mathematical and technical material which is relevant to the specific problems of nuclear rockets. As a foundation and as a source of fundamental information for both the general and the specialized reader, "Nuclear Rocket Propulsion" is both unique and timely in this rapidly expanding field. However, perhaps its greatest service will be to stimulate further ideas and research in the whole provocative and challenging area of nuclear energy and rocket propulsion.

Norris E. Bradbury, DIRECTOR
LOS ALAMOS SCIENTIFIC LABORATORY

PREFACE

This text is presented to introduce a relatively new field—nuclear rocket propulsion—to engineers and scientists engaged in work in similar fields. As will be seen, the field of nuclear rocket propulsion is very broad in scope, covering aspects of the separate regimes of heat transfer, structural analysis, fluid flow, thermodynamics, ballistic flight, reactor physics, and radiation safety. The text presents the features of each of these regimes which are of particular pertinence to nuclear rocket propulsion.

The presentation is done primarily in a descriptive fashion. Results of careful analyses are presented and verbal arguments for the realistic physical bases of these arguments are given, but no real effort is made to demonstrate the mathematical proofs necessary for the rigorous foundation of any of the final working equations or physical conclusions. These proofs can be found by recourse to the large quantity of available literature referenced in each chapter. In a sense, to paraphrase a point of view expressed by H. Etherington:* A complete knowledge of these proofs is not necessary to the understanding of the field or the use of this text. This text shows us how to tell the time. The mathematical rigor shows what makes the clock go. Knowing how to tell the time is the important thing here, and if we tinker too much with the innards of the clock, we may find ourselves without a timepiece. It is sufficient here to know that the required mathematical foundation exists.

Thus it is seen that this text will be of most practical value to the research and development engineer, rather than to the pure scientists. However, it is hoped that from this text the scientist can gain a greater appreciation and understanding of the morass of engineering problems which beset development work in this field.

It will also be noted that different units are used in different portions of the text and that some duplication of symbols prevails from one section to the next. However, every effort has been made to adhere to those units and symbols which are in common use in the particular field under discussion. For example, heat-transfer rates are given in

* H. Etherington, "Reactor Calculations for Amateurs," notes informally circulated at Argonne National Laboratory, note 5, p. 26 of the series, June 9, 1952.

Btu/(hr)(ft²), while gamma-photon mass absorption coefficients are in cm²/gm. This multiplicity or confusion of units and symbols prevails even after ten years of work in the nuclear-reactor engineering field and is compounded here by the fusion of reactor engineering with the conventions of the missile engineering field. Rather than crusade, this text accepts the status quo of confusion and urges that workers in the field become as adept in the cgs and mks as in the English system of units. To ease the transition from one system to the next a comprehensive table of conversion factors is given in an appendix.

Nothing written herein should be construed as reflecting any work now underway or contemplated by any organizations working in this field. In particular this text is not intended as an exposition of any present status of development in nuclear rocket propulsion—rather, as mentioned above, as an introduction to this new field. It is hoped that this text will enable those interested in and working in this and allied fields to keep pace with continued growth in the application of nuclear energy to rocket propulsion. Security permitting, it is anticipated that revised versions of this text will be issued in forthcoming years as it becomes pertinent to do so.

Few technical books are completely the work of the authors whose names are listed on the title page, and this text is no exception to the general rule. However, so many people have helped in one way or another in the production of this book that it is quite impossible to acknowledge all our debts of gratitude. The interest and comments of many of our colleagues have been of great help in this endeavor. The support of the Los Alamos Scientific Laboratory through its Director, N. E. Bradbury, and Technical Associate Director, D. K. Froman, is particularly appreciated. The efforts of L. M. Redman, head of the Document Classification Group, and R. W. Spence, who clarified classification problems and steered the manuscript through the shoals of Security, were also of vital importance to this publication. Of additional help were the critical technical reviews by R. E. Schreiber, Division Leader, and R. W. Spence, Alternate Division Leader of the Nuclear Propulsion Division at the Laboratory. And lastly, we gratefully acknowledge the help of Carol Schweitzer and Della Baldock, who valiantly transmuted the manuscript from written to typed form.

R. W. Bussard
R. D. DeLauer

CONTENTS

Foreword   vii

Preface   ix

Chapter 1. INTRODUCTION   1
   1-1 Introduction and Purpose   1
   1-2 Generalized Missile System   2
   1-3 Scope of Text   3

Chapter 2. BASIC ROCKET PERFORMANCE   6
   2-1 Vehicle Performance   6
   Free Fall; Earth's Field; Atmospheric Effects; Multi-
   stage Rockets; Ballistic Flight, Satellites, and Escape
   Conditions
   2-2 Nozzle Performance   18
   Isentropic Expansion; Real Nozzles
   2-3 Propellant Characteristics   24
   Liquids; Gases; Dissociation and Recombination; Perform-
   ance

Chapter 3. SYSTEM ANALYSIS   45
   3-1 Components   45
   Propellant; Tanks and Structure; Pumping Equipment;
   Nuclear Rocket Motor and Thrust Structure; Dead Load
   3-2 Comparative Analysis   60
   Nuclear Vehicle Performance; Comparative Chemical
   Rocket Performance; Region-of-interest Study; Optimization Studies
   3-3 Limitations of System Analysis   83

Chapter 4. HEAT TRANSFER AND FLUID FLOW   86
   4-1 Convective Heat Transfer   86
   Boundary Layer; Laminar Flow; Turbulent Flow; Porous
   Flow; Experimental Correlation; Mean Temperature
   Difference
   4-2 Conduction   106
   Steady-state Conduction; Nonsteady Heat Conduction;

Numerical Methods; Analog Methods
4-3 Geometric Considerations   116
Stacked Plates; Tubes; Solid Rods; Packed Spheres
4-4 Power Density   119
4-5 Fluid Friction and Pressure Drop   122
Pressure Drop Due to Friction in Tubes; Plenum Effects;
Pressure-Temperature Relation for a Constant-area Flow
with Heat Transfer and Friction
4-6 System Stability   126
Laminar-Turbulent Flow; Porous Flow; Choking; Two-
phase Flow

Chapter 5.   MATERIALS   **138**
5-1 Basic Requirements   138
Fuel Elements; Moderators and Reflectors; Control Elements; Structural Components
5-2 Properties   141
Physical Properties; Nuclear Characteristics; Interaction
Effects
5-3 Special Problems   164
Thermal Strain and Stress; Corrosion and Erosion; Radiation Effects

Chapter 6.   NUCLEONICS   **189**
6-1 Reactor Statics
The Self-sustaining Fission Reaction; Mathematical Description of the Process; Approximate Methods of Analysis;
Results of Calculations
6-2 Reactor Kinetics   212
The Time-dependent Fission Process; Reactivity Coefficients
6-3 Reactor Geometries   219
6-4 Gamma and Neutron Absorption and Leakage   221
Heating Effects; Radiation Dose Levels

Chapter 7.   SYSTEM CONTROL   **244**
7-1 Typical System   244
Major Components; Performance; System Dynamics
7-2 Mathematical Methods   247
Method of Laplace Transform; Feedback and System Stability
7-3 Simulation   260
Electronic Analog Computer; Applications

7-4 Operational Considerations 268
Initial Start-up; Power Range; Shutdown
7-5 Control Instrumentation 272
Proportional Counter; Fission Chambers; Compensated Ion
Chambers

Chapter 8. TESTING **277**
8-1 Component Development Testing 277
Nonnuclear; Nuclear Testing
8-2 Full-scale Testing 287
Static Tests; Flight Tests; Facilities
8-3 Instrumentation 300
Structural Instrumentation; Hydrodynamic Instrumentation; Thermal Instrumentation; Thrust Instrumentation
8-4 Health Hazards and Radiation Safety 304
Biological Effects; Radiation Dose Units; Expected Doses;
Radiation Safety

Chapter 9. ADVANCED AND EXOTIC SYSTEMS **313**
9-1 Fusion Energy 314
9-2 Decay Energy 315
Heat Sources; Direct Momentum
9-3 Fission Energy 319
Direct Momentum; Fission-fragment Heating; Gaseous
Reactors or "Fizzlers"
9-4 Reactor Systems 327
Thermomechanical Cycles; Electrical Heating; Accelerators
9-5 In Conclusion 339

Appendix **341**
Table A-1. Conversion Factors 341
Table A-2. Physical Constants 344
Figure A-1. Chart of the Nuclides (with List of the 345
Elements)

Index 361

CHAPTER 1

INTRODUCTION

1-1. Introduction and Purpose. With the application of nuclear energy to weapons, stationary power plants, and propulsion of ships and aircraft, it was inevitable that nuclear power sources be considered for rocket propulsion. Nuclear rockets are not a new concept; ever since the advent of the controlled fission process, many schemes have been presented[1,2]* for the utilization of nuclear energy in thrust-producing devices, and the potential superiority of nuclear-powered rockets over their chemical brothers has been amply demonstrated.[3,4] Indeed, assuming the successful development of high-performance nuclear rocket motors, it is evident that nuclear rockets will supplant conventional chemical rockets, at least for vehicle missions involving very heavy payloads and long ranges such as for the establishment and continuing supply of large earth satellites. Beyond such applications it seems clear that nuclear power offers the only present practical hope for travel between the planets and their satellites in the solar system.

The inherent exploratory curiosity of mankind ensures the eventual development of space travel. The establishment of manned satellites, the exploration of the moon, expeditions to Mars and Venus, and many other fanciful prognostications of fiction writers of years past will surely come to pass, but only as rapidly as the talents of the world's scientists and engineers can be directed to the problems of space flight. Therefore, as we stand upon the threshold of this new age of exploration, it is pertinent to discuss the presently most difficult of these problems, the nuclear propulsion of rocket vehicles.

Throughout the last decade the application of neutron physics to engineering problems has resulted in many advances in nuclear-reactor technology, and while the literature abounds in contributions[5,6] dealing with large stationary power reactors, nothing has yet been presented on the problems of high-power-density mobile (flyable) reactor systems. The solution of these problems is largely in the domain of the engineer, since proper heat generation and removal, fluid (coolant) distribution and flow, and structural integrity must be achieved in order to construct

* Superscript numbers indicate references listed at end of chapter.

1

successful high-power-density mobile reactors. Accordingly, one of the purposes of this text is to present to the engineer a basis for understanding the engineering problems of such reactors and how these problems are affected by and related to the aspects of neutron physics characterizing reactor types of interest.

There is more to nuclear rockets than high-power-density reactor design. The performance requirements for nuclear rocket power plants will be determined by the performance required of the rocket vehicle itself. Accordingly, analyses of the internal and external ballistic behavior of nuclear rockets are presented in sufficient detail to enable those just entering the rocket and missile field, as well as those now engaged in such work, to obtain a reasonable understanding of the subject. No attempt is made to include chemical rockets per se, as the literature in the field is extensive and readily available.

1-2. Generalized Missile System. The basic difference between chemical and nuclear-powered rockets of the sort considered herein is in the method of obtaining the energy required for vehicle propulsion. The chemical rocket fills its energy needs from the combustion or decomposition of its propellants; the working fluid of the nuclear rocket provides no intrinsic energy but is heated by the kinetic energy of fission fragments released in the controlled fission process within a nuclear reactor. Since rockets move by virtue of the principle of conservation of momentum, it is desirable that the working fluid (propellant) of the nuclear rocket be expelled rearward at a velocity as high as is possible. This requires high working-fluid temperature and low molecular weight. It is for the latter reason that nuclear rockets seem attractive; since the propellant can be chosen without regard to consideration of its combustion characteristics, low-molecular-weight fluids such as pure hydrogen may be used.

In studying the utilization of a nuclear heat source in a rocket motor, the application of such a motor to a missile system must also be investigated. For the purposes of this text a generalized missile system will be employed, with the vehicle being a single-stage device as shown schematically in Fig. 1-1. It should not be too surprising that the schematic diagram looks very much like that for a conventional chemical rocket, with the exception of the section labeled "nuclear rocket motor." The *dead load* carried by the vehicle may be located at the nose of the rocket, just forward of the propellant and propellant tanks, in order to achieve maximum use of the propellant for radiation shielding of the reactor and to obtain the maximum geometrical separation of the dead load and reactor. This dead load (Sec. 3-1) could include a crew, in the case of manned satellite rockets, and thus such radiation-shielding considerations may be necessary. The propellant tanks, essentially thin-skinned pressurized metal balloons, are located forward of the pumping-equipment compartment. The propellant pumps, pump-drive turbines, reactor, and power-plant control mechanisms are all assumed to be located in the aft end of the rocket vehicle.

For our purposes the following sequential operation is assumed. Propellant carried in the tank section is pumped to the reactor by turbine-driven centrifugal pumps, as is commonly done in large liquid-fueled chemical rockets. The working fluid is vaporized and heated to the desired temperature within the reactor and is then exhausted through a converging-diverging nozzle to produce the thrust which propels the rocket.

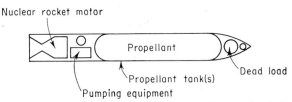

FIG. 1-1. Schematic diagram of generalized nuclear rocket vehicle.

In analyzing the generalized system, consideration is given to launching-site requirements, system-readiness capability, and other factors of importance not directly influencing the vehicle flight performance. No attempt is made to define a guidance system specifically applicable to nuclear rockets, this being a separate field in itself; it is assumed that proper guidance systems can be developed. However, certain missile-guidance criteria which affect the nuclear rocket motor or control-system design (e.g., thrust programming) are discussed.

1-3. Scope of Text. In order to produce a worthwhile text in a field as large as nuclear rocket propulsion, it is necessary to exclude some areas from discussion and to assume a certain level of knowledge on the part of the reader. As mentioned previously, characteristics of rocket-vehicle behavior and rocket-motor performance peculiar to chemical rockets are excluded from discussion herein. The entire field of low-power-density reactor design and analysis (as for stationary power reactors) is also ruled out of consideration. In order to minimize the amount of elementary material presented, it is assumed that the reader has a basic knowledge of reactor physics, a sound background in fluid mechanics, and a familiarity with basic heat-transfer processes. A knowledge of chemical rocket behavior will be helpful but is not necessary for a thorough understanding of the material.

First, basic rocket performance is presented in order to establish the performance parameters that characterize a given rocket-vehicle and -motor design. Using these performance parameters, a systems approach to over-all missile performance is developed. The application of this method of system analysis is then discussed with particular reference to the determination of the general performance regions for which nuclear rockets are of interest and to the optimization of various design variables. The next section, on heat exchange and fluid flow, reviews the fundamentals of convective and conductive heat transfer for various heat-exchange geometries. Fluid-pressure-drop and flow-system-stability considerations are also presented. A discussion of materials follows, dealing with the basic requirements for reactor fuel elements, moderators, and structural materials, as well as presenting their physical and nuclear properties. In addition, special problems associated with thermal stress and strain, creep, and corrosion-erosion are considered. The chapter on nucleonics presents a condensed version of reactor neutronic theory and its application to particular reactor geometries. The presentation here, as throughout the text, is from an engineering viewpoint. Reactor kinetic behavior is discussed, and equations are developed for use in the analysis of reactor control. Gamma- and neutron-heating and -shielding problems are presented, along with methods of approach to the solution of these problems. The requirements for reactor start-up, steady-state operation, and shutdown of a typical system are presented in the section on reactor system control. Mathematical and simulation techniques applicable to control-system studies are indicated. The testing of nuclear rockets and rocket motors is next discussed, and various pertinent testing criteria are defined. The normal radiation and health hazards associated with reactor testing are discussed, as well as those which may arise from accidential failure of a reactor or nuclear rocket undergoing test. Finally, in order to stimulate imagination in the field, some possibilities are suggested for advanced, high-performance nuclear propulsion systems.

Although many of the things discussed in the following pages may seem flights of fancy to the staid engineer of yesteryear, it is perhaps encouraging to recall the words of the late Dr. R. H. Goddard, who wrote* (in 1919) that "these developments involve many experimental difficulties, to be sure; but they depend upon nothing that is really impossible."

REFERENCES

1. Bonestell, C., and W. Ley: "The Conquest of Space," chap. 2, pp. 49ff., The Viking Press, Inc., New York, 1949.
2. Murray, Raymond L.: "Introduction to Nuclear Engineering," chap. 19, sec. 19.5, Prentice-Hall, Inc., Englewood Cliffs, N.J., 1954.
3. Tsien, H. S.: "Rockets and Other Thermal Jets Using Nuclear Energy" in Clark

* By permission from R. H. Goddard, A Method of Reaching Extreme Altitudes, *Smithsonian Misc. Collections*, vol. 71, no. 2, p. 57, 1919.

Goodman (ed.), "The Science and Engineering of Nuclear Power," vol. II, chap. 11, Addison-Wesley Publishing Company, Reading, Mass., 1949.

4. Shepherd, L. R., and A. V. Cleaver: The Atomic Rocket—1, 2, 3, and 4, *J. Brit. Interplanet. Soc.*, vol. 7, no. 5, September; no. 6, November, 1948; vol. 8, no. 1, January; no. 2, March, 1949.

5. Charpie, R. A., et al. (eds.): "Reactors," Progress in Nuclear Energy, ser. II, vol. 1, McGraw-Hill Book Company, Inc., New York, 1956.

6. "The Reactor Handbook," vols. 1 and 2 ("Physics" and "Engineering"), *AECD*-3645 and *AECD*-3646, 1955.

CHAPTER 2

BASIC ROCKET PERFORMANCE

Before the application of nuclear energy to rockets can be discussed, it is necessary to understand the characteristics of rocket-motor gas dynamics and the inherent features of ballistic-rocket-vehicle flight. Fundamental equations expressing the various pertinent phenomena are derived and summarized in this chapter. Also of interest are the physical and chemical characteristics of the best potential nuclear rocket working fluids or propellants. These are discussed, and estimates of performance are presented based upon the previously developed gas-dynamic equations.

2-1. Vehicle Performance. *Free Fall.* In *free-fall* flight the rocket vehicle is acted upon by no forces other than those due to the action of the vehicle power plant. By definition, actions in a coordinate system whose origin is based upon a body in free fall take place in a space free of external force fields whether the body is moving in a closed orbit about the earth or in intergalactic space (neglecting the field due to the body itself). A force field due to the presence of the body itself acts in this hypothetical coordinate system but is trivial for rocket vehicles of reasonable size. The earth is in free fall about the sun; thus its inhabitants act relatively independently of the sun's gravitational field; however, the great mass of the earth results in a powerful local force field whose strength at the surface is sometimes called the force of gravity.

A rocket vehicle moves by the reaction force due to the directed expulsion of matter from the vehicle. Classic examples given in more basic books for the layman[1,2] describe the forces and motions associated with one's stepping from a small boat to the dock or the motion of a boat caused by throwing large boulders out the rear. The principles involved are the same as those which describe rocket flight; if a mass m (man) leaves a mass M (boat) with relative velocity v, then M will move in the opposite direction with velocity $V = (m/M)v$, sometimes assuring a dunking for m.

Assume a rocket vehicle of mass m, as shown in Fig. 2-1, moving with velocity v relative to some fixed point in space and losing mass at a constant rate $-dm/dt$. Assume that a fraction α of the expelled mass

6

leaves with a constant velocity v_L relative to the vehicle and that a fraction β leaves with constant relative velocity v_e. This expulsion of mass causes a vehicle velocity change dv over the time interval dt. A simple balance of forces leads at once to

$$m \frac{dv}{dt} = -\frac{dm}{dt}(\alpha v_L + \beta v_e) \qquad (2\text{-}1)$$

Elimination of the time parameter reduces this to the more familiar conservation-of-momentum expression

$$m\,dv = -dm\,(\alpha v_L + \beta v_e) \qquad (2\text{-}2)$$

Integration of this expression from an arbitrary initial velocity v_0 over the rocket-motor operating time t_b and a vehicle velocity change Δv_b gives a relation between vehicle masses and velocities as

$$\int_{v_0}^{v_0 + \Delta v_b} \frac{dv}{\alpha v_L + \beta v_e} = -\int_{m_0}^{m_b} \frac{dm}{m} \qquad (2\text{-}3)$$

which leads to

$$\frac{\Delta v_b}{\alpha v_L + \beta v_e} = \ln \frac{m_0}{m_b} \quad \text{or} \quad \frac{m_0}{m_b} = \exp \frac{\Delta v_b}{\alpha v_L + \beta v_e} \qquad (2\text{-}4)$$

where m_0 is the initial vehicle mass and m_b is the final or "burnt" mass. This is called the mass-ratio equation in free fall or free space. At burn-

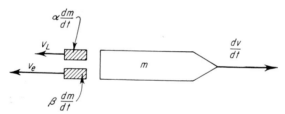

FIG. 2-1. Forces on rocket vehicle in free space.

out, the total rocket-motor energy expenditure is distributed between kinetic energy of the vehicle and energy remaining in the exhaust gases after expulsion from the vehicle.

Earth's Field. While the free-space equations are very useful for comparative vehicle analyses, when properly used, and can also be used to describe the maximum performance capability of a given vehicle, they are not rigorously applicable to most rocket vehicles of immediate practical interest, which will be launched while under the influence of the earth's gravitational field. For upward flight at an angle θ between the vehicle axis and the local horizon (or tangent plane to the local gravitational equipotential surface), as shown in Fig. 2-2, the basic vehicle performance equation becomes

$$m \left(\frac{dv}{dt} + g \sin \theta \right) = - \frac{dm}{dt} (\alpha v_L + \beta v_e) \tag{2-5}$$

The thrust and vehicle axes are here assumed to coincide. Integration of Eq. (2-5) over the previously defined operating conditions gives

$$(\alpha v_L + \beta v_e) \int_{m_0}^{m_b} \frac{dm}{m} = \int_{v_0}^{v_0 + \Delta v_b} dv + \int_{t_0}^{t_0 + t_b} g \sin \theta \, dt \tag{2-6}$$

which reduces to

$$\frac{m_0}{m_b} = \exp \frac{\Delta v_b + t_b \, \mathbf{g \sin \theta}}{\alpha v_L + \beta v_e} \tag{2-7}$$

where $\mathbf{g \sin \theta}$ is the integrated time-average value of the local gravitational field strength times the sine of the instantaneous flight angle. This

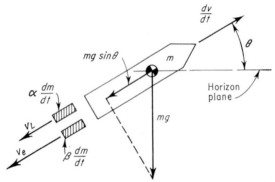

FIG. 2-2. Forces on rocket vehicle in the earth's field.

term has the effect of reducing the free-space velocity potential of the vehicle. Here part of the energy output of the rocket motor goes into suspension of the vehicle within the gravitational field and part into potential energy associated with height above the earth's surface. The remainder is split between vehicle kinetic energy and residual internal and kinetic energy of the exhaust gases.

For the case of rocket vehicles operating under a variable-thrust program designed to give constant vehicle acceleration, the mass-ratio equations are the same as for the constant-thrust case previously discussed. While aesthetically attractive for passenger-carrying applications, the constant-acceleration case is less practical than constant thrust (constant propellant-weight flow rate), since continuous throttling of rocket-motor flow and power output is required to reduce thrust as propellant is expelled. Such a throttling process does not make full use of the handling capabilities of pumps, lines, valves, and rocket motor except at start-up at initial maximum propellant flow rates, and it leads to longer required operating times than the constant-propellant-flow-rate (approximately constant-thrust) system. Although not considered further herein, the performance characteristics of constant-acceleration rocket vehicles have been thoroughly analyzed in other studies.[3] Individual analysis will be necessary for vehicles using thrust programs other than constant thrust or constant acceleration.

Atmospheric Effects. Not only will most nuclear rocket vehicles of interest be launched within the influence of the earth's field, they will also be affected in their flight by the earth's atmosphere. Flight within the atmosphere requires the expenditure of energy to overcome frictional and momental retarding forces (drag) acting upon the rocket vehicle. The sum of such forces is commonly expressed by

$$D = C_D A_f \frac{\rho_a v^2}{2g_c} \tag{2-8}$$

where ρ_a = local air density

$\quad g_c$ = force-to-mass conversion factor

$\quad A_f$ = frontal cross-sectional area of vehicle (assumed wingless)

$\quad C_D$ = dimensionless drag coefficient

Experiments have shown that C_D is principally dependent upon the vehicle shape (particularly the nose shape), the flight velocity, and the angle between the vehicle axis and the flight path. An example[4] of the variation is shown in Fig. 2-3.

Momentum changes of the air surrounding the vehicle in flight at a nonzero angle of attack result in sideward forces (lift) on the vehicle. Such forces are grossly described in the same manner as drag forces by

$$L = C_L A_f \frac{\rho_a v^2}{2g_c} \tag{2-9}$$

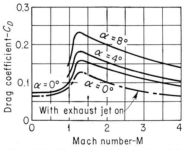

FIG. 2-3. Drag coefficient of a finless RM-10 missile.

An example[4] of the variation in body-lift coefficient due to angle of attack and flight velocity is shown in Fig. 2-4 for a typical rocket vehicle. The addition of lifting surfaces such as wings and fins leads to wing-body interaction effects in addition to greatly increased lifting forces at low angles of attack. While of great importance in the analysis of aircraft and in the study of guidance and stability of rocket vehicles, the subject of aerodynamics is beyond the scope of this text and is of immediate concern only as it has a major effect on the flight performance, and hence power-plant requirements, of rocket vehicles. The most important effect in this sense is the loss of velocity or waste of energy required to overcome drag forces.

Assuming zero lift, a force balance for an atmospheric vehicle leads to

$$\Delta v_b + t_b \, \mathbf{g} \, \mathbf{sin} \, \boldsymbol{\theta} + \int_{t_0}^{t_0+t_b} \frac{Dg_c \, dt}{m} = (\alpha v_L + \beta v_e) \ln \frac{m_0}{m_b} \tag{2-10}$$

Making use of the relations

$$m = m_0 - w_p(t - t_0) \tag{2-11}$$

for constant propellant flow rate $w_p = dm/dt$, and

$$F = \frac{w_p(\alpha v_L + \beta v_e)}{g_c} \tag{2-12}$$

the force equation can be reduced to

$$\frac{m_0}{m_b} = \exp \frac{\Delta v_b + t_b \, \mathbf{g} \, \mathbf{sin} \, \boldsymbol{\theta}}{(\alpha v_L + \beta v_e)(1 - \zeta)} \tag{2-13}$$

where ζ is the integrated time-average value of the ratio of drag to thrust.

Another reduction in vehicle performance is that resulting from the atmospheric back pressure at the rocket-motor nozzle-exit section. A nozzle designed for high-altitude use or for use in vacuum may expand the propellant gases to very low static pressures at the nozzle exit. Such expansion increases the exhaust velocity (Sec. 2-2), thus improving performance. However if such a nozzle is operated at ambient pressures appreciably higher than the nominal exhaust-gas exit pressure, the exhaust jet will break away from the nozzle walls and the gas will leave the nozzle at a lower bulk velocity than if this separation had not occurred. If the vehicle force balance is rewritten to include this effect, it will appear in the mass-ratio equation as a multiplicative correction factor χ in the exponent denominator. This factor is defined as the ratio of the integrated time-average exhaust velocity to the ideal free-space (no atmosphere) exhaust velocity with the same nozzle. The complete mass-ratio

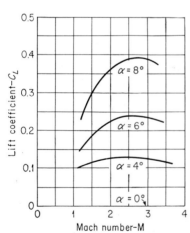

FIG. 2-4. Lift coefficient of a finless RM-10 missile.

equation then becomes

$$\frac{m_0}{m_b} = \exp \frac{\Delta v_b + t_b \, \mathbf{g} \, \mathbf{\sin} \, \boldsymbol{\theta}}{(\alpha v_L + \beta v_e)(1 - \zeta)(\chi)} = e^{\xi} \tag{2-14}$$

where ξ denotes the complete exponent.

For a constant propellant flow rate the total rocket-motor operating time is related to the ratio of propellant weight to gross vehicle weight by

$$t_b = (\alpha v_L + \beta v_e)\frac{m_p}{a_0 m_0} \tag{2-15}$$

where a_0 is the initial vehicle acceleration.

Applying this to the complete mass-ratio equation and rearranging the left-hand side results in a transcendental equation in m_p/m_0:

$$\frac{m_p}{m_0} = 1 - \exp - \frac{\Delta v_b + (\alpha v_L + \beta v_e)(m_p/a_0 m_0) \, \mathbf{g} \, \mathbf{\sin} \, \boldsymbol{\theta}}{(\alpha v_L + \beta v_e)(1 - \zeta)\chi} \tag{2-16}$$

Analytic solution of this is not possible; however, numerical solution enables the determination of a unique set of ratios m_p/m_0 for an equivalent set of Δv_b for any given propellant-gas performance parameters and specified drag and atmospheric factors. A more detailed discussion of vehicle performance analysis is presented in Chap. 3.

Determination of the values of ζ and χ, as well as $\mathbf{g} \, \mathbf{\sin} \, \boldsymbol{\theta}$, requires knowledge of the vehicle velocity and position in space as a function of time and of the variation of atmospheric density with altitude. This latter is given approximately by

$$\rho_a(h) = 0.075 \exp \left(-7.4 \times 10^{-6} h^{1.15}\right) \tag{2-17}$$

and is shown in Fig. 2-5 for an NACA standard day.[5] The variation of g with height is of course given by

$$g(h) = g_0 \left(\frac{R_e}{R_e + h}\right)^2 \tag{2-18}$$

where R_e is the radius of the earth and g_0 is the acceleration of gravity at sea level (altitude zero).

For launching from the earth's surface, the relation between height, time, and vehicle velocity can be found from integration of the equation

$$\frac{d^2 h}{dt^2} = a(t) \tag{2-19}$$

where $a(t)$ is the instantaneous upward acceleration. For a constant-thrust (approximately constant-flow-rate) vehicle it can be shown that $a(t)$ is given by

$$a(t) = a_0 \left\{ 1 + K\frac{t}{t_b} - \frac{\zeta(v,h)}{1 - [a_0 t/(\alpha v_L + \beta v_e)]} \right\} \sin \theta(t) - g(h) \tag{2-20}$$

where $K = (a_b - a_0)/a_0$ and a_0 and a_b are initial and final (burnt) vehicle accelerations. Forces and motions due to curvature of the vehicle flight path and the rotation of the earth are neglected here. The present analysis is given to illustrate the difficulties involved in accounting for atmospheric effects rather than to encompass all features of ballistic orbits.

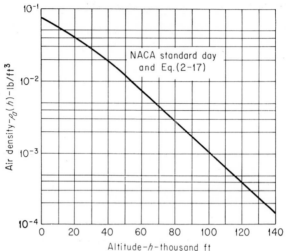

FIG. 2-5. Density of earth's atmosphere.

Since $\zeta(v,h)$ depends upon the instantaneous velocity and atmospheric density (thus height), it is clearly impossible to solve Eqs. (2-19) and (2-20) in closed form. However, a series of successive numerical approximations can be made, each using the values of $\zeta(v,h)$ determined by the previous iteration. This process will rapidly converge upon the true solution; in fact it is often sufficient to determine $\zeta(v,h)$ from the velocity-height-time relations established by integration of Eq. (2-20), neglecting the term involving ζ. For example, assuming $\theta(t)$ is constant at 90° (vertical flight path) and g invariant over the height of interest, Eqs. (2-19) and (2-20) can be combined to yield

$$a(t) = \frac{d^2h}{dt^2} = a_0 \left(1 + K \frac{t}{t_b}\right) - g \qquad (2\text{-}21)$$

$$v(t) = \frac{dh}{dt} = a_0 \left(t + \frac{K}{2} \frac{t^2}{t_b}\right) - gt \qquad \text{for } v(0) = 0 \qquad (2\text{-}22)$$

$$h(t) = \frac{a_0}{2} \left(t^2 + \frac{K}{3} \frac{t^3}{t_b}\right) - \frac{gt^2}{2} \qquad \text{for } h(0) = 0 \qquad (2\text{-}23)$$

From the density-height relation given in Eq. (2-17) and Fig. 2-5 and the velocity-height-time relations determined as in Eqs. (2-22) and (2-23), the drag may be determined from Eq. (2-8) and graphs such as that in

Fig. 2-3 for a specific vehicle design. Having drag as a function of time, it is a simple matter to estimate the integrated time-average value of ζ for use in the vehicle performance equations. In order to save time, refined solutions are best obtained by use of computing machines.

Multistage Rockets. A *multistage* or *step* rocket consists of a number of rocket vehicles stacked one upon the other and fired in series so that each section starts with an initial velocity equal to the final velocity of the sum of all the previously fired rockets. Each rocket uses its predecessors as steps upon which to climb—thus arises the name "step rockets." The advantage of such an assembly is that the burnout velocity of the final rocket can be many times greater than it would have been if fired alone.

The maximum velocity attainable by a rocket is generally determined by constructional limits on the maximum fraction of vehicle weight which can be devoted to propellant. Experience has shown that it is difficult to build structurally sound vehicles which have more than 85 to 90 per cent by weight of propellant. A practical upper limit at the present time appears to be about 90 per cent of propellant by weight.

The mass-ratio equation for the ith step of an n-step rocket is

$$\frac{m_{0_i} + \sum_{1}^{i-1} m_{0_j}}{m_{b} + \sum_{1}^{i-1} m_{0_j}} = e^{\xi_i} \tag{2-24}$$

where the steps are numbered in order from the smallest (last-fired) to largest (launching stage). If the substitutions

$$\lambda_i = \frac{1}{m_{0_i}} \sum_{1}^{i-1} m_{0_j} \qquad \text{and} \qquad \delta_i = \frac{m_{b_i}}{m_{0_i}}$$

are made, Eq. (2-24) reduces to

$$\frac{1 + \lambda_i}{\delta_i + \lambda_i} = e^{\xi_i} \tag{2-25}$$

λ_i is just the ratio of the full weight of all the $i - 1$ steps plus the payload to the full weight of the ith step itself, while δ_i is the ratio of empty (burnt) weight to full weight for the ith step alone. λ_i has been called a "payload factor,"[6] while δ_i is evidently a structural parameter determining the allowable propellant-weight fraction of the ith vehicle. Now, it is of interest to determine whether or not there is a value of λ_i or a variation of δ_i with i which leads to maximum performance for a given weight. Maximum performance is obtained with maximum ξ_i, and hence maximum Δv_b. Solving Eq. (2-25) for ξ_i, rearranging, and differentiating with respect to i yields

$$\frac{d\xi_i}{di} = \left[\frac{\delta_i - 1}{(\lambda_i + 1)(\lambda_i + \delta_i)} \right] \frac{d\lambda_i}{di} \qquad (2\text{-}26)$$

For optimum this must equal zero. Since the term in brackets is always finite, except for the trivial case $\delta_i = 1$ (for which $\xi_i = 0$), it is obvious that the derivative of λ_i with respect to i must be zero. This can only be the case if λ_i itself is zero or a constant. It is easily verified that this condition leads to a maximum rather than a minimum.[7] For a constant λ_i and fixed δ_i, the mass-ratio exponent will be constant; thus optimum performance results from each stage's producing its proportionate, uniformly distributed share of the required over-all velocity potential.

Ballistic Flight, Satellites, and Escape Conditions. After burnout above the earth's atmosphere, a rocket vehicle moves primarily under the action of the gravitational attraction of the earth. The influence of other astronomical bodies, such as the moon, is relatively unimportant in the case of motion of rocket vehicles which are launched from and return to the surface of the earth. On the other hand the effect of the moon cannot be neglected in accurate calculations of perturbations of satellite orbits.

Derivation of the general equations of motion of a particle moving in an elliptic orbit about a fixed or rotating earth has been thoroughly covered elsewhere[8,9] and will not be repeated here. It can be shown that the ballistic ground range, on a nonrotating spherical earth, of a rocket which ceases firing at a height h_b above the earth's surface and is moving at an angle θ_b with the horizontal at burnout is approximately given by

$$S = 2R_e \cot^{-1} \left\{ \left[\frac{g_0 R_e}{(v_b \cos \theta_b)^2} - 1 \right] \cot \theta_b \right\} + h_b \cot \theta_b \qquad (2\text{-}27)$$

where $h_b \ll R_e$. Here R_e is the radius of the earth and v_b is the velocity of the vehicle at burnout. Neglecting the term $h_b \cot \theta_b$ as being small compared to S, the optimum burnout angle for maximum range can be determined by differentiation of Eq. (2-27) with respect to the flight angle at burnout. Solution for optimum θ_b then yields the relation

$$\theta_{b_m} = \tan^{-1} \left(1 - \frac{v_b^2}{g_0 R_e} \right)^{\frac{1}{2}} \qquad (2\text{-}28)$$

Combining Eqs. (2-27) and (2-28), the maximum range is approximately

$$S_m = 2R_e \cot^{-1} \left[2 \frac{g_0 R_e}{v_b^2} \left(1 - \frac{v_b^2}{g_0 R_e} \right)^{\frac{1}{2}} \right] + h_b \left(1 - \frac{v_b^2}{g_0 R_e} \right)^{-\frac{1}{2}} \qquad (2\text{-}29)$$

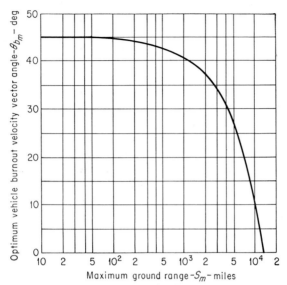

Fig. 2-6. Optimum vehicle-burnout angle.

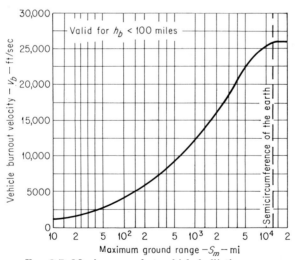

Fig. 2-7. Maximum rocket-vehicle ballistic range.

By combination of Eqs. (2-28) and (2-29) it is possible to relate the optimum burnout angle and the maximum range. This relation is shown graphically in Fig. 2-6. Figure 2-7 shows the maximum attainable ballistic range as a function of burnout velocity, as given by Eq. (2-29).

Determination of the characteristics of ballistic flight from a rotating earth is considerably complicated by the fact that the range and optimum burnout angle are functions of the latitudes of the burnout and impact points on the earth. Strictly speaking, the foregoing equations are valid only for a nonrotating earth. Corrections due to the earth's rotation will generally be within 10 per cent of the calculational results based upon a nonrotating earth.

Much of the popular and some of the technical literature published concerning rockets has dealt with the possibilities of establishing artificial satellites of the earth or of escape from the earth by rocket vehicle.[10–12] Discussion of the advantages and disadvantages of satellites and other extraterrestrial vehicles is beyond the scope of this text; however, it is germane to consider briefly the fundamental energy and velocity requirements for such devices.

Consider a vertically launched rocket which ends its motor operation above the atmosphere, so that drag effects may be neglected after burnout. If it is to "escape" the earth's gravitational field, the upward-directed kinetic energy of the vehicle at burnout must equal the kinetic energy it would have at that height if it had fallen from nearly zero velocity at infinity. This kinetic energy must be equal to the potential energy of the vehicle at infinity less that at the height of interest within the earth's field. From this simple energy balance (neglecting the rotation of the earth) it is possible to determine the escape velocity. Recalling, from Eq. (2-18), that the variation of gravitational field strength with height is

$$g(h) = g_0 \left(\frac{R_e}{R_e + h}\right)^2 \qquad (2\text{-}18)$$

the energy balance for a vehicle escaping from a height h above the surface can be written as

$$E_k = \frac{m}{2}[v_{esc}(h)]^2 = mg_0 \int_h^\infty \left(\frac{R_e}{R_e + h}\right)^2 dh = mg_0 R_e \frac{R_e}{R_e + h} \qquad (2\text{-}30)$$

from which the escape velocity is

$$v_{esc}(h) = R_e \left(\frac{2g_0}{R_e + h}\right)^{1/2} \qquad (2\text{-}31)$$

At sea level ($h = 0$), the escape velocity is about 36,700 ft/sec. It falls slowly with increasing altitude, as shown in Fig. 2-8.

To establish a vehicle in a stable circular orbit at height h the centripetal acceleration due to the curvature of the orbit must exactly balance the gravitational acceleration of the earth's field at that height, thus

$$\frac{[v_{sat}(h)]^2}{R_e + h} = g_0 \left(\frac{R_e}{R_e + h}\right)^2 \qquad (2\text{-}32)$$

from which the orbital velocity of the satellite can be determined to be

$$v_{sat}(h) = R_e \left(\frac{g_0}{R_e + h} \right)^{\frac{1}{2}} = \frac{v_{esc}}{\sqrt{2}} \qquad (2\text{-}33)$$

The sum of the orbital kinetic energy and the potential energy due to height above the earth's surface is required to establish a vehicle of mass m in a stable oribit. This energy is given by

$$E_k + E_p = E_{tot} = \frac{m}{2} [v_{sat}(h)]^2 + m g_0 \int_0^h \left(\frac{R_e}{R_e + h} \right)^2 dh \qquad (2\text{-}34)$$

The time of revolution $\tau(h)$ is determined from Eq. (2-33) and the relation $[\tau(h)][v_{sat}(h)] = 2\pi (R_e + h)$. This is

$$\tau(h) = 2\pi \frac{R_e + h}{R_e} \left(\frac{R_e + h}{g_0} \right)^{\frac{1}{2}} \qquad (2\text{-}35)$$

The orbital velocity and time of revolution are shown as functions of height in Fig. 2-8. It is interesting to note that the orbital periods are

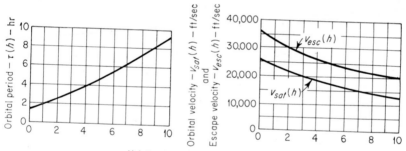

Height above surface — h — thousand mi

FIG. 2-8. Orbital characteristics.

only a few hours for heights up to several thousand miles above the earth's surface. A satellite in a low-altitude orbit would thus circle the earth about ten times in the course of one day. When thinking of using such vehicles as extraterrestrial observation posts, it is well to remember that, while affording a grand over-all view of our globe, the details of the surface are rushing under the satellite with an apparent velocity of about 5 miles/sec. Much better observational stability can be achieved by recourse to a 24-hr orbit in which the satellite orbital plane lies between 60°N and 60°S latitudes. Here the relative surface satellite velocity will never exceed about 1,000 miles/hr and the satellite will simply move north and south along a fixed longitude line. For the special case in which the orbital plane coincides with the equator, the satellite will sit in space above a fixed point on the earth. Unfortunately for observational purposes, the 24-hr orbit is at a height of about 22,400 miles above the surface.

2-2. Nozzle Performance. It has been shown [Eq. (2-16) and others] that the flight performance of a rocket vehicle is dependent primarily upon the propellant exhaust velocity and secondarily upon the character-istics of the flight path chosen. The effective propellant exhaust veloc-ity is determined chiefly by the thermodynamic properties of the propel-lant gas, the geometry of the rocket-motor nozzle, and the operating conditions within the rocket motor. The effective exhaust velocity is thus the parametric link between exterior ballistics of the vehicle and

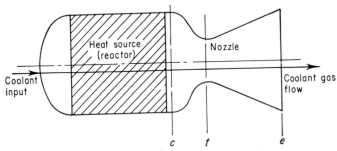

FIG. 2-9. Typical rocket-motor geometry.

interior design parameters of the power plant. As such it is of funda-mental significance in the analysis of any rocket vehicle and consequently will be given due attention here.

Isentropic Expansion. Consider a rocket-motor geometry as shown in Fig. 2-9. For adiabatic expansion of gases from the chamber through the converging-diverging nozzle by an energy-conservative process, the ideal gas velocity at any downstream station (here shown as the nozzle exit) is given by

$$v_{ei}^2 - v_c^2 = 2Jg_c c_p (T_c - T_e) \qquad (2\text{-}36)$$

where J is a thermal-mechanical energy-conversion factor (778 ft-lb/Btu), all temperatures are in absolute units, and c_p denotes the integrated temperature-averaged specific heat at constant pressure over the range T_e to T_c. As is well known,[13–15] the temperature is related to the static pressure at any station by

$$\frac{T_e}{T_c} = \left(\frac{P_e}{P_c}\right)^{(\gamma-1)/\gamma} \qquad (2\text{-}37)$$

where γ is defined as the average value of the ratio of specific heat at constant pressure to that at constant volume over the given temperature range. Simple combination of Eqs. (2-36) and (2-37) shows that

$$v_{ei}^2 - v_c^2 = 2Jg_c c_p \eta_c T_c \qquad (2\text{-}38)$$

where η_c is the Carnot-cycle efficiency of the expansion process. It is defined by

$$\eta_c = 1 - \frac{T_e}{T_c} = 1 - \left(\frac{P_e}{P_c}\right)^{(\gamma-1)/\gamma} \qquad (2\text{-}39)$$

This ideal-cycle efficiency is shown in Fig. 2-10 as a function of nozzle pressure ratio for several values of γ.

From the basic thermodynamic relations

$$c_p - c_v = \frac{R_u}{J\,\mathfrak{M}} \qquad \text{and} \qquad \gamma = \frac{c_p}{c_v} \qquad (2\text{-}40)$$

it can be shown that

$$c_p = \frac{R_u}{J\,\mathfrak{M}}\frac{\gamma}{\gamma-1} \qquad (2\text{-}41)$$

where R_u is the universal gas constant [1,544 (lb/ft²)ft³/(lb mole)(°R)] and $\mathfrak{M}$ is the temperature-averaged molecular weight of the exhaust

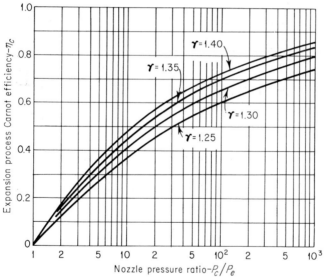

FIG. 2-10. Nozzle expansion-process characteristics.

gases. Combining this with Eq. (2-38), the ideal propellant-gas exhaust velocity is expressed as

$$v_{ei}^2 - v_c^2 = \frac{2\gamma g_c}{\gamma-1}\frac{R_u}{\mathfrak{M}}T_c\eta_c = v_{mi}^2\eta_c \qquad (2\text{-}42)$$

The *maximum* theoretical exhaust velocity v_{mi} occurs for an infinite expansion ratio (expansion to zero pressure), hence for 100 per cent Carnot-cycle efficiency. Assuming chamber velocity small compared to exit velocity, the ideal exhaust velocity is plotted in Fig. 2-11 as a function of $T_c/\mathfrak{M}$ for several values of the parameter $\gamma\eta_c/(\gamma - 1)$.

From Eq. (2-42) it is at once evident that high exhaust velocity is obtained by operation at high chamber temperature, large expansion ratio P_c/P_e, or by use of low-molecular-weight propellants. It is this latter factor which gives nuclear rockets their potential advantage over rockets deriving their energy from chemical combustion. The average

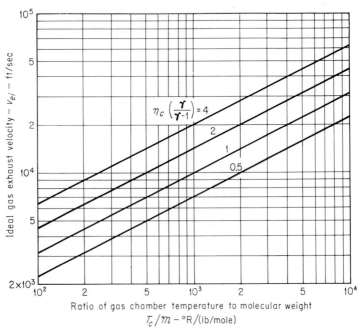

FIG. 2-11. Ideal exhaust velocity.

molecular weight of optimum mixtures of typical combustible rocket propellants such as gasoline-oxygen or nitric acid–aniline is about 20 to 25. On the other hand, diatomic hydrogen gas has a molecular weight of 2. Since a nuclear-reactor coolant can be chosen without regard to its combustion characteristics, the use of low-molecular-weight gases is desirable. For use of hydrogen the nuclear rocket can have an exhaust velocity of the order of 3 times as high as conventional chemical rockets operating at the same maximum gas temperature. Since the exhaust velocity enters exponentially into the mass-ratio equations, the nuclear rocket has an enormous potential weight advantage over chemical rockets for the same vehicle performance.

From the principle of conservation of mass, the continuity equation for propellant flow can be written as

$$\rho_e A_e v_{ei} = \rho_c A_c v_c = \rho_t A_t v_t \tag{2-43}$$

where the subscripts refer to the axial stations shown in Fig. 2-9. The symbol A denotes area normal to the flow axis, and ρ is the local gas density. The gas velocity at the nozzle throat is sonic and is given by

$$v_t = \left(\gamma g_c \frac{R_u}{\mathfrak{M}} T_t\right)^{\frac{1}{2}} \quad \text{or} \quad v_t = \left(\frac{2\gamma g_c}{\gamma + 1} \frac{R_u}{\mathfrak{M}} T_c\right)^{\frac{1}{2}} \quad (2\text{-}44)$$

For perfect gases

$$P = \frac{\rho T R_u}{\mathfrak{M}} \quad (2\text{-}45)$$

Combination of this with Eqs. (2-37), (2-43), and (2-44) gives the geometrical relation

$$\frac{A_t}{A_e} = \left(\frac{\gamma + 1}{2}\right)^{1/(\gamma-1)} \left(\frac{P_e}{P_c}\right)^{1/\gamma} \left\{\frac{\gamma + 1}{\gamma - 1}\left[1 - \left(\frac{P_e}{P_c}\right)^{(\gamma-1)/\gamma}\right]\right\}^{\frac{1}{2}} \quad (2\text{-}46)$$

This is useful in specifying the dimensions of a nozzle required for a given performance. By proper manipulation of the foregoing equations the nozzle throat area can be found from

$$w = A_t P_c \left[\frac{\gamma g_c \mathfrak{M}}{R_u T_c}\left(\frac{2}{\gamma + 1}\right)^{(\gamma+1)/(\gamma-1)}\right]^{\frac{1}{2}} \quad (2\text{-}47)$$

for any desired weight flow rate.

The ideal thrust from this isentropic system is

$$F_i = \frac{w v_{ei}}{g_c} + (P_e - P_a)A_e \quad (2\text{-}48)$$

By means of Eqs. (2-42), (2-46), and (2-47) the theoretical thrust per unit propellant flow rate, called the ideal specific impulse I_{sp_i}, can be reduced to a function of chamber conditions, gas thermodynamic properties, and nozzle exit and atmospheric pressures. For operation in vacuum ($p_a = 0$) this relation is

$$I_{sp_i} = \frac{F_i}{w} = \left[\frac{2\gamma}{\gamma - 1} \frac{R_u}{\mathfrak{M}g_c} T_c\eta_c + \left(\frac{v_c}{g_c}\right)^2\right]^{\frac{1}{2}} + \left(\frac{P_e}{P_c}\right)^{(\gamma-1)/\gamma}\left(\frac{\gamma - 1}{2\gamma} \frac{R_u}{\mathfrak{M}g_c} \frac{T_c}{\eta_c}\right)^{\frac{1}{2}}$$

$$(2\text{-}49)$$

Real Nozzles. Ideal isentropic performance is not realizable in practice. Losses due to wall friction, radial (nonaxial) motion of the expanding gases, use of nonperfect gases, radiation to space down the nozzle axis, dissociation and recombination within the nozzle, the effect of a finite boundary layer, and shock waves within the supersonic flow region all lead to a reduction in over-all nozzle performance.

Radial gas velocity does not produce thrust. Use of a conical expansion section in the nozzle produces flow along a series of conical streamlines or stream surfaces so that the bulk average axial velocity is less than for pure parallel flow at all stations downstream of the throat. Simple geometric considerations show this reduced velocity to be

$$\frac{v_{\text{conical}}}{v_{\text{parallel}}} = \frac{1}{2}(1 + \cos \psi) \qquad (2\text{-}50)$$

where ψ is the cone half angle. For a cone half angle of 20° this factor is 0.97, thus indicating only a 3 per cent loss in exhaust velocity. For a high-performance rocket even this small loss is undesirable and should be avoided by use of other nozzle shapes designed to yield parallel flow at the nozzle exit section. Such parallel-flow nozzles assure near-maximum exhaust velocity with no geometric losses. In principle the flow parallelism is achieved by turning the flow before it reaches the nozzle exit. To do so requires that the nozzle wall be curved inward toward the flow axis near the end of the expansion section. However, in order to permit proper over-all expansion from the throat, without excessive nozzle length, the nozzle wall must curve outward beyond the throat. The shape of such a nozzle is therefore roughly as shown in Fig. 2-12.

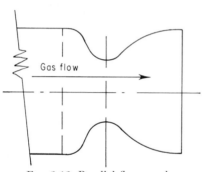

FIG. 2-12. Parallel-flow nozzle.

Detailed design of this type of nozzle is a complex and difficult procedure based upon use of the method of characteristics for supersonic flow. Exposition of this procedure can be found in texts on supersonic aerodynamics[16] and in the extensive literature dealing with rocket-motor design principles.[17-20] The major losses in this type of nozzle are a result of shock-wave interactions in the supersonic-flow regime. For large nozzles these seldom cause more than about a 1 per cent reduction in bulk exhaust velocity.

Thermal radiation to space from the gases downstream of the throat is small. Black-body radiation at 3000°R can transfer only 0.04 Mw/ft² of radiating area; in this case the area is that of the nozzle cross section. On the other hand the rate of kinetic-energy transfer through a typical rocket exhaust nozzle is the order of 100 Mw/ft² of nozzle cross section. It is clear that thermal-radiation losses of the magnitude discussed are trivial.

Chemical reaction phenomena such as dissociation and recombination result in change in mixture molecular weight and heat release and absorption in the supersonic-flow region of the nozzle. Generally the molecular weight increases during gas passage through the nozzle, leading to higher local gas densities and hence flow rates per unit area larger than predicted by the simple theoretical equations. These processes are discussed more fully in Sec. 2-3.

Friction with the nozzle walls results in heat transfer to the walls, thus rendering the flow nonadiabatic. This effect becomes smaller for larger nozzles because the amount of heat transferred depends upon the surface area available ($\propto D^2$), while the total flow rate depends upon the volume ($\propto D^3$). Nonadiabatic flow in a real nozzle leads to lower-than-theoretical bulk gas temperatures at any point, hence to higher-than-ideal densities. This increased density results in a higher mass flow rate per unit area than is given by theoretical equations such as Eq. (2-47). Flow velocities in a finite boundary layer range from zero at the wall surface to full free-stream velocity at the boundary between "buffer" layer and turbulent core.[21] For a boundary layer of finite thickness (true for all real gases) the effective full-velocity flow area is thus less than the theoretical flow area; hence the mass flow rate per unit area will be less than the ideal.

Two other effects befog the correct determination and prediction of nozzle throat area required for a given flow rate. One is the familiar vena contracta resulting from radially inward-directed gas momentum introduced in the converging section connecting throat and rocket-motor chamber. This tends to increase the density slightly above theoretical at the throat, and hence lead to higher-than-ideal mass flow densities. The other results from the fact that the *true* throat is really the sonic surface in the gas flow stream, which may or may not coincide exactly with the minimum diameter of the nozzle. In most real nozzles the Mach 1.0 surface is convex outward from the chamber and intersects the nozzle walls at or slightly downstream of the minimum-diameter point within the nozzle. This gives a *true* throat area greater than the geometrical planar throat area, which in turn gives an effect of higher-than-ideal mass flow rate per unit geometrical throat area.

The net result of all these effects is that the mass flow rate in a real nozzle differs from that in an ideal nozzle, usually by being greater than ideal. This leads to difficulty for the designer who must specify the nozzle size required for a given thrust. Common practice in the rocket industry has been to make use of a nozzle "discharge coefficient" ν_d, defined as the ratio of actual to theoretical flow per unit geometrical area, based upon experiments on nozzles with gases and flow conditions similar to those under design. Some reduction in exhaust velocity also results from these effects. Here again it is customary to use a nozzle-velocity coefficient to convert calculated theoretical exhaust velocities to real velocities. This coefficient is defined as the ratio of actual to theoretical exhaust velocity and is given by

$$\nu_v = \frac{v_{ea}}{v_{ei}} \qquad (2\text{-}51)$$

Using this, Eq. (2-42) can be rewritten as

$$v_{ea} = v_v \left(\frac{2\gamma g_c}{\gamma - 1} \frac{R_u}{\mathfrak{M}} T_c \eta_c + v_c^2 \right)^{1/2} \tag{2-52}$$

Making use of the correction factors v_v and v_d, the actual thrust per unit propellant flow rate, and hence the actual specific impulse for a rocket operating in vacuum, becomes

$$I_{sp} = \frac{F_a}{w} = v_v \left[\frac{2\gamma}{\gamma - 1} \frac{R_u}{\mathfrak{M} g_c} T_c \eta_c + \left(\frac{v_c}{g_c} \right)^2 \right]^{1/2}$$
$$+ \frac{1}{v_d} \left(\frac{P_e}{P_c} \right)^{(\gamma-1)/\gamma} \left(\frac{\gamma - 1}{2\gamma} \frac{R_u}{\mathfrak{M} g_c} \frac{T_c}{\eta_c} \right)^{1/2} \tag{2-53}$$

Note that this is

$$I_{sp} = \frac{v_{ei}}{g_c} \left[v_v + \frac{1}{v_d} \left(\frac{1}{\eta_c} - 1 \right) \frac{\gamma - 1}{2\gamma} \right] \tag{2-54}$$

for operation with a motor geometry for which $v_c \ll v_e$. The actual specific impulse is related to the effective exhaust velocity by

$$v_e = g_c I_{sp} \tag{2-55}$$

It is this effective velocity which should be used in vehicle performance calculations as described in the previous section. Figure 2-13 shows the parameter $v_e \sqrt{\mathfrak{M}/T_c}$ as a function of the pressure ratio P_c/P_e for several values of specific-heat ratio γ when the velocity and discharge coefficients are chosen to be 0.98 and 1.05, respectively.

For use of a liquid propellant the power output of the rocket motor must be sufficient to vaporize and heat the propellant to peak temperature at the desired weight flow rate. This is

$$P_r = K \left(\frac{v_{mi}^2}{2J g_c} + H_v \right) w \tag{2-56}$$

where H_v is the heat of vaporization of the liquid propellant and J and K are thermal-mechanical and thermal-electrical conversion factors respectively. In the English system of units the values of these are $J = 778$ ft-lb/Btu and $K = 1.055 \times 10^{-3}$ (Mw)(sec)/Btu.

2-3. Propellant Characteristics. Having developed and presented the fundamental vehicle and nozzle performance equations, it is now necessary to consider the properties of the propellants which are of interest for use in a nuclear rocket motor. Since low molecular weight is the fundamental criterion, the elements hydrogen, helium, lithium, beryllium, and boron are worth mention, together with their dissociable compounds such as the various hydrocarbons (for example, CH_4, C_3H_8, CH_2) and metallic hydrides (for example, LiH and BH). Nitrogen gas is of little interest as a propellant because it is extremely stable and does not dissociate appreciably until temperatures above 6000°F are reached. Even if completely dissociated, its molecular weight would be about 14, seven times higher than that of diatomic hydrogen. However, several of the easily dissociated hydrogen-bearing compounds of nitrogen such as NH_3 and N_2H_4 are of potential usefulness as nuclear rocket propellants. Other compounds of interest include water and several of the dissociable

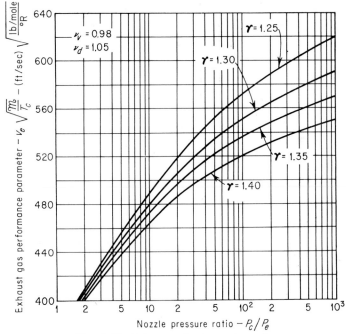

FIG. 2-13. Exhaust velocity, real nozzle.

alcohols. Throughout the discussion which follows, the propellants are regarded as monopropellants only. Since heating of the gases is to be accomplished by a nuclear reactor rather than by combustion processes, it is not necessary to utilize a chemically reactive mixture.

Liquids. The problems of handling, storing, and utilizing solid or gaseous propellants for nuclear rockets are so formidable compared to those associated with the use of liquids that only liquid propellants are considered herein. This excludes the normal solids—lithium, beryllium, and boron—mentioned above. Investigation of the properties of these materials discloses that natural lithium and boron are both strong absorbers of thermal neutrons and are thus not desirable as major components of nuclear reactors. Beryllium, while an excellent neutron moderator, is very costly and does not offer any real performance advantage over dissociated ammonia or any of the potentially useful hydrocarbons. It will not be further considered as a propellant. On the other side of the fence is the element helium, which can only be liquefied at great effort and expense because of its extremely low boiling point (7.5°R at 1 atm) and its low heat of vaporization (10.8 Btu/lb, about one-hundredth that of water). These two facts make helium very undesir-

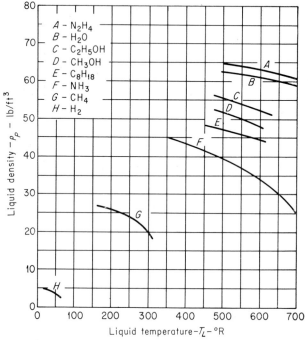

Fig. 2-14. Density of various liquid propellants.

able from the standpoint of production, handling, and storage. As a consequence of its low heat of vaporization, internal heat generation by energy absorption from the radiation field surrounding the nuclear-reactor power plant (Chap. 6) would require that large amounts of non-thrust-productive weight be carried to shield any liquid helium aboard a nuclear rocket vehicle. For these reasons and in spite of its nonreactive nature, helium will not be discussed further herein for use as a propellant for nuclear rockets. The list of useful materials is thus reduced to a single element, hydrogen, and its compounds.

Some of the characteristic features of liquid hydrogen and the various hydrogen compounds are discussed in detail in this section. To provide a ready reference, values of the most needed and pertinent physical, thermal, and chemical properties of these liquids are summarized in

Table 2-1 and Figs. 2-14 and 2-15, which show liquid densities and vapor pressures as functions of temperature.

WATER.   Water, H_2O, is a clear colorless liquid familiar to us all.   It is perhaps surprising to find it included in a list of nuclear rocket propellants.   It is here primarily because it is so readily available and so easy to handle, transport, and store.   Corrosion of storage tanks is not a

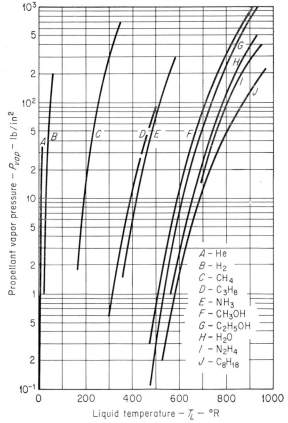

A – He
B – H_2
C – CH_4
D – C_3H_8
E – NH_3
F – CH_3OH
G – C_2H_5OH
H – H_2O
I – N_2H_4
J – C_8H_{18}

FIG. 2-15. Vapor pressure of various liquid propellants.

problem if active pure metals such as aluminum and iron are avoided. Stainless steel, copper, or anodized (surface-oxidized) aluminum tanks will hold water indefinitely.   Water is an excellent neutron moderator because of its high nuclear density and the fact that two out of every three nuclei are those of hydrogen.

ALCOHOLS.   Two typical alcohols, methyl, CH_3OH, and ethyl, C_2H_5OH, are readily available colorless liquids with some properties similar to those of water.   Both their freezing and boiling points are lower than

TABLE 2-1. PROPERTIES OF LIQUID PROPELLANTS

Property	Propellant								
	Hydrogen	Ammonia	Hydrazine	Methyl alcohol	Ethyl alcohol	Methane	Propane	Octane	Water
Chemical formula	H_2	NH_3	N_2H_4	CH_3OH	C_2H_5OH	CH_4	C_3H_8	C_8H_{18}	H_2O
Molecular weight $\mathfrak{M}$, lb/mole	2.016	17.03	32.05	34.04	46.07	16.04	44.09	114.23	18.02
Melting point, °F	−434.5	−108	34.5	−144	−180	−299	−310	−70	32
Boiling point, °F	−423	−28	237	148	174	−259	−44	258	212
Heat of vaporization at 1 atm H_v, Btu/lb	197	589	602	473	367	248	183	128	970
Heat capacity of liquid c_p, Btu/(lb)(°F)	1.75 (−434°F) 2.33 (−424°F)	1.05 (−76°F) 1.48 (212°F)	0.75 (80°F)	0.57 (32°F) 0.60 (68°F)	0.54 (32°F) 0.58 (77°F)	0.811 (−280°F) 0.861 (−226°F)	0.576 (32°F)	0.52 (68°F) 0.63 (200°F)	1.00 (32–212°F)
Viscosity of liquid μ, lb mass/(hr)(ft)	0.03 (−424°F)	0.64 (−28°F)	2.71 (35°F) 2.35 (68°F)	1.98 (32°F) 1.45 (68°F)	4.29 (32°F) 2.91 (68°F)	. . . .	. . . .	1.71 (32°F) 1.31 (68°F)	4.34 (32°F) 2.42 (68°F)
Thermal conductivity of liquid k, Btu/(hr)(ft)(°F)	0.068 (−424°F)	0.29 (45°F)	. . . .	0.120 (68°F)	0.105 (68°F)	. . . .	. . . .	0.082 (70–104°F)	0.33 (32°F) 0.38 (140°F)
Critical pressure, atm	12.8	111.5	145	78.7	63.1	45.8	43	24.6	217.7
Critical temperature, °F	−399.7	270.3	716	464	242.9	−114.5	204.1	564.8	706.3
Approximate relative cost	4–5	1	3	1	1	2	1.5	1	1

those of water, but their liquid ranges are considerably greater than that of water. Corrosion of storage tanks is not a problem for these liquids, but considerable fire hazard results from mixtures of alcohol vapors and air over a moderate range of alcohol concentration. Prolonged inhalation of alcohol vapors results in dullness of perception and can lead to serious internal-tissue damage. The pure (100 per cent) liquids are excellent drying agents and can "burn" the skin by local dehydration. Water flushing and shower facilities should be provided for personnel working with pure alcohol. The high nuclear density of hydrogen and carbon in methyl and ethyl alcohols assures their usefulness as neutron moderators.

HYDROCARBONS. Hydrocarbons from CH_4 to CH_2 are potentially useful nuclear rocket propellants provided that appreciable dissociation of the primary compound occurs in its passage through the reactor heat source. A large choice of freezing and boiling points is available; there are literally hundreds of potentially useful compounds. Like the alcohols, the major hazard in storage is that resulting from the formation of combustible mixtures of hydrocarbon vapors and air. Methane, in particular, forms explosive mixtures over an exceedingly wide range of concentration.[22] Liquid hydrocarbons are not corrosive and may be stored in mild-steel tanks for prolonged periods. Health hazard due to inhalation of fumes is not severe. Like most other hydrogen compounds, the liquid hydrocarbons are excellent neutron moderators.

NITROGEN COMPOUNDS. The two most obviously useful compounds of nitrogen and hydrogen are ammonia, NH_3, and hydrazine, N_2H_4. Both are colorless liquids which present severe health hazards. Prolonged inhalation of vapors of hydrazine or ammonia can result in temporary blindness, collapse, and shock. Pure ammonia is a powerful drying agent and can give severe burns if liquid drops fall on exposed skin. Although ammonia–air vapor mixtures are not readily combustible, hydrazine vapors do form highly explosive mixtures with air. Hydrazine itself can spontaneously decompose under certain conditions, liberating large amounts of energy. The liquid properties of hydrazine are similar to those of water, but ammonia is liquid at 1 atm only below $-28°F$ and so must be either stored under pressure or refrigerated. The presence of nitrogen impairs the usefulness of these compounds as moderators compared to those previously discussed, since thermal-neutron absorption due to nitrogen in a molecule of the compound is about two to three times that for the hydrogen in the molecule.

HYDROGEN. Liquid hydrogen has several of both the most and the least desirable characteristics for use as a nuclear rocket propellant. Its low molecular weight gives it a performance capability superior to all other propellants; however, its extreme low temperature (liquid below

−423°F) makes handling and storage difficult, embrittles metals, solidifies air, and requires a relatively costly production process. Not only must insulation be provided for liquid-hydrogen storage tanks, but continuous refrigeration may be required to remove the heat released in conversion from the ortho to para phase of the molecular structure if this conversion is not accomplished at the liquefaction plant. Storage-tank corrosion is not a problem, but combustible mixtures of gas and air are

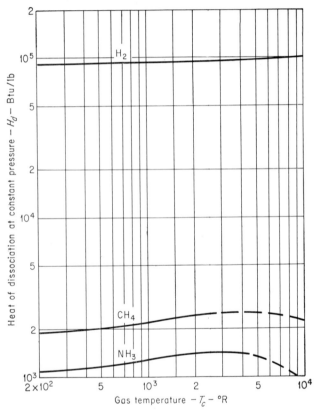

Fig. 2-16. Heat of dissociation of propellant gases.

easily formed[22] and provide a safety hazard. The health hazard of liquid hydrogen is chiefly due to its low temperature, as severe frostbite can result from brief exposure to the liquid. In the liquid state, hydrogen has high nuclear density and acts as a fair moderator, comparable in some respects to water. However, the low liquid temperature reduces its effectiveness, and liquid hydrogen alone is a poor choice for moderator compared to the other propellants considered.

Gases. It is principally as gases that the propellants previously discussed are used in a nuclear rocket motor. The liquid propellant is vaporized either by radiation heating before it reaches the reactor core or by fission heating in the first few inches of travel through the fissioning-core volume. It is as gases that the propellants leave the nozzle, producing thrust to drive the vehicle. Most of the heat transfer to the propellant takes place to gaseous material. The word "gases," as used in this sense, refers to the propellant material after it has received its heat of vaporization, or "energy of disorder," whether the reactor heat-transfer system is operating at subcritical or supercritical pressures.

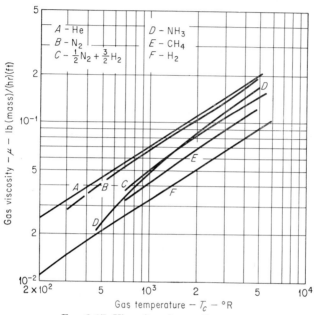

Fig. 2-17. Viscosity of propellant gases.

General characteristics of the gases resulting from vaporization of the propellants previously considered are discussed in this section. Physical, thermal, and chemical properties of interest are shown as functions of temperature in Figs. 2-16 through 2-20. The phenomena of dissociation and recombination are treated at some length to illustrate the approach necessary to obtain an accurate estimate of the molecular weight and other pertinent properties characteristic of the gas flowing through the reactor and nozzle.

WATER. Water vapor (steam) has been used for many years as the working fluid in conventional power plants. As is well known, high-temperature steam is highly corrosive, especially when in contact with oxygen (as in air). Water is extremely stable and will not dissociate appreciably at moderate pressures until temperatures above 4000°F have been reached. However, even at lower temperatures hydroxyl radicals and some free oxygen molecules are present, giving rise to an oxidizing action at moderate temperatures. Because of water's stable molecular structure, the molecular weight of gaseous water will be close to 18 at elevated temperatures and pressures.

ALCOHOLS. Alcohols decompose at temperatures above 3000°F at moderate pressures to form, principally, hydrogen and carbon monoxide, together with some acetylene and higher hydrocarbons, hydroxyl radicals, and free oxygen. The gaseous mixture thus has both oxidizing and

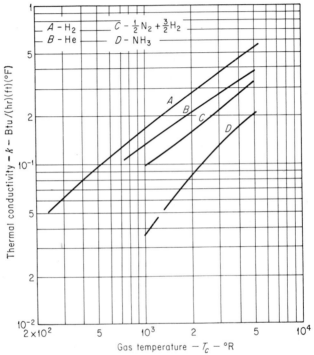

FIG. 2-18. Thermal conductivity of propellant gases.

reducing components and potentially can attack most materials. Since the formation and destruction of active radicals is a heterogeneous (wall effects) as well as homogeneous (gas phase) reaction, it is not unreasonable to suppose that the two-way corrosive capability will cancel out at physical boundaries of the system so that the gas mixture will act as either an oxidizer or a reducer but not as both simultaneously at any given pressure and temperature. The molecular weight of decomposed alcohols will be about 9 to 10, or roughly half that of water.

HYDROCARBONS. The potentially useful hydrocarbons decompose to form hydrogen, free carbon, acetylene, and small amounts of higher hydrocarbons at temperatures above 3500°F at pressures of several atmospheres. The gaseous mixture is often highly reducing, with excess hydrogen, and can react corrosively with many carbon compounds such as wood, plastic, various solid hydrocarbons, and carbon itself. Hot hydrogen will also react with some metals to form hydrides and will cause intergranular corrosion or cracking of others. This last is sometimes referred to as hydrogen "embrittlement." However, if the gas mixture is carbon-rich, the free carbon present can condense in the gas phase or

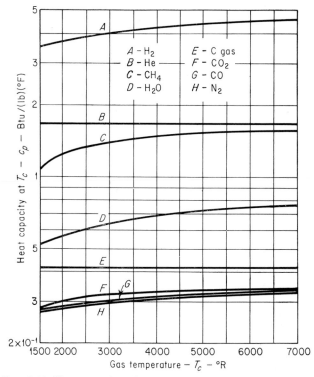

FIG. 2-19. Heat capacity of pure gases at constant temperature.

"plate" on the surfaces of the channel containing the gas. Either event may result in reduction of flow or plugging of flow channels. The energy of vaporization of carbon is about 28,000 Btu/lb, so that a large amount of heat is released in the condensation process. The molecular weight of decomposed hydrocarbons varies from 5.5 to 8 at elevated temperatures and pressures of interest.

NITROGEN COMPOUNDS. Both ammonia and hydrazine decompose rapidly at temperatures above 2500°F at moderate pressures to form nitrogen and hydrogen. Since diatomic nitrogen cannot be formed by the decomposition of a single ammonia molecule and the three hydrogen atoms released can form only one diatomic molecule, the instantaneous products of decomposition must include some monatomic nitrogen and hydrogen. This being the case, ammonia acts as a highly reducing gas at temperatures well below those for corrosive action by the other propellants, water excepted. The mechanism of dissociation of hydrazine is not well understood, but it probably goes through an ammonia-like

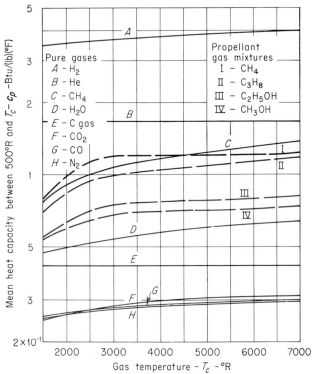

FIG. 2-20. Mean heat capacity of pure gases and of propellant gases at equilibrium conditions at 100 atm.

stage before complete breakup of the molecule occurs, and thus its chemical-reactivity characteristics should not markedly differ from those of ammonia. The free hydrogen present will attack carbon and many carbon compounds as well as most metals, notable exceptions being molybdenum and platinum. The molecular weights of the products of decomposition are about 8.5 for ammonia and 10.5 for hydrazine.

HYDROGEN. Hydrogen is relatively stable to temperatures as high as 4000°F at moderate pressures, remaining in the diatomic state. Hot hydrogen is highly reducing and will react with carbon or graphite, some metals, and many hydrocarbon compounds. Its attack on graphite is believed to be by intergranular chemical corrosion of the binding material holding the graphite matrix together. This action results in a loose, sandy surface with little adherence strength at the graphite-gas interface. If the hydrogen gas is moving past the surface with an appreciable velocity, the weakly held grains of graphite will be blown away, thus exposing fresh intergranular joints to the chemical attack of hot hydrogen. The molecular weight of hydrogen is roughly 2 at most temperatures and pressures useful for rocket motor and reactor design.

Dissociation and Recombination. Determination of the characteristics of the propellant gases leaving the reactor and entering the nozzle requires knowledge of the constitution of these gases, hence of the degree of dissociation occurring in the reactor. Accurate estimation of nozzle and propellant performance also requires knowledge of the gas constitution throughout the nozzle. A true determination of this latter information necessitates calculations involving the rate at which chemical recombination reactions take place in a rapidly expanding gas stream.

EQUILIBRIUM. Since the time of residence of gases within a nuclear reactor serving as a rocket-motor energy source is long (e.g., 50 msec) compared with the dissociation time of any of the gases considered, at temperatures above 3000°F, the assumption of chemical equilibrium at the reactor exit (nozzle entrance) is reasonable.

Consider a gas-phase dissociation-recombination reaction taking place as

$$\sum_{}^{j} m_i A_i \rightleftharpoons \sum_{}^{k} n_i B_i \tag{2-57}$$

where A_i denotes the ith component of the j reacting materials and B_i is the ith component of the k products of reaction. The equilibrium constant for this reaction, assumed to occur at a pressure P (in atmospheres), is given by

$$K_p = \frac{\prod_{1}^{k} \mathbf{N}_i^{n_i}}{\prod_{1}^{j} \mathbf{M}_i^{m_i}} P^{\left(\sum_{1}^{k} n_i - \sum_{1}^{j} n_i\right)} \tag{2-58}$$

where the symbol Π denotes "the product of," such as

$$\prod_{1}^{r} \alpha_i = \alpha_1 \alpha_2 \cdots \alpha_{r-1} \alpha_r$$

Here $\mathbf{N}_i$ and $\mathbf{M}_i$ are mole fractions of the products B_i and reactants A_i in the equilibrium mixture. The mole fractions are defined as

$$\mathbf{M}_i = \frac{m_i}{\sum_{1}^{j} m_i + \sum_{1}^{k} n_i} \quad \text{and} \quad \mathbf{N}_i = \frac{n_i}{\sum_{1}^{j} m_i + \sum_{1}^{k} n_i} \tag{2-59}$$

It is easily seen from this definition that

$$\sum_{1}^{j} \mathbf{M}_i + \sum_{1}^{k} \mathbf{N}_i = 1 \tag{2-60}$$

The equilibrium constant K_p, generally a sensitive function of temperature, is tabulated[23-25] for many simple reactions. Values of K_p for several reactions of interest herein are shown in Fig. 2-21.

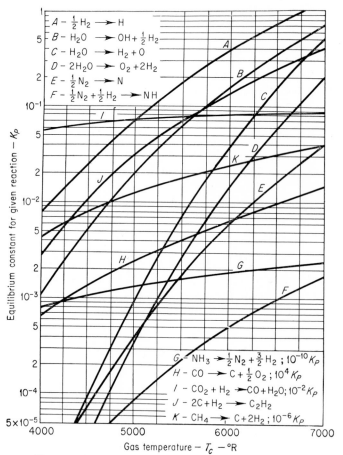

FIG. 2-21. Equilibrium constants for various reactions.

Determination of the values of $\mathbf{M}_i$ and $\mathbf{N}_i$ is often laborious. One equation involving the $j + k$ unknowns (the $\mathbf{M}_i$ and $\mathbf{N}_i$) results from Eq. (2-60). In a multielement system involving e elements, a set of $e - 1$ equations involving the $\mathbf{M}_i$ and $\mathbf{N}_i$ can be determined by a mass balance or atom balance on the complete system. The total number of atoms of any given element must be related to those of any other by the same ratio as that obtaining in the initial reactant mixture. Other equations may be obtained by use of Eq. (2-58). Since it is not likely that values of K_p will be available for the complete reaction of a multielement, multicomponent system, it is necessary to choose $j + k - e$ dissociation-recombination reactions which are pertinent to the problem and for which values of the equilibrium constants are available. For these reactions, $j + k - e$ equilibrium equations may then be written, following Eq. (2-58). If this is done, a set of $j + k$ simultaneous equations in $j + k$ unknowns is available, enabling the complete solution of the problem for any desired system pressure and temperature. Pressure enters the equations directly, while temperature affects only the values of the $j + k - e$ equilibrium constants (Fig. 2-21).

As an example of the use of this technique, consider the dissociation of water, as follows:

$$\mathbf{M}_1 H_2 O \rightleftharpoons \mathbf{N}_1 H_2 + \mathbf{N}_2 O_2 + \mathbf{N}_3 OH + \mathbf{N}_4 O + \mathbf{N}_5 H \qquad (2\text{-}61a)$$

Application of Eq. (2-60) leads to

$$\mathbf{M}_1 + \mathbf{N}_1 + \mathbf{N}_2 + \mathbf{N}_3 + \mathbf{N}_4 + \mathbf{N}_5 = 1 \qquad (2\text{-}61b)$$

An atom balance for the complete system results in

$$\frac{2\mathbf{M}_1 + 2\mathbf{N}_1 + \mathbf{N}_3 + \mathbf{N}_5}{\mathbf{M}_1 + 2\mathbf{N}_2 + \mathbf{N}_3 + \mathbf{N}_4} = \frac{\text{H atoms}}{\text{O atoms}} = 2 \qquad (2\text{-}61c)$$

Since $j = 1$ and $k = 5$, there are six unknowns, thus requiring four additional equations to permit solution of the problem. Four simple dissociation-recombination equations whose equilibrium constants are known can be chosen. These may be

$$H_2 \rightleftharpoons 2H \qquad \text{here } K_{p_1} = \frac{\mathbf{N}_5{}^2}{\mathbf{N}_1} P \qquad (2\text{-}61d)$$

$$O_2 \rightleftharpoons 2O \qquad \text{here } K_{p_2} = \frac{\mathbf{N}_4{}^2}{\mathbf{N}_2} P \qquad (2\text{-}61e)$$

$$H_2 O \rightleftharpoons H_2 + \tfrac{1}{2} O_2 \qquad \text{here } K_{p_3} = \frac{\mathbf{N}_1 \sqrt{\mathbf{N}_2}}{\mathbf{M}_1} \sqrt{P} \qquad (2\text{-}61f)$$

$$H_2 O \rightleftharpoons \tfrac{1}{2} H_2 + OH \qquad \text{here } K_{p_4} = \frac{\mathbf{N}_3 \sqrt{\mathbf{N}_1}}{\mathbf{M}_1} \sqrt{P} \qquad (2\text{-}61g)$$

Solution of this system is straightforward, though time-consuming. Equation (2-61g) may be solved for $\mathbf{N}_1 = f_1(\mathbf{N}_3, \mathbf{M}_1)$. Substitution of this into Eq. (2-61f) yields $\mathbf{N}_2 = f_2(\mathbf{N}_3, \mathbf{M}_1)$. Repetition of this for Eqs. (2-61e) and (2-61d) gives $\mathbf{N}_4 = f_4(\mathbf{N}_3, \mathbf{M}_1)$ and $\mathbf{N}_5 = f_5(\mathbf{N}_3, \mathbf{M}_1)$. These four equalities can then be substituted into Eqs. (2-61b) and (2-61c) to obtain two equations in the two unknowns N_3 and M_1. Solution for these immediately leads to values for all the N_i. Unfortunately, even this simple system results in equations as high as sixth order; thus if a large number of operating conditions (that is, P and T) are to be investigated for a given problem, automatic computing machines can profitably be used.

RATE PHENOMENA. It has become standard practice in the chemical rocket industry to compute propellant flow through nozzles by assuming either "frozen" or constant-composition flow, or instantaneous chemical equilibrium within the nozzle. For the first case the gas is usually assumed frozen at the nozzle-entrance conditions throughout its expansion process through the nozzle. This assumption appears plausible because the gas particles move through the nozzle in a very short time (a millisecond or less) and are continually becoming less dense as the flow proceeds down the nozzle; thus they have neither the time nor opportunity to react with each other once they leave the chamber. However, the assumption is obviously not reasonable for reactions with recombination reaction times which are very much shorter than the time of residence of gas particles within the nozzle. The second case, instantaneous equilibrium composition at the static gas pressure and temperature at all nozzle sections, assumes an infinite reaction rate. It is apparent that neither case is correct for real gases, but certainly all real gases will fall between the two extremes. The assumption of instantaneous equilibrium results in calculated exhaust velocities generally higher than those obtained for the constant (chamber) composition condition. Use of frozen flow, although incorrect, is thus conservative. Exact solution for the flow constitution throughout the nozzle requires the introduction of reaction-rate equations into the system of molar-balance equations used for instantaneous equilibrium calculations. This procedure has not been followed extensively in the field, partly because it greatly complicates the problem but primarily because of the paucity of kinetic data for the various recombination reactions of interest.

Accurate calculation of the gas exhaust velocity by this method requires specification of the gas velocity prior to entering the nozzle, hence can only be carried out for specific geometries. This is because the nozzle throat-area conditions (and hence all conditions downstream of the throat) must be determined by the kinetic-equilibrium properties of the gas at the throat, which in turn depend upon the velocity and temperature profiles upstream of the throat section. For this reason it is not possible to perform kinetic-equilibrium calculations of general validity. The dissociation of hydrogen, $H_2 \rightleftharpoons 2H$, and the water-gas reaction, $H_2O + CO \rightleftharpoons CO_2 + H_2$, have been studied from the kinetic viewpoint.[26–30] The reaction-rate constant for recombination of hydrogen is high, and reaction times are short (order of microseconds) compared to the residence time in typical nozzles. The estimated kinetic-equilibrium composition therefore closely follows that computed on the basis of instantaneous equilibrium. The opposite picture is presented by the water-gas recombination reaction. Here the formation of CO_2 and H_2

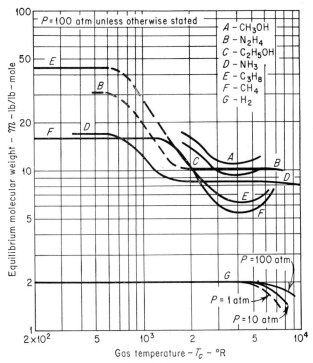

FIG. 2-22. Molecular weight of propellant gases.

proceeds so slowly throughout the nozzle that the gas mixture acts as though it is frozen at the nozzle-entrance composition throughout the flow. For a complete treatment of these two cases and to gain familiarity with the difficulties involved in such calculations, the references given should be consulted. For purposes of this text the dissociation of hydrogen is assumed to follow instantaneous equilibrium, while all other reactions are treated as frozen at the equilibrium constitutions at the nozzle entrance (reactor exit).

Performance. Equilibrium values of molecular weights, as computed by methods outlined in the preceding section, are presented in Fig. 2-22 as functions of temperature for the various propellant gases of interest.

For expansion of hydrogen, with instantaneous nozzle equilibrium, average values of molecular weight and synthesized values of specific-heat ratio may be used to compute exhaust velocity by use of the adiabatic-

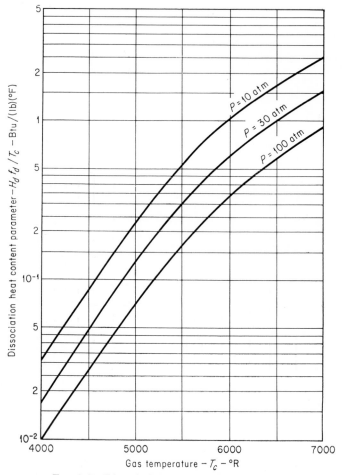

FIG. 2-23. Dissociation parameter for hydrogen.

flow equations derived previously. For nozzle-exit temperatures so low (less than about 1500°F) that complete recombination can be assumed in the gas stream, the synthetic specific-heat ratio can be determined entirely by an energy balance based upon the mole fraction of hydrogen dissociated at the nozzle entrance. From Eq. (2-40) it is found that

$$\gamma = \frac{\mathfrak{M}c_p}{\mathfrak{M}c_p - R_u/J} = \frac{\mathfrak{M}c_p}{\mathfrak{M}c_p - 1.99} \qquad (2\text{-}62)$$

For expansion to low temperature the effective heat capacity of the gas is given by

$$c'_p = c_p + \frac{H_d f_d}{T_c} \qquad (2\text{-}63)$$

where H_d is the heat of dissociation (Fig. 2-16) and f_d is the weight fraction of hydrogen that is dissociated. Combination of Eqs. (2-62) and (2-63) gives the required synthetic over-all specific-heat ratio. Values of the parameter $H_d f_d / T_c$ are shown for convenience in Fig. 2-23 as a function of temperature for several rocket-motor chamber pressures.

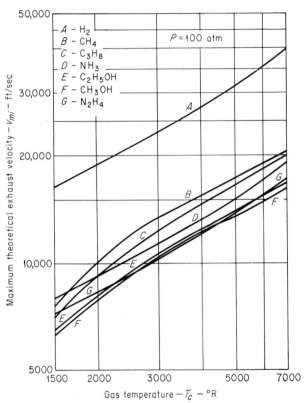

FIG. 2-24. Propellant-gas exhaust velocity.

Using the values of c_p presented in Fig. 2-20 together with those for hydrogen obtained from combination of the data in Figs. 2-21 and 2-23, the ideal maximum exhaust velocity can be computed for all the propellants of interest. Results of such calculations are shown in Fig. 2-24, which presents ideal maximum exhaust velocity as a function of temperature. A chamber pressure of 100 atm was assumed in order to facilitate calculations for all the propellants. The effective exhaust velocity depends upon the nozzle-velocity and -discharge coefficients, as shown by Eqs. (2-54) and (2-55), as well as upon the ideal maximum exhaust velocity. Data given in the figures, together with the equations pre-

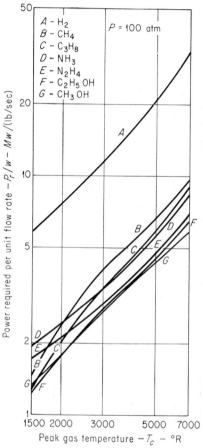

FIG. 2-25. Propellant specific-power consumption.

sented, enable the determination of effective exhaust velocity for any propellant considered at all conditions of interest in nuclear rocket motors.

The power consumption per unit flow rate can be determined by combination of the ideal maximum exhaust velocities shown in Fig. 2-24, the heat-of-vaporization data from Table 2-1, and the relation given in Eq. (2-56). This specific power consumption is shown in Fig. 2-25 as a function of peak gas temperature for all the propellants of interest.

REFERENCES

1. Ley, W.: "Rockets, Missiles, and Space Travel," 2d printing, chap. 3, pp. 62–63, The Viking Press, Inc., New York, 1951.
2. Zim, Herbert S.: "Rockets and Jets," chap. II, pp. 14ff., Harcourt, Brace and Company, Inc., New York, 1945.
3. Kooy, J. M. J., and J. W. H. Uytenbogaart: "Ballistics of the Future," chap. IX, pp. 209–239, McGraw-Hill Book Company, Inc., New York, 1946.
4. *a.* Esenwein, F. T., L. J. Obery, and C. F. Schueller: Aerodynamic Characteristics of NACA RM-10 Missile in 8- by 6-foot Supersonic Wind Tunnel at Mach Numbers from 1.49 to 1.98, *NACA RM* E50D28, July, 1950.
   b. Piland, R. O.: Drag Measurements on a $\frac{1}{6}$ Scale, Finless, Sting Mounted NACA RM-10 Missile in Flight at Mach Numbers from 1.1 to 4.04 Showing Some Reynolds Number and Heating Effects, *NACA RM* L54H09, October, 1954.
   c. Stoney, W. E., Jr., and J. F. Royall: Zero-lift Drag of a Series of Bomb Shapes at Mach Numbers from 0.60 to 1.10, *NACA RM* L56D16, July, 1956.
5. Wood, K. D.: "Airplane Design," 10th ed., pp. A1:2–A1:4, published by author at Boulder, Colo., 1954. Data taken from C. N. Warfield, Tentative Tables for the Properties of the Upper Atmosphere, *NACA TN* 1200.
6. Sutton, G. P.: "Rocket Propulsion Elements," chap. 8, p. 247, John Wiley & Sons, Inc., New York, 1949.
7. Leitman, G.: Optimum Pay-load-ratio Relation for Multiple-stage Rockets, *NAVORD Rept.* 5064, U.S. Naval Ordnance Test Station, China Lake, Calif., Apr. 17, 1956.
8. Rauscher, Manfred: "Introduction to Aeronautical Dynamics," chap. 2, pp. 31–42, John Wiley & Sons, Inc., New York, 1953.
9. Ref. 3, chap. VI, pp. 112–167.
10. Ref. 1, chaps. 11 and 12, pp. 281–345.
11. Symposium on Satellite Vehicles, Second International Congress on Astronautics, London, 1951, as published in *J. Brit. Interplanet. Soc.*, vol. 10, no. 6, pp. 245–304, November, 1951.
12. On the Utility of an Artificial Unmanned Earth Satellite, *J. Am. Rocket Soc.*, vol. 25, no. 2, pp. 71–78, February, 1955.
13. Dodge, Barnett F.: "Chemical Engineering Thermodynamics," chap. VII, pp. 261ff., McGraw-Hill Series in Chemical Engineering, McGraw-Hill Book Company, Inc., New York, 1944.
14. Young, Vincent W., and Gilbert A. Young: "Elementary Engineering Thermodynamics," 3d ed., chap. IV, pp. 48ff., McGraw-Hill Book Company, Inc., New York, 1947.
15. Zucrow, M. J.: "Principles of Jet Propulsion and Gas Turbines," chap. 3, pp. 67ff., John Wiley & Sons, Inc., New York, 1948.
16. Liepmann, Hans Wolfgang, and Allen E. Puckett: "Introduction to Aerodynamics of a Compressible Fluid," chap. 13, pp. 210ff., John Wiley & Sons, Inc., New York, 1947.
17. Dillaway, Robert B.: A Philosophy for Improved Rocket Nozzle Design, *Am. Rocket Soc. Paper* 362-56, November, 1956.
18. Foelsch, Kuno: The Analytical Design of an Axially Symmetric Nozzle for a Parallel and Uniform Jet, *J. Aeronaut. Sci.*, vol. 16, no. 1, pp. 161–166, 188, January, 1949.

19. Puckett, Allen E.: Supersonic Nozzle Design, *J. Appl. Mechanics*, vol. 13, no. 4, pp. 265–270, December, 1946.
20. Beckwith, Ivan E., and John A. Moore: An Accurate and Rapid Method for the Design of Supersonic Nozzles, *NACA TN* 3322, February, 1955.
21. Schlichting, Hermann: "Boundary Layer Theory," chap. II, pp. 22–27, chap. VII, pp. 94–113, McGraw-Hill Book Company, Inc., New York, 1955.
22. Lewis, Bernard, and Guenther von Elbe: "Combustion, Flames and Explosions of Gases," appendix B, pp. 749–763, Academic Press, Inc., New York, 1951.
23. Ref. 22, appendix A, pp. 739–748.
24. Hirschfelder, J. O., F. T. McClure, and C. F. Curtiss: Thermochemistry and the Equation of State of the Propellant Gases, *NDRC Rept.* A-48 *OSRD*-547, table XXXI, pp. 54–56, May, 1942.
25. Huff, Vearl N., Sanford Gordon, and Virginia E. Morrell: General Method and Thermodynamic Tables for Computation of Equilibrium Composition and Temperature of Chemical Reactions, *NACA Rept.* 1037, 1951.
26. Penner, S. S., and D. Altman: Adiabatic Flow of Hydrogen Gas through a Rocket Nozzle with and without Composition Change, *J. Franklin Inst.*, vol. 245, pp. 421–432, 1948.
27. Altman, D., and S. S. Penner: Chemical Reaction during Adiabatic Flow through a Rocket Nozzle, *J. Chem. Phys.*, vol. 17, pp. 56–61, 1949.
28. Penner, S. S.: Maintenance of Near Equilibrium during Isentropic Expansions through a Nozzle, *J. Am. Chem. Soc.*, vol. 71, pp. 788–791, 1949.
29. Krieger, F. J.: Chemical Kinetics and Rocket Nozzle Design, *J. Am. Rocket Soc.*, vol. 21, pp. 179–185, November, 1951.
30. Ref. 22, chap. III, pp. 83–88.

CHAPTER 3

SYSTEM ANALYSIS

The relative advantage accruing from use of a particular design condition or rocket-vehicle component-performance parameter can only be determined by an analysis of its effect on complete vehicle performance. As an example, high rocket-motor chamber pressure produces high exhaust velocities and yields thrust units of high specific power output, but requires larger, more powerful, and heavier propellant-pumping equipment than that for lower-pressure use. The choice of *optimum* operating pressure for maximum vehicle performance can only be determined by analyzing the performance capabilities of *vehicles* over a wide range of chamber pressure. The effect of changing propellant-tank pressure, vehicle initial acceleration, payload weight, and many other parameters must be determined by similar methods. System analysis attempts to do this by relating generalized functional weight and performance equations for each component to the fundamental vehicle performance equations given in Chap. 2.

3-1. Components. In order to analyze the performance of a rocket vehicle system, the dependence of the weights of its components upon some characteristic vehicle performance or weight parameter must be known. Rocket-vehicle system analysis is possible only because the weights of all functional components depend strongly upon either the reactor power output (hence thrust or gross weight) or the total energy released in powered flight (hence propellant weight or vehicle total impulse). The gross weight of a nuclear rocket vehicle is the sum of the weights of propellant (m_p), tankage and structure (m_t and m_s), pumping equipment (m_e), nuclear rocket motor and associated thrust structure (m_r and m_f), and dead load (m_d). Each of these functional units is discussed in turn in this section. Conspicuous by its absence is the weight of the aerodynamic fins so typical of rockets the size of the World War II V-2 and smaller. Modern large rockets do not require external fins for flight stability, this being accomplished most effectively by side forces resulting from the deflection of exhaust gas by movable vanes in the exhaust jet or from off-axis thrust caused by tilting the primary thrust-unit axis relative to the vehicle axis.[1,2]

Propellant. A working fluid is required in order to cool the nuclear-reactor heat source and to propel the vehicle (Chap. 2). This working fluid is called the propellant, and its weight is denoted by the symbol m_p. The weight of propellant is proportional to the total energy output of the system by virtue of the fact that it determines the maximum possible energy output. The amount of heat which can be generated by the reactor is limited to the amount which can be absorbed by the propellant in the vehicle. Not all of the propellant carried aboard a rocket vehicle can be used for thrust. Some is lost by being trapped in the finite piping and pump volumes after the tanks have run dry. Some is required to provide a heat sink for cooling various auxiliary equipment. Other propellant is used to drive the pump turbines. This latter is first heated to moderate temperature ($\sim$1500°F) in the reactor core, then withdrawn, passed through the turbines, and exhausted to the atmosphere (or to space) through high-pressure-ratio nozzles in order to gain as much thrust as possible from this "waste" propellant. Still other losses occur by vaporization of propellant within the tanks. This is caused partly by internal heat generation due to the absorption of energy from the radiation field surrounding the reactor and partly by heat transferred to the propellant from the tank walls which are, in turn, heated by aerodynamic skin friction as the rocket vehicle moves rapidly through the atmosphere. Losses due to radiation heating can be minimized by the use of shielding, and those due to skin-friction heating can be cut down by tank insulation. The sum of all such losses is defined to be a fraction α of the total propellant weight. For a constant-thrust, constant-flow-rate rocket motor, this means that a fraction α of the flow goes into non-thrust-productive uses. Note that much of this fraction does not go through the reactor; thus the reactor need not be designed to handle flow based upon the total propellant weight divided by the operating time.

For vertical launching and ascent through the atmosphere at space accelerations from $\frac{1}{3}$ to $1g_0$ (range of near-optimum accelerations for large rockets), experiments[3,4] and analyses show that the maximum skin temperature achieved on the vehicle side (tank) walls due to aerodynamic heating is about 300°F. Estimation of the heat transferred to the propellant requires a knowledge of the heat-transfer coefficients as well as the temperatures on both sides of the tank skin. Measurements have been made of skin heating of rocket vehicles ascending vertically through the atmosphere.[3] Typical results of such tests are shown in Fig. 3-1, where the air-side heat-transfer coefficient is plotted as a function of the time after take-off. Also shown are the tank-skin temperature and the "adiabatic wall" temperature of the ambient air. Heat transfer to quiescent liquid nitrogen, oxygen, and hydrogen has not been extensively studied, and the available data[5] are not in good agreement; how-

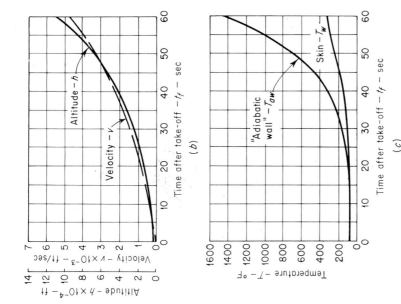

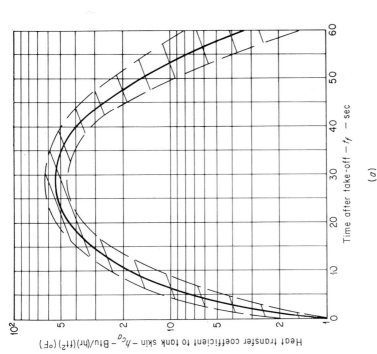

FIG. 3-1. (a) Heat transfer to skin of V-2 missile rising vertically through the atmosphere. (b) Altitude and velocity history, V-2 flight. (c) Typical temperature history, V-2 flight. (W. W. Fischer and R. H. Norris, Supersonic Convective Heat Transfer Correlation from Skin-temperature Measurements on a V-2 Rocket in Flight, Trans. ASME, vol. 71, no. 59, pp. 457–469, July, 1949.)

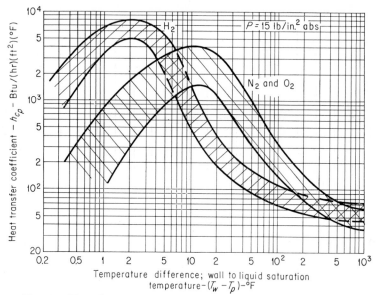

Fig. 3-2. Forced-convection heat transfer to liquid H_2, N_2, and O_2.

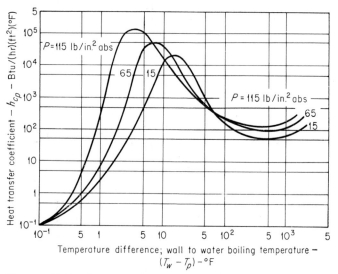

Fig. 3-3. Free-convection heat transfer to water. (*E. A. Farber and R. L. Scorah, Heat Transfer to Water Boiling under Pressure, Trans. ASME, vol. 70, no. 5, pp. 369–381, May, 1948.*)

ever, those shown in Fig. 3-2, which plots liquid-side coefficient as a function of the difference between wall temperature and liquid boiling temperature, are sufficiently good for rough estimation of the heat transfer to cryogenic liquids in single-skinned propellant tanks. To a first approximation the data shown for nitrogen and oxygen can be assumed adequate for use with methane and other liquids of comparable boiling point. Heat transfer to water has been extensively studied. Typical curves of heat-transfer coefficient for free convection to water are shown in Fig. 3-3 as a function of temperature difference.[6,7] Data shown for the liquid free-convection range should be applicable for use with water, the room-temperature hydrocarbons, hydrazine, and the alcohols as propellants. Data shown in Fig. 3-3 in the film-boiling range are reasonably applicable for use with ammonia propellant.

Neglecting transient effects (e.g., wall heat capacity) and the thermal resistance of the tank wall, heat transfer per unit area to the propellant is given by

$$\frac{q}{A_t} = U(T_{aw} - T_p) \tag{3-1}$$

where T_{aw} and T_p are air-adiabatic-wall (Chap. 4) and liquid-propellant temperatures, respectively, and U is an over-all heat-transfer coefficient defined by

$$\frac{1}{U} = \frac{1}{h_{c_a}} + \frac{1}{h_{c_p}} \tag{3-2}$$

The heat-transfer coefficients can be chosen from Figs. 3-1, 3-2, and 3-3 to satisfy the temperature conditions of the problem. Assuming the propellant is carried in a cylindrical tank of diameter D, the fraction of propellant vaporized is given by

$$\alpha_v = \frac{m_{pv}}{m_p} = \frac{4f_v}{D\rho_p H_v} \int_0^{\tau_h} \frac{q}{A_t} \, dt \tag{3-3}$$

where ρ_p = propellant density
H_v = heat of vaporization of liquid
τ_h = effective heating time

The coefficient f_v is the fraction of heat transferred which goes into vaporization of propellant; $(1 - f_v)$ is that which goes to heating of the liquid. For purposes of rough heat-transfer calculations, the missile skin and air temperature–time history shown in Fig. 3-1 may be assumed. For such conditions the air- and liquid-side heat-transfer coefficients can be found from the data given in Figs. 3-1 to 3-3, thus permitting a numerical solution of Eq. (3-3). A more exact analysis requires detailed knowledge of the vehicle flight trajectory. In this manner the fraction of propellant vaporized by aerodynamic heating of the tank skin can be found as a function of propellant-tank diameter. A set of curves showing the ratio

α_v/f_v as a function of tank diameter is given in Fig. 3-4 for various propellants. Note that water, hydrazine, methyl and ethyl alcohol, and the room-temperature hydrocarbons (such as gasoline) do not appear on the figure. Their losses due to heating as discussed are negligible, even under the assumption that all heat transferred goes into the vaporization

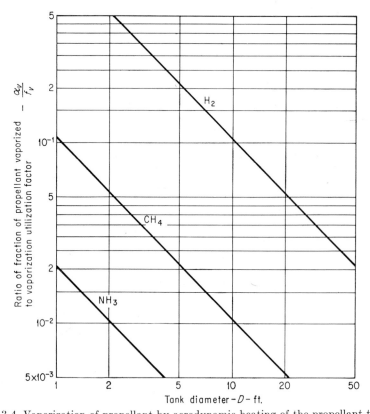

FIG. 3-4. Vaporization of propellant by aerodynamic heating of the propellant tanks.

of propellant ($f_v = 1.0$). For liquid hydrogen, assuming a vaporization utilization factor of $f_v = 0.2$, the loss does not exceed 5 per cent until tanks less than 5 ft in diameter are used.

Tanks and Structure. The propellants must be carried in flight; thus a tank or set of tanks is an obvious necessity. The weight of such tanks is divided between the tank skin and structural members required to support and stiffen the tank assembly. Modern practice in the design of large rockets often utilizes gas pressure in the tank to carry thrust loads to the vehicle nose and the tank skin is used as the vehicle skin or outer surface. Careful analysis[8] shows that double-walled tank construction is undesirable weightwise on large rockets, while the preceding section shows that, even with cryogenic propellants such as liquid hydrogen, the propellant losses due to liquid vaporization are small for *large* single-skin tanks. The tank itself is very much like a pressurized metal-skinned balloon, and stiffening structure is needed only at the tank end caps and at points of attachment to the payload compartment and propulsion system. The excess structure weight can thus be kept to a minimum. The structure weight can be expressed as a function of the tank-skin weight by

$$m_s = A_1 m_t \qquad (3\text{-}4)$$

A typical value for A_1 is between 0.1 and 0.3, based upon present practices. The surface area of a cylindrical tank fitted with $2:1$ ellipsoidal end caps is given by

$$A_t = \pi D_t^2 (B + 0.69) \qquad (3\text{-}5)$$

where $B = L_t/D_t$, the ratio of tank length to diameter. For operation at uniform pressure P_t the wall thickness required in a tank of this size is

$$t_t = \frac{f_s P_t D_t}{2\sigma_t} \qquad (3\text{-}6)$$

where f_s is a design safety factor and σ_t is the yield strength of the tank material. The pressure at any height within the tank is the sum of the gas overpressure and the liquid pressure due to hydrostatic head within the acceleration field of the rocket. The load pressure will thus vary with height from a minimum value at the top of the liquid column to a maximum at the bottom. True optimum minimum-weight design requires that the tank gas overpressure be varied to produce a constant pressure at the tank outlet throughout the time of flight. In such a system the tank pressure at burnout will be uniform throughout the tank, being due to gas pressure alone; thus the tank must be designed with walls of uniform thickness.

The total volume of such a tank is

$$V_t = \frac{\pi}{4} D_t^3 (B + \tfrac{1}{3}) \qquad (3\text{-}7)$$

A small fraction f_u of this total volume must always be left empty at the top of the tank to provide space for thermal expansion of the liquid propellant in the remainder of the tank and to permit accumulation and removal of propellant vapors without entrainment of liquid propellant. This volume is called the tank ullage fraction. The allowable propellant volume is thus

$$V_p = (1 - f_u) V_t \qquad (3\text{-}8)$$

Combination of Eqs. (3-5) through (3-8) with the appropriate material densities leads to a relation between tank-skin weight and weight of propellant carried.   This is given by

$$\frac{m_t}{m_p} = \frac{2f_sP_t}{(1 - f_u)\sigma_t}\frac{B + 0.69}{B + \frac{1}{3}}\frac{\rho_t}{\rho_p} = A_2 \tag{3-9}$$

Values of A_2 are shown in Fig. 3-5 as a function of the parameter $f_sP_t\rho_t/\sigma_t\rho_p$ for zero ullage fraction and for several values of B.

The total tank-skin and -structure weight is thus

$$m_t + m_s = A_3m_p \tag{3-10}$$

where $A_3 = A_2(A_1 + 1)$.

Pumping Equipment.   A pumping plant is necessary to transport the liquid propellant from its storage tank at relatively low pressure to the nuclear reactor operating at high pressure.   Piping and valves associated with the pump and turbine-drive system are considered as part of the pumping equipment.   It is not possible to analyze accurately pump and turbine weights by means of general design equations for a wide range of operating conditions; consequently, dimensional-analysis methods must be employed to obtain the form of the functional variation of component weights.   Such dimensionally determined correlation equations can then be related to the real world by normalization to the measured weights of existing equipment of comparable or similar performance.

For geometrically similar pumps operating at fixed maximum impeller-tip speed, and hence for a given flow velocity, the liquid-handling capacity of any pump is proportional to the through-flow area of the pump, hence to the square of some characteristic linear dimension D.   The weight of the pump (casing, impeller, etc.) is proportional to surface area and mean thickness of its structural members, and hence to D^2t.   The structure thickness, in turn, is directly proportional to the product of pump operating (discharge) pressure and passage diameter.   This simple dimensional argument thus indicates that the weight of geometrically similar pumps is related to their discharge pressure and volumetric flow capacity, for fixed maximum impeller-tip speed, by

$$m_{\text{pump}} \propto P_dQ_f^{3/2} \tag{3-11}$$

To obtain a weight relation which holds for pumps over a wide range of flow rates and discharge pressures it is necessary to examine the way in which optimum pump geometry varies with changes in these two parameters.   One performance parameter characterizing liquid pumps is called the specific speed N_s.   It is defined as directly proportional to the product of pump speed and the square root of flow rate, divided by the fluid-pressure rise raised to the 0.75 power.   However, the fluid-pressure rise across the pump is proportional to the square of pump speed, so that

$$N_s \propto \frac{NQ_f^{1/2}}{(P_d - P_0)^{3/4}} \propto \frac{Q_f^{1/2}}{(P_d - P_0)^{1/4}} \tag{3-12}$$

where P_0 is the pump inlet pressure. Experience in the development of high-performance pumps has shown that the most efficient shapes and impeller geometries vary with the design specific speed. Low specific speeds lead to radial-flow centrifugal pumps as optimum, while axial-flow pumps are superior for use at high-specific-speed conditions. Between these two extremes lie a multitude of "mixed" flow, part radial, part axial, designs. The optimum pump configuration thus changes from a disklike geometry at low N_s to a cylindrical shape at high N_s. It is

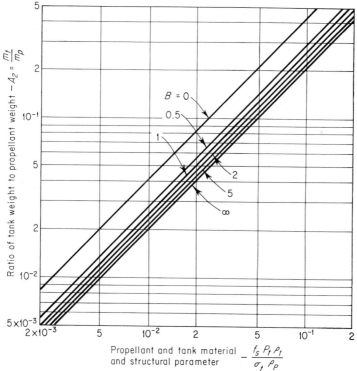

Fig. 3-5. Propellant-tank-weight coefficient.

clear that geometric similarity is not preserved over a wide range of specific speeds or volumetric flow rates. The foregoing dimensional analysis is thus incorrect to the extent that geometrical similarity was assumed at all flow rates and for all fluid pressures. In low-speed centrifugal pumps the pump diameter is large compared to the "eye" diameter and the limiting flow area is not proportional to D^2, but rather to the product of the pump-impeller passage thickness and impeller diameter. The casing and impeller are still centrifugally and pressure-loaded over the diameter D; thus their weight is proportional to D^3, as before. In the transition from centrifugal- to axial-flow pumps, the ratio of structural surface to pump volume drops for pumps of equal volumetric capacity; hence the axial-flow pump requires less structural material per unit volumetric flow rate than does the centrifugal pump. These nonanalytic changes result in reducing the dependence of pump weight on flow rate below that given in Eq. (3-11). For a given flow rate the system horsepower is directly proportional to the fluid-pressure rise across the pump, so that drive shaft and gear weights are also proportional to discharge pressure (for $P_d \gg P_0$). Many of the structural features of the pump, such as shaft mountings, bearings, flanges, seals, casing supports, etc., are not strongly or directly dependent upon discharge pressure. The result of this is to reduce the dependence of over-all pump weight on discharge pressure below that given in Eq. (3-11).

A fundamental dimensional analysis for the turbine weight, similar to that previously given for the pump, leads to

$$m_{\text{turbine}} \propto (P_d Q_f)^{3/2} \tag{3-13}$$

for geometrically similar turbines operating at fixed impeller-speed and gas-pressure conditions. Considerations of geometrical and other changes similar to those given previously for the pumps indicate that the turbine weight for optimum turbine performance is less dependent upon pump discharge pressure and volumetric flow rate than is indicated by Eq. (3-13).

A simple geometric analysis shows that the weight of piping is related to the volumetric flow rate by

$$m_{\text{pipe}} = \frac{2L\rho}{\sigma v_f} P_f Q_f \propto P_f Q_f \tag{3-14}$$

where L, ρ, and σ are, respectively, the length, wall density, and material tensile strength of the pipe. P_f is the liquid pressure and v_f is the flow velocity within the pipe. Note that this weight is independent of pipe diameter.

The weight of valves is proportional to their size and thickness, thus is also given by

$$m_{\text{valves}} \propto P_f Q_f \tag{3-15}$$

The pipe liquid pressure will be equal to pump inlet pressure for most of the piping, but will be at pump discharge pressure within those sections connecting the pump and nuclear reactor.

Taking all these factors into account, a reasonable functional relationship for the pumping-equipment weight is

$$m_e = A_4 Q_f P_d^{2/3} + A_5 \tag{3-16}$$

The constant A_5 is added to take account of the fact that a pump-turbine system for nearly zero flow rate will have a finite weight, principally resulting from the weight of mounting brackets and other support structures and the necessity of using finite thickness in all component parts. Typical values of the constants, based upon modern rocket pumping-plant weights,[9,10] are

$$A_4 = 1 \text{ (lb-sec/ft}^3)/(\text{lb/in.}^2)^{2/3} \qquad \text{and} \qquad A_5 = 100 \text{ lb}$$

Propellant flow through the pump must include that passing through the reactor to produce thrust β and that withdrawn from the reactor to drive the pump turbines α_t. The pump volumetric flow rate is thus

$$Q_f = \frac{(\beta + \alpha_t)w_p}{\rho_p} \tag{3-17}$$

where ρ_p is the propellant liquid density and w_p is the total rate of propellant loss from the vehicle and is equal to the total propellant weight divided by the system operating time. Assuming the non-thrust-productive fraction of propellant is expelled with zero velocity ($v_L = 0$), the thrust of the rocket motor is given by

$$F = \frac{\beta w_p v_e}{g_c} = \frac{a_0}{g_0} m_0 \tag{3-18}$$

where a_0 is the initial-force acceleration of the vehicle. Combining Eqs. (3-16), (3-17), and (3-18), the pumping-equipment weight becomes

$$m_e = A_4 \frac{\beta + \alpha_t}{\rho_p \beta v_e} a_0 P_d^{2/3} m_0 + A_5 = A_6 m_0 + A_5 \tag{3-19}$$

The coefficient A_6/A_4 is shown in Fig. 3-6 as a function of $(\beta + \alpha_t)/\rho_p \beta v_e$ for several values of $(a_0/g_0)P_d^{2/3}$.

Required pumping power is obtained from the product of volumetric flow rate and pump discharge pressure (assuming inlet pressure small compared to discharge pressure). This power is

$$HP_p = \frac{0.262(\beta + \alpha_t)w_p P_d}{\lambda_p \rho_p} \tag{3-20}$$

where λ_p is the pump energy efficiency. This must be equal to the shaft-power output of the turbine, which is given by

$$HP_t = 1.415 c_{pt} \Delta T_t \lambda_t \alpha_t w_p \tag{3-21}$$

where the turbine is assumed to be driven by hot gas from the reactor. The gas-temperature drop across the turbine is ΔT_t and the average specific heat is c_{pt} over this temperature range. λ_t is the energy-conversion efficiency of the turbine. The amount of propellant required to run the pumping-plant turbine is found by combination of Eqs. (3-20) and (3-21) as

$$\frac{\alpha_t}{\beta + \alpha_t} = \frac{w_t}{w_p} = \frac{0.185 P_d}{\lambda_p \lambda_t \Delta T_t \rho_p c_{pt}} \tag{3-22}$$

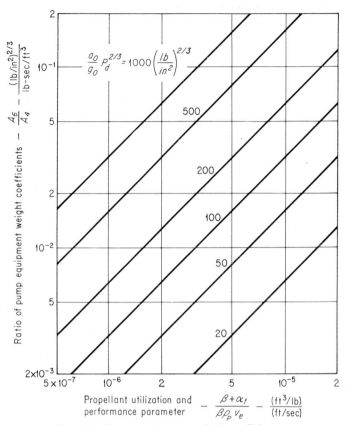

FIG. 3-6. Pump-equipment-weight coefficients.

TABLE 3-1. TYPICAL PUMPING-PLANT TURBINE-DRIVE GAS REQUIREMENTS

Requirement	Propellant				
	H_2	CH_4	NH_3	C_8H_{18}	C_2H_5OH
Heat capacity of gas, Btu/(lb)(°F)..	3.55	0.95*	0.84*	0.80*	0.62*
Liquid density, lb/ft³..............	4.4	26	43	47	55
Fraction of propellant to drive turbines, α_t......................	0.047	0.030	0.021	0.020	0.022
Pumping-system operating conditions	$P_d = 1{,}000$ lb/in.² $\beta + \alpha_t = 1$				
	$\Delta T_t = 1400 - 900°F = 500°F$ $\lambda_p \lambda_t = 0.5$				

* Heat capacity of fully dissociated products, over the given range of ΔT_t.

where w_t is the turbine-gas flow rate. Several typical values for α_t are given in Table 3-1 for the performance conditions listed.

High pump discharge pressure is desirable in a nuclear rocket-propulsion system for several reaons. As is shown in Chap. 4, the local heat-transfer coefficient from a solid reactor fuel element to a gaseous coolant is strongly dependent on system operating pressure. High pressure results in high heat-transfer coefficients and permits high power density within the reactor core. This leads to use of small cores and low-weight reactors, hence to a high power output per unit system weight. In addition, since the propellant mass flow rate per unit core flow area is proportional to the difference between the squares of the reactor-core inlet and outlet static pressures, high system pressure serves to reduce pressure-drop loads on core components. It may also be desirable, in some cases, to operate the reactor at a pressure above the critical pressure of the propellant. This eliminates the problems associated with flow of a two-phase mixture of liquid and gas. Internal dynamic coupling between liquid slugs and compressible gas bubbles in two-phase flow often results in low effective choking velocities for such flow through long pipes, holes, or other heat-transfer channels of low aspect ratio. High system pressure also assures small rocket-motor exhaust nozzles by virtue of the fact that the mass flow per unit nozzle throat area will be high. This is an important consideration when the design of nozzles with area expansion ratios greater than 20:1 is considered. Pump discharge pressures (reactor operating pressures) as high as 100 to 150 atm can be considered for use in nuclear rocket power plants. Choice of the true optimum system pressure depends upon the exact conditions of the problem and the desired performance of the vehicle.

Nuclear Rocket Motor and Thrust Structure. In a nuclear reactor the fissioning volume, or core, is usually surrounded by a layer of nonfissionable material which thermalizes fast neutrons leaving the core and returns them to the core as thermal neutrons. This outer shell, called a neutron reflector or tamper, helps to conserve neutrons and thus reduce the mass of fissionable fuel required for criticality. Much of the usefulness of such a reflector would be lost if it were placed outside the required structural pressure shell, for here thermal neutrons returning from the reflector to the core would be nonproductively absorbed by material of the nonmoderating shell. The reflector and core should thus both be carried within the reactor pressure shell. A nozzle is attached to the reactor-outlet end of the pressure shell. Thrust produced by expansion of propellant through this nozzle is transmitted to the rocket vehicle by means of a fixed or gimbaled thrust structure attached to the shell at a point which minimizes the difficulties of introducing propellant into the reactor from the pump system.

The power output of the nuclear rocket reactor is given by Eq. (2-56), which in this case takes the form

$$P_r = \left[\frac{0.678}{g_c} \left(\frac{v_{mi}}{10^3} \right)^2 + 1.055 \times 10^{-3} H_v \right] (\beta + \alpha_t) w_p = A_7 w_p \quad (2\text{-}56)$$

Values of A_7 are given in Sec. 2-3, Fig. 2-25. This power is generated at a volumetric rate K_c by fission heating within a core of volume V_c; thus the power can be written as

$$P_r = K_c V_c \quad (3\text{-}23)$$

The bulk core power density is of course dependent upon the average heat-transfer coefficient h_{cg} within the core and the specific heat-transfer surface A_{sp} available per unit core volume. For a core operating at constant temperature T_r with coolant (propellant) gas entering at T_0 and leaving at T_e, the bulk power density is given by

$$K_c = 2.93 \times 10^{-7} A_{sp} h_{cg} \Delta T_{LM} \quad (3\text{-}24)$$

where ΔT_{LM} is the log-mean temperature difference (Chap. 4) defined by

$$\Delta T_{LM} = \frac{(T_r - T_0) - (T_r - T_e)}{\ln \dfrac{T_r - T_0}{T_r - T_e}} \quad (3\text{-}25)$$

The numerical coefficient in Eq. (3-24) is a conversion factor from Btu per hour to megawatts.

Possible values of average core heat-transfer coefficients for each of the propellant gases of interest can be obtained from information given in the next chapter by making use of the relation

$$h_{cg} = \frac{\displaystyle\int_{T_0}^{T_e} h_c(T) \, dT}{T_e - T_0} \quad (3\text{-}26)$$

The specific heat-transfer surface area is entirely a function of the "fineness" of the heat-transfer structure, coarse construction leading to low values of A_{sp} and fine structure to high A_{sp}. This parameter is also discussed in Chap. 4.

The weight of the core is of course the product of its average bulk density ρ_c and volume, so that

$$m_{\text{core}} = \rho_c V_c = \frac{\pi}{4} D_c^2 L_c \rho_c \quad (3\text{-}27)$$

The reflector weight is

$$m_{refl} = \rho_{refl} V_{refl} \quad (3\text{-}28)$$

where the reflector volume for a cylindrical reactor core is approximately

$$V_{refl} \approx \frac{3\pi}{2} D_c^2 L_c \frac{t_{refl}}{D_c} = 6 \frac{t_{refl}}{D_c} V_c \qquad \text{for } D_c > 6 t_{refl} \quad (3\text{-}29)$$

The volume of the reactor pressure-shell material is determined in a manner similar to that used in a preceding section for the determination of propellant-tank skin-material volume. The pressure shell must contain an internal pressure P_c, is constructed of material with a tensile yield strength σ_{sh}, and is designed to include a safety factor f_s. The shell volume, including the converging section down to the nozzle throat, is then roughly

$$V_{sh} \approx \pi \frac{f_s P_c}{\sigma_{sh}} D_c^2 L_c = 4 \frac{f_s P_c}{\sigma_{sh}} V_c \qquad (3\text{-}30)$$

and the weight is

$$m_{sh} = \rho_{sh} V_{sh} \qquad (3\text{-}31)$$

Combination of Eqs. (3-23) and (3-24) with (3-27) to (3-31) to obtain a relation between nuclear-reactor weight and reactor power gives

$$\frac{m_r}{P_r} = \frac{\rho_c + 6\rho_{refl} t_{refl}/D_c + 4\rho_{sh} f_s P_c/\sigma_{sh}}{2.93 \times 10^{-7} A_{sp} h_{cg} \Delta T_{LM}} = A_8 \qquad (3\text{-}32)$$

Values of A_8 less than 3 lb/Mw are attainable by refined design and construction. The reactor weight can be related to the gross vehicle weight by combination of Eqs. (3-18) and (3-32) with Eq. (2-56), so that

$$m_r = A_9 m_0 + A_{10} \qquad (3\text{-}33)$$

where A_{10} is a fixed weight, characteristic of the minimum size reactor which will go critical, and A_9 is

$$A_9 = A_7 A_8 \frac{a_0}{\beta v_e} \qquad (3\text{-}34)$$

Reasonable values for A_{10} lie between 500 and 4,000 lb, depending upon the type of reactor under consideration.

The nozzle weight is defined to include only the expansion section from the throat to the exit plane. The weight of the transition section from the reactor-core exit to the throat plane is included in the equations given previously for pressure-shell weight. The pressure loads over much of the expansion section of a large nozzle are small, regardless of chamber pressure, and the nozzle wall thickness in this region will be nearly constant at a minimum value determined by cooling requirements and buckling stability under the axial thrust loading. The weight of this section will therefore be roughly directly proportional to the nozzle surface area. For geometrically similar nozzle shapes the nozzle surface area is directly proportional to the area expansion ratio ϵ and the throat area; thus the weight can be denoted by

$$m_{noz} \propto \epsilon D_t^2 \qquad (3\text{-}35)$$

The total thrust is grossly proportional to the product of the reactor pressure and the nozzle throat area. This proportionality combined with that given for the nozzle surface area leads to a functional relationship giving the weight of the nozzle (expansion section) as

$$m_{noz} \propto \frac{\epsilon F}{P_c} \tag{3-36}$$

Application of Eq. (3-18) leads to the expression

$$m_{noz} = A_{11} \frac{a_0 \epsilon}{g_0 P_c} m_0 = A_{12} m_0 \tag{3-37}$$

Normalization of Eq. (3-37) to typical modern high-performance nozzles gives A_{11} a range of values from $0.05/\text{in.}^2$ to $0.25/\text{in.}^2$

The size and weight of gimbaled or fixed thrust-transmitting members is obviously determined by the thrust loads which must be transmitted. The functional relation

$$m_{\text{thrust}} \propto F \tag{3-38}$$

can immediately be written. Making use of this in combination with the expression for thrust given by Eq. (3-18), the thrust structure weight is

$$m_{\text{thrust}} = A_{13} \frac{a_0}{g_0} m_0 = A_{14} m_0 \tag{3-39}$$

Simple structural analyses show that typical values of A_{13} fall between 10^{-3} lb/lb for fixed structure and 3×10^{-3} lb/lb for gimbaled (to permit angular motion of the rocket motor) mountings.

Summing up all these weight relations, it is found that the nuclear rocket motor and thrust structure weight is given by

$$m_r + m_f = A_{15} m_0 + A_{10} \tag{3-40}$$

where $A_{15} = A_9 + A_{12} + A_{14}$.

Dead Load. Despite its name, the dead load is the most important weight group in the rocket vehicle, since it includes the weight of the payload which the rocket is built to carry. The dead-load weight is the sum of the weights of all the nonfunctional items, in the thrust-producing sense, aboard the rocket vehicle. It includes guidance and communications equipment, auxiliary electrical power supplies, the payload, crew and crew-compartment weight (if any), radiation shielding as required to protect the crew, payload, or other components, necessary structural supports for attachment to the body of the missile, and proper aerodynamic covering (vehicle skin) for all these items. It is denoted by the symbol m_d.

3-2. Comparative Analysis. Analysis of the size, weight, and flight performance of different nuclear rocket vehicles allows choice of the optimum design conditions for a given required performance. Here the optimum vehicle is not necessarily the minimum-weight vehicle. For example, although lighter than those using other propellants, nuclear rockets which use liquid hydrogen may be considerably larger because of the low density of the liquid propellant. If ease of vehicle handling, transport, and storage are prime considerations, then for some ranges of performance, higher-density propellants which yield heavier but smaller-volume vehicles may be chosen as optimum.[11] Specification of the optimum vehicle for a given job is clearly not an analytical procedure, since much must be left to the judgment of the vehicle designer and the ultimate user. In spite of this, vehicle performance analyses are not often made by studying the vehicle weight required for a given performance. This is done partly because the performance equations are easily handled in terms of weights (Chap. 2) and partly because gross weight is indeed a valid and useful parameter to judge the vehicle's worth. The relative usefulness of nuclear and chemical rockets is easily assessed on this basis by a comparison of the vehicle weight required to carry a given payload or dead load to any desired velocity. Such a comparison results in determination of an optimum-performance region of interest for each type of vehicle. Other studies can be made to show the effect of varying selected design parameters such as reactor specific weight, operating pressure, vehicle initial acceleration, tank pressure, and others. These are often called optimization studies, although it is not always possible to achieve a true optimum in the mathematical sense of maxima or minima.

Nuclear Vehicle Performance. The gross weight of a nuclear rocket is simply the sum of all its component weights:

$$m_0 = m_p + m_t + m_s + m_e + m_r + m_f + m_d \qquad (3\text{-}41)$$

Using the weight relations developed in the preceding section, this is given by

$$m_0(1 - A_6 - A_{15}) = m_p(1 + A_3) + m_d + A_5 + A_{10}$$

$$= m_p(1 + A_3) + m_L \qquad (3\text{-}42)$$

where m_L is the sum of all the fixed weights of the complete vehicle. Dividing through by the gross weight m_0, Eq. (3-42) can be related to the vehicle velocity performance capability by substitution of m_p/m_0 obtained from Eq. (2-16). The resulting equation, obtained after some manipulation, relates the ratio of gross weight to dead-load weight to the vehicle velocity exponent ξ by

$$\frac{m_0}{m_d} = \frac{1 + C_3/m_d}{C_1 - C_2(1 - e^{-\xi})} \qquad \text{or} \qquad \frac{m_0}{m_L} = \frac{1}{C_1 - C_2(1 - e^{-\xi})} \qquad (3\text{-}43)$$

The C_i coefficients are combinations of the various component-weight-equation coefficients.   These are

$$C_1 = 1 - (A_6 + A_{15})$$
$$C_2 = A_3 + 1 \qquad\qquad (3\text{-}44)$$
$$C_3 = A_5 + A_{10}$$

Note that the ratio of gross weight m_0 to dead load m_d is a function of the dead-load weight, approaching a minimum limiting value as the dead-load weight approaches infinity.   For vehicle comparisons on a volume basis, Eqs. (3-42) and (3-43) can be rearranged to show the propellant volume per unit dead load as

$$\frac{V_p}{m_L} = \frac{1}{\rho_p} \frac{m_p}{m_0} \frac{m_0}{m_L} = \frac{1 - e^{-\xi}}{\rho_p[C_1 - C_2(1 - e^{-\xi})]} \qquad (3\text{-}45)$$

Referring to Eq. (2-16), the exponent ξ is defined as

$$\xi = \frac{\Delta v_b + g\,\sin\,\theta\, t_b}{(\alpha v_L + \beta v_e)(1 - \zeta)\chi} = \frac{\Delta v_b + g\,\sin\,\theta\, \dfrac{\alpha v_L + \beta v_e}{a_0}\dfrac{m_p}{m_0}}{(\alpha v_L + \beta v_e)(1 - \zeta)\chi} \qquad (3\text{-}46)$$

Equation (3-43) can be rearranged to permit solution for ξ for any desired ratio of gross weight to dead load.   Rearranged, the equation appears as

$$\xi = \ln \frac{C_2}{C_2 - C_1 + \dfrac{m_d}{m_0}\left(1 + \dfrac{C_3}{m_d}\right)} = \ln \frac{C_2}{C_2 - C_1 + \dfrac{m_L}{m_0}} \qquad (3\text{-}47)$$

This solution permits study of the effect of variation of gross weight on vehicle performance with fixed dead load and clearly shows that the vehicle velocity performance reaches a maximum for a finite fixed dead-load weight as the gross weight is increased to infinity.   This maximum value is given by

$$\xi_m = \ln \frac{C_2}{C_2 - C_1} \qquad (3\text{-}48)$$

For reference purposes the coefficients in the component-weight equations are listed in Table 3-2 to show their dependence upon vehicle and power-plant design parameters.   Complete expressions for the factors C_1, C_2, and C_3 can be obtained from Table 3-2 and the definitions in Eq. (3-44).   These expressions are given in full in Table 3-3.   Though formidable in appearance, substitution of reasonable values of the pertinent design parameters shows that $0.5 < C_1 < 1.0$ and $1.0 < C_2 < 1.4$ for all propellants of interest.   Typical values are $C_1 \sim 0.9$ and $C_2 \sim 1.1$. The factor C_3 is simply the sum of the fixed weights of the power-plant components and is typically about 1,000 lb.

Curves showing the variation of m_0/m_L with ξ for several values of

TABLE 3-2. DEFINITION AND SUMMARY OF COEFFICIENTS IN VEHICLE COMPONENT-WEIGHT EQUATIONS

A_1 = weight of tank structure per unit tank skin weight (~ 0.15 lb/lb)

$$A_2 = \frac{2f_s P_t}{(1 - f_u)\sigma_t} \frac{3B + 2.07}{3B + 1} \frac{\rho_t}{\rho_p}$$

$A_3 = (1 + A_1)A_2$

A_4 = coefficient in pump-weight equation [~ 1 (lb-sec/ft^3)/(lb/in.^{2})$^{2/3}$]

A_5 = fixed (minimum) pumping-equipment weight (~ 100 lb)

$$A_6 = A_4(\beta + \alpha_t) \frac{a_0 P_d^{2/3}}{\rho_p \beta v_e}$$

$$A_7 = (\beta + \alpha_t) \left[\frac{0.678}{g_c} \left(\frac{v_{mi}}{10^3} \right)^2 + 1.055 \times 10^{-3} H_v \right]$$

$$A_8 = \frac{\rho_c + 6\rho_{refl} t_{refl}/D_c + 4\rho_{sh} f_s P_c/\sigma_{sh}}{2.93 \times 10^{-7} A_{sp} h_{cg} \, \Delta T_{LM}}$$

$$A_9 = A_7 A_8 \frac{a_0}{\beta v_e}$$

A_{10} = minimum critical reactor weight ($\sim 2{,}000$ lb)

A_{11} = coefficient in nozzle-weight equation ($\sim 0.15/$in.^{2})

$$A_{12} = A_{11} \frac{a_0 \epsilon}{g_0 P_c}$$

A_{13} = coefficient in thrust-structure-weight equation
$$[10^{-3} \text{ (fixed) to } 3 \times 10^{-3} \text{ (gimbaled)}]$$

$$A_{14} = A_{13} \frac{a_0}{g_0}$$

$A_{15} = A_9 + A_{12} + A_{14}$

$$A_{16} = A_7 \frac{g_0}{\beta v_e}$$

A_{17} = chemical rocket-motor weight per unit thrust (~ 0.0167 lb/lb)

TABLE 3-3. DEFINITION AND SUMMARY OF COEFFICIENTS IN VEHICLE PERFORMANCE EQUATIONS

$$C_1 = 1 - A_6 - A_{15} = 1 - A_4(\beta + \alpha_t) \frac{a_0 P_d^{2/3}}{\rho_p \beta v_e} - A_{11} \frac{a_0 \epsilon}{g_0 P_c}$$

$$- \frac{a_0}{\beta v_e} (\beta + \alpha_t) \left[\frac{0.678}{g_c} \left(\frac{v_{mi}}{10^3} \right)^2 + 1.055 \times 10^{-3} H_v \right]$$

$$\frac{\rho_c + 6\rho_{refl} t_{refl}/D_c + 4\rho_{sh} f_s P_c/\sigma_{sh}}{2.93 \times 10^{-7} A_{sp} h_{cg} \, \Delta T_{LM}} - A_{13} \frac{a_0}{g_0}$$

$$C_2 = C_5 = C_{12} = 1 + (1 + A_1) \frac{2f_s P_t}{(1 - f_u)\sigma_t} \frac{3B + 2.07}{3B + 1} \frac{\rho_t}{\rho_p}$$

$C_3 = A_5 + A_{10}$

$$C_4 = 1 - A_6 - A_{12} - A_{14} = 1 - A_4(\beta + \alpha_t) \frac{a_0 P_d^{2/3}}{\rho_p \beta v_e} - A_{11} \frac{a_0 \epsilon}{g_0 P_c} - A_{13} \frac{a_0}{g_0}$$

$C_5 = C_2$

$$C_6 = A_{16} = (\beta + \alpha_t) \frac{g_0}{\beta v_e} \left[\frac{0.678}{g_c} \left(\frac{v_{mi}}{10^3} \right)^2 + 1.055 \times 10^{-3} H_v \right]$$

$$C_{11} = 1 - A_6 - A_{17} = 1 - A_{17} - A_4(\beta + \alpha_t) \frac{a_0 P_d^{2/3}}{\rho_p \beta v_e}$$

$C_{12} = C_2$

$C_{13} = A_5$

C_1 are shown in Figs. 3-7 through 3-12. Each figure presents curves for a different value of C_2. The limiting value ξ_m is shown in these figures. To analyze the performance of a nuclear rocket vehicle it is necessary to evaluate the coefficients C_1 and C_2, from their definitions given in Table 3-3, by use of the vehicle and reactor design conditions and pertinent properties characterizing the chosen propellant. The ratio of gross weight to dead load plus fixed power-plant weights can then be determined for any value of ξ from the curves shown in Figs. 3-7 through

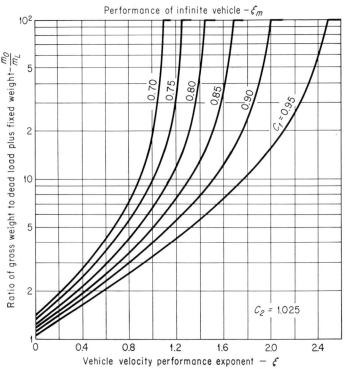

FIG. 3-7. Generalized vehicle performance. $C_2 = 1.025$.

3-12, or by use of Eq. (3-43). For a given value of this ratio, the ratio of propellant weight to gross weight can be found from Eq. (3-42). Having this and specifying the flight-path parameters permits evaluation of the second term in the numerator of Eq. (3-46). Propellant performance (effective exhaust velocity) can be determined by the methods described in Secs. 2-2 and 2-3. Estimates of drag and other atmospheric effects then permit the determination of vehicle Δv_b from the known value of ξ for each ratio m_0/m_L. For any value of m_0/m_L the ratio of gross weight to dead load m_0/m_d can then be found for a given set of reactor and pump design conditions [Eq. (3-43) and Table 3-2]. To illustrate this method Figs. 3-13 and 3-14 show the performance of two typical single-stage nuclear rockets determined by this method. The propellants chosen for comparison are those most often proposed[11-13] for use in nuclear rockets: hydrogen and ammonia. The curves show the ratio of gross weight m_0 to dead-load weight m_d for various values of dead load as a function of vehicle burnout velocity. As a matter of interest, curves showing the ratio of propellant volume to dead load [from Eq. (3-45)] as a function of vehicle burnout velocity are presented in

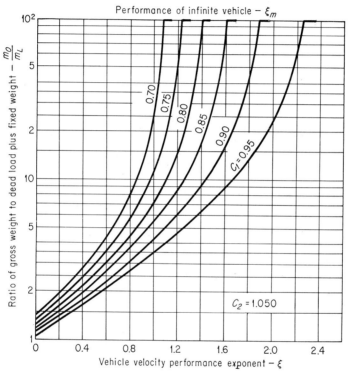

FIG. 3-8. Generalized vehicle performance. $C_2 = 1.050$.

Figs. 3-15 and 3-16 for these two propellants. Note that the ammonia-propellant vehicle is smaller than the hydrogen-propellant vehicle over a large range of burnout velocities, even though it is much heavier. The assumed design and operating conditions are listed in Table 3-4 on page 71 for both vehicles.

Comparative Chemical Rocket Performance. To determine the relative advantages of nuclear and chemical rockets it is necessary to set up generalized equations to describe the chemical rocket component weights and vehicle performance, as was done for the nuclear-powered vehicles.

This can be done rather simply, since the equations previously derived

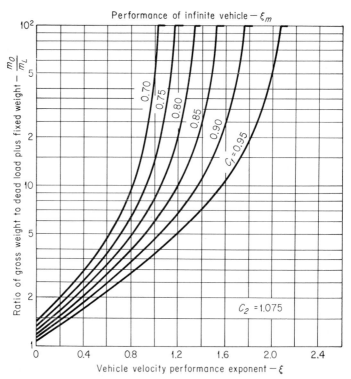

FIG. 3-9. Generalized vehicle performance. $C_2 = 1.075$.

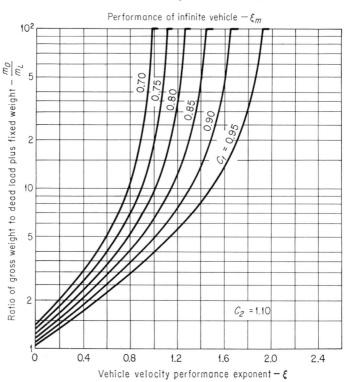

FIG. 3-10. Generalized vehicle performance. $C_2 = 1.10$.

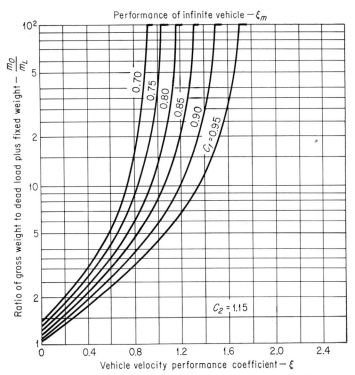

FIG. 3-11. Generalized vehicle performance. $C_2 = 1.15$.

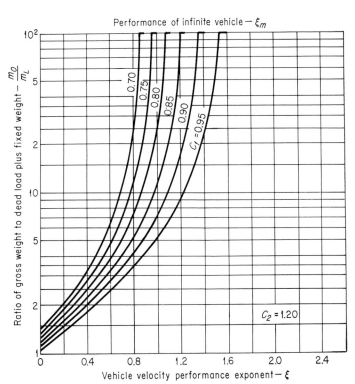

FIG. 3-12. Generalized vehicle performance. $C_2 = 1.20$.

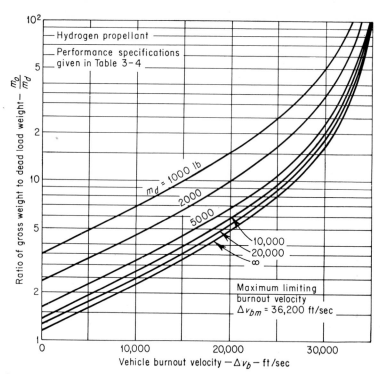

FIG. 3-13. Nuclear rocket performance. Weight basis, hydrogen propellant.

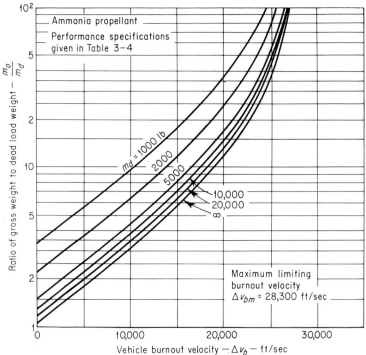

FIG. 3-14. Nuclear rocket performance. Weight basis, ammonia propellant.

for all components of the nuclear rocket power plant except the rocket motor are reasonably valid for use in the chemical rocket system. A thorough analysis and discussion of chemical rocket motors is not within the province of this text. It is sufficient here to recognize that the motor weight for large chemical rocket vehicles can be approximately expressed by

$$m_r + m_f = A_{17}m_0 \frac{a_0}{g_0} \tag{3-49}$$

Data on existing and past large ballistic rockets such as the V-2 and Viking indicate that a reasonable value for A_{17} is 0.0167 lb/lb. No fixed

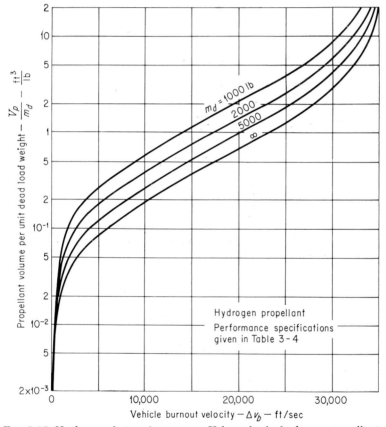

Fig. 3-15. Nuclear rocket performance. Volume basis, hydrogen propellant.

minimum weight is included here because there is no minimum critical size (as for nuclear reactors) for combustion chambers. This leads to considerable simplification in the presentation of performance curves, as only one curve is required for all values of dead load if the fixed weight

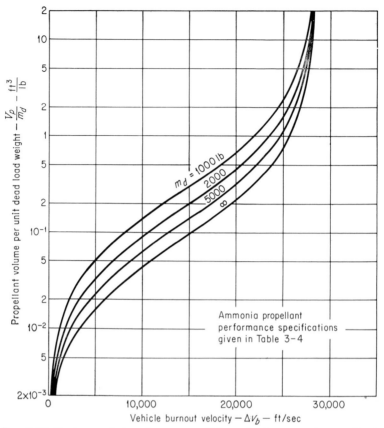

FIG. 3-16. Nuclear rocket performance. Volume basis, ammonia propellant.

of pumping equipment is small compared to the dead-load weight.

Using the component-weight relations previously obtained for the nuclear rocket system together with Eq. (3-49), the gross weight of a chemical rocket is found from

$$m_0(1 - A_6 - A_{17}) = m_p(1 + A_3) + m_d + A_5$$
$$= m_p(1 + A_3) + m_L \quad (3\text{-}50)$$

Since the mass-ratio equations given in Chap. 2 are valid for any rocket, the ratio of gross weight to dead load can be determined as before. This is

$$\frac{m_0}{m_d} = \frac{1 + C_{13}/m_d}{C_{11} - C_{12}(1 - e^{-\xi})} \quad \text{or} \quad \frac{m_0}{m_L} = \frac{1}{C_{11} - C_{12}(1 - e^{-\xi})} \quad (3\text{-}51)$$

where $C_{11} = 1 - A_6 - A_{17}$
$C_{12} = A_3 + 1$
$C_{13} = A_5$

TABLE 3-4. PERFORMANCE PARAMETERS FOR TYPICAL HYDROGEN- AND AMMONIA-PROPELLED NUCLEAR ROCKET VEHICLES

Reactor: Eqs. (3-24) to (3-32)

$\dfrac{m_r}{V_c} = 200$ lb/ft³ of core $\qquad\qquad$ $P_c = P_d = 1,000$ lb/in.²

$\dfrac{P_r}{V_c} = K_c = 100$ Mw/ft³ of core (Sec. 4-4) $\qquad$ $A_8 = 2$ lb/Mw

Propellant Tankage: Eq. (3-9)

$P_t = 15$ lb/in.² for H_2	$P_t = 50$ lb/in.² for NH_3	$B = 5$
$f_s = 1.7$	$\rho_t = 175$ lb/ft³ (aluminum)	
$f_u = 0.02$	$\sigma_t = 30,000$ lb/in.²	

Vehicle Performance: Eq. (3-46)

$\dfrac{a_0}{g_0} = 1.5$ $\qquad\qquad$ $f_v = 0.2$ (Fig. 3-4) $\quad$ $\sin \theta = 0.3$

$\alpha_v = 0.02$ for H_2 (Fig. 3-4)

$\alpha_t = 0.05$ for H_2 (Table 3-1) $\qquad\qquad\qquad$ $\alpha_v = 0$ for NH_3 (Fig. 3-4)

$\beta = 0.93$ for H_2 $\qquad\qquad\qquad\qquad\qquad$ $\alpha_t = 0.02$ for NH_3 (Table 3-1)

$\zeta = 0.04$ for H_2 $\qquad$ $\zeta = 0.02$ for NH_3 $\qquad$ $\beta = 0.98$ for NH_3

$\qquad\qquad\qquad\qquad\qquad\qquad\qquad\qquad\qquad$ $\chi = 0.98$

Propellant: Secs. 2-2 and 2-3

H_2	NH_3
$T_c = 5000°R$ (Refs. 11 to 13)	$T_c = 5000°R$ (Refs. 11 to 13)
$\gamma = 1.35$ (Fig. 2-20) $\quad \epsilon = 20$	$\gamma = 1.34$ (Fig. 2-20) $\quad \epsilon = 20$
$v_L = 0 \quad \dfrac{P_c}{P_e} = 330$ [Eq. (2-46)]	$v_L = 0 \quad \dfrac{P_c}{P_e} = 320$ [Eq. (2-46)]
$v_e = 27,800$ ft/sec (Figs. 2-13, 2-22)	$v_e = 13,400$ ft/sec (Figs. 2-13, 2-22)
$v_{mi} = 31,300$ ft/sec (Fig. 2-24)	$v_{mi} = 15,200$ ft/sec (Fig. 2-24)
$\dfrac{A_7}{\beta + \alpha_t} = 20.7$ Mw-sec/lb (Fig. 2-25)	$\dfrac{A_7}{\beta + \alpha_t} = 6.05$ Mw-sec/lb (Fig. 2-25)
$\rho_p = 4.4$ lb/ft³	$\rho_p = 43$ lb/ft³

Miscellaneous: Tables 3-2 and 3-3

$A_1 = 0.15$ lb/lb $\qquad$ $A_4 = 1$ (lb-sec/ft³)/(lb/in.²)$^{2/3}$ $\qquad$ $A_5 = 100$ lb

$A_{10} = 2,000$ lb $\qquad$ $A_{11} = 0.15/in.²$ $\qquad\qquad\qquad\qquad$ $A_{13} = 2 \times 10^{-3}$ lb/lb

For H_2	For NH_3
$C_1 = 0.875$	$C_1 = 0.940$
$C_2 = 1.082$	$C_2 = 1.028$
$C_3 = 2,100$	$C_3 = 2,100$
$C_4 = 0.951$	$C_4 = 0.985$
$C_5 = C_2$	$C_5 = C_2$
$C_6 = 0.0253$	$C_6 = 0.0148$

A comparison of chemical rocket and nuclear rocket performance is not possible by use of a set of general performance curves like those given in Figs. 3-7 through 3-12 for nuclear rocket vehicles. Such a comparison can only be made between true performance curves for specific rocket vehicles such as those shown in Figs. 3-13 through 3-16. For this reason

1. German BMW X-4 (WW-II)
2. German Taifun
3. U.S. unboosted Aerobee
4. U.S. WAC Corporal
5. German Wasserfall
6. U.S. Viking
7. German A-4 (V-2)
8. U.S. WAC Cpl + V-2 (2-stage)
9. German A-9 + A-10 (2-stage)

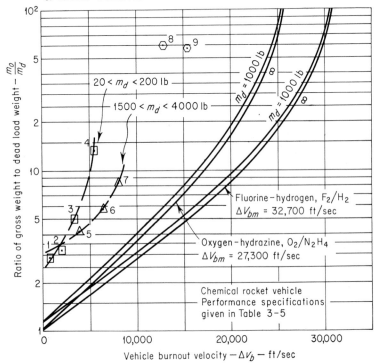

FIG. 3-17. Chemical rocket performance. Weight basis.

no generalized plots of Eq. (3-51) are presented. Rather, the performance of two specific vehicles is considered. One of these is specified as using liquid oxygen and hydrazine as propellants. This combination has a propellant performance[14] typical of that found in large modern rocket engines. The other vehicle uses an optimum mixture ratio of liquid fluorine and liquid hydrogen. The performance[15] of this combination roughly represents the practical upper limit for chemical combustion-powered rockets. Following the method of analysis described in the preceding section, the ratio of gross weight m_0 to dead-load weight m_d for single-stage vehicles is shown in Fig. 3-17 as a function of vehicle burnout velocity for each of these chemical rockets. Note that the spread in the curves is slight for all the dead loads shown, since the value of A_5, the pumping-equipment fixed weight, is always small compared to the dead load for all dead-load weights of interest. Also shown in the figure are points and curves for several past and present chemical rocket vehicles. For comparison Fig. 3-18 shows the propellant volume

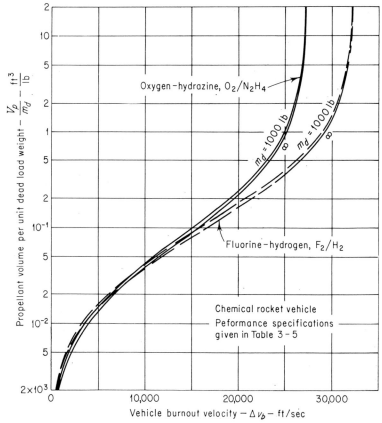

FIG. 3-18. Chemical rocket performance. Volume basis.

per unit dead load for these two chemical rockets. The pertinent assumptions with regard to vehicle and motor design parameters required for evaluation of the performance-equation constants are given in Table 3-5.

The chief difference between the chemical and nuclear rocket design conditions is in choice of chamber pressure. Little incentive exists to operate above about 50 atm pressure in the chemical motor. However the weight of the nuclear reactor is strongly dependent on pressure

TABLE 3-5. PERFORMANCE PARAMETERS FOR TYPICAL FLUORINE-HYDROGEN- AND OXYGEN-HYDRAZINE-PROPELLED CHEMICAL ROCKET VEHICLES

Motor: Eq. (3-49), Sec. 2-2, and Table 3-2

$P_c = 500$ lb/in.^{2}	$P_d = 750$ lb/in.^{2}
$\epsilon = 20$	$\nu_d = 1.05$ [Eq. (2-54)]
	$\nu_v = 0.98$ [Eq. (2-54)]

Propellant Tankage: Eq. (3-9)

$P_t = 70$ lb/in.^{2}	$B = 5$
$f_s = 1.7$	$\rho_t = 500$ lb/ft^3 (chrome steel or Inconel X)
$f_u = 0.02$	$\sigma_t = 90,000$ lb/in.^{2}

Vehicle Performance: Eq. (3-46)

$\dfrac{a_0}{g_0} = 1.5$		$\sin \theta = 0.3$
$\zeta = 0.02$ for F$_2$-H$_2$		$\zeta = 0.01$ for O$_2$-N$_2$H$_4$
$\chi = 0.96$ for F$_2$-H$_2$		$\chi = 0.98$ for O$_2$-N$_2$H$_4$
$\alpha_v = 0.01$ for F$_2$-H$_2$	$\alpha_t = 0.02$	$\alpha_v = 0$ for O$_2$-N$_2$H$_4$
$\beta = 0.97$ for F$_2$-H$_2$		$\beta = 0.98$ for O$_2$-N$_2$H$_4$

Propellant: Refs. 14 and 15, Secs. 2-2 and 2-3

F$_2$-H$_2$	O$_2$-N$_2$H$_4$
Mixture ratio = 15.7 (oxidizer/fuel)	Mixture ratio = 0.7 (oxidizer/fuel)
$\rho_p = 43$ lb/ft^3 of mixture	$\rho_p = 65$ lb/ft^3 of mixture
$T_c = 7750°$R $\quad \gamma = 1.16$	$T_c = 5750°$R $\quad \gamma = 1.23$
$v_L = 0 \quad \dfrac{P_c}{P_e} = 170$ [Eq. (2-46)]	$v_L = 0 \quad \dfrac{P_c}{P_e} = 215$ [Eq. (2-46)]
$v_{ei} = 13,700$ ft/sec	$v_{ei} = 10,300$ ft/sec
$v_e = 14,300$ ft/sec [Eq. (2-54)]	$v_e = 10,600$ ft/sec [Eq. (2-54)]

Miscellaneous: Tables 3-2 and 3-3

$A_1 = 0.15$ lb/lb	$A_5 = 100$ lb
$A_4 = 1$ (lb-sec/ft^3)/(lb/in.^{2})$^{2/3}$	$A_{17} = 0.0167$ lb/lb

For F$_2$-H$_2$	For O$_2$-N$_2$H$_4$
$C_{11} = 0.9684$	$C_{11} = 0.9691$
$C_{12} = 1.0379$	$C_{12} = 1.0251$
$C_{13} = 100$	$C_{13} = 100$

through the pressure sensitivity of the average core heat-transfer coefficient (Chap. 4). For this reason pressures as high as the order of 100 atm may be advantageous in a nuclear rocket motor. The exhaust velocity for the chemical rockets was taken from data presented in Refs. 14 and 15. It is evident from Figs. 3-17 and 3-18 that these single-stage chemical rockets reach a point of diminishing return, weightwise, at vehicle burnout velocities of the order of 17,000 and 21,000 ft/sec for the oxygen-hydrazine and fluorine-hydrogen vehicles respectively. If burnout velocities higher than these are desired, the minimum gross weight–dead load ratio will occur for vehicles of more than one stage. Following the methods outlined in Sec. 2-1, the performance of multistage chemical rockets was determined by using the previously given propellants and design conditions. The ratio of gross weight of all stages

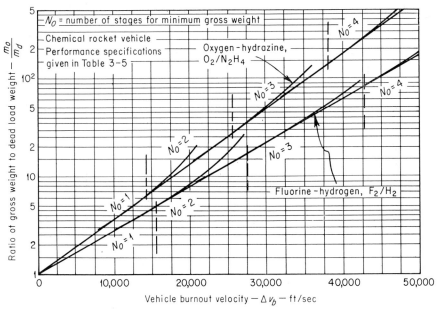

FIG. 3-19. Multistage chemical rocket performance. Weight basis.

to dead-load weight is shown in Fig. 3-19. The optimum range of burnout velocity for each integer number of stages is marked along the curves in the figures.

Region-of-interest Study. A direct comparison of the performance conditions for which nuclear rockets are superior to chemical, or vice versa, is called a region-of-interest study, for it helps to define the areas of performance in which nuclear and chemical rocket vehicles are of most practical interest. Such a study must be based upon consideration of specific vehicles, since the number and complexity of variables which determine the over-all vehicle performance is so vast that no general comparison is possible. An example of this type of study can be shown by comparison of the assumed vehicles whose performance curves are shown in Figs. 3-13 through 3-19. By superposition of the chemical- and nuclear-vehicle performance curves, points of equal gross weight–

dead load ratio and vehicle burnout velocity can be found, for different values of dead-load weight, at the intersections of the curves for chemical and nuclear rocket vehicles.   Having determined these points, a curve of dead-load weight for vehicles of equal gross weight–dead load ratio can be drawn as a function of vehicle burnout velocity.   Such a curve is often called a "break-even" curve.   Break-even curves for comparison

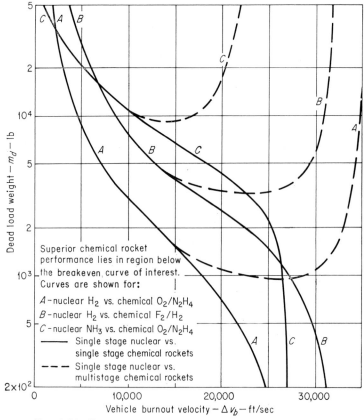

Fig. 3-20. Comparative rocket performance.   Weight basis.

of the single-stage nuclear rockets with the single- and multistage chemical rockets previously discussed are shown in Fig. 3-20.   Such presentations are sometimes more graphic when related to vehicle ballistic range rather than burnout velocity, since ballistic range is a sensitive function of burnout velocity when velocities greater than 20,000 ft/sec are considered.   The relation between true ballistic range and vehicle burnout velocity for optimum initial ballistic flight angle is shown in Fig. 2-7. Using this figure, the break-even curves shown in Fig. 3-20 are replotted vs. range in Fig. 3-21.

Optimization Studies. The optimum values of any given design parameter can best be determined by analyzing the dependence of the vehicle performance on the parameter in question. No general method exists for such optimization: each parameter of interest must be treated individually in a fashion best suited to display the essential parameter-performance relationship. Several examples of such analyses are presented here to illustrate the approach required for successful optimization.

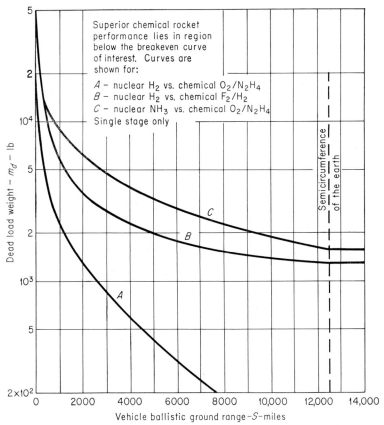

Superior chemical rocket performance lies in region below the breakeven curve of interest. Curves are shown for:

A – nuclear H_2 vs. chemical O_2/N_2H_4
B – nuclear H_2 vs. chemical F_2/H_2
C – nuclear NH_3 vs. chemical O_2/N_2H_4
Single stage only

FIG. 3-21. Comparative rocket performance. Weight basis.

INCENTIVE FOR HIGH POWER DENSITY. One of the parameters left to the choice of the nuclear rocket designer is the power output per unit reactor-core volume, and thus indirectly the power output per unit reactor weight. At first thought it seems reasonable to expect that increasing reactor specific power (megawatts per pound) leads to continuously increasing vehicle performance. To test the validity of this assertion it is necessary to set up the performance equations in such a way that a fundamental dependence on reactor specific power is embodied within them. This can only be done by treating the reactor weight independently of the weight of nozzle and thrust structure.

From Eq. (3-32) the reactor weight is related to reactor power by

$$m_r = A_8 P_r \qquad (3\text{-}52)$$

Here the coefficient A_8 is the inverse of reactor specific power. Making use of the relations given in Eqs. (2-56) and (3-18), the reactor power is given by

$$P_r = A_7 \frac{a_0}{\beta v_e} m_0 \qquad (3\text{-}53)$$

for a vehicle in which the "waste" propellant is expelled with zero axial velocity ($v_L = 0$).

The sum of the nozzle and thrust-structure weight is obtained from Eqs. (3-37) and (3-39) as

$$m_f = (A_{12} + A_{14}) m_0 \qquad (3\text{-}54)$$

Combining Eqs. (3-52) and (3-53), it is noted that the analysis can be made more general, to include the effect of initial acceleration as it influences the relation between vehicle performance and reactor specific power, by introducing the parameter specific power per unit initial acceleration, denoted by the symbol Ω. To keep this parameter in specific power units the initial acceleration is expressed in terms of the standard gravitational acceleration. Thus

$$m_r = A_7 A_8 \frac{g_0}{\beta v_e} \frac{a_0}{g_0} m_0 = A_{16} \frac{m_0}{\Omega} \qquad (3\text{-}55)$$

where $\qquad A_{16} = A_7 \frac{g_0}{\beta v_e} \qquad$ and $\qquad \Omega = \frac{1}{A_8 a_0 / g_0} \qquad (3\text{-}56)$

Combining Eqs. (3-54) and (3-55) and the previously developed weight equations for other vehicle components with the fundamental definition of vehicle gross weight given in Eq. (3-41), the gross weight can be expressed by

$$m_0 \left[1 - (A_6 + A_{12} + A_{14}) - \frac{A_{16}}{\Omega} \right] = m_p (A_3 + 1) + m_d + A_5 \qquad (3\text{-}57)$$

The propellant weight is of course given by

$$m_p = m_0 (1 - e^{-\xi}) \qquad (3\text{-}58)$$

Using this in Eq. (3-57) and rearranging, the ratio of rocket-vehicle gross weight to dead load plus fixed pump-equipment weight is given by

$$\frac{m_0}{m_d + A_5} = \frac{m_0}{m_L} = \left[C_4 - C_5 (1 - e^{-\xi}) - \frac{C_6}{\Omega} \right]^{-1} \qquad (3\text{-}59)$$

where the coefficients are defined as

$$C_4 = 1 - (A_6 + A_{12} + A_{14})$$
$$C_5 = A_3 + 1 \tag{3-60}$$
$$C_6 = A_{16}$$

Graphical illustration of the effect of reactor specific power per unit acceleration can best be shown by consideration of specific rocket vehicles. The variation of m_0/m_L with Ω for several values of the velocity-performance exponent ξ is shown in Figs. 3-22 and 3-23 for the two nuclear

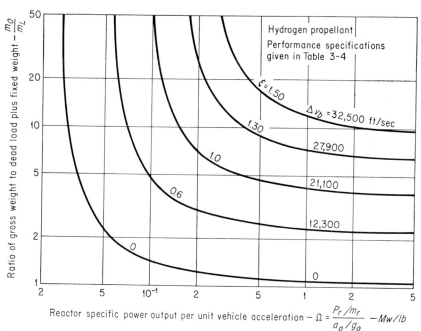

Reactor specific power output per unit vehicle acceleration $- \Omega = \dfrac{P_r/m_r}{a_0/g_0}$ $-Mw/lb$

FIG. 3-22. Nuclear rocket performance as a function of reactor specific power. Hydrogen propellant.

rockets previously used as illustrative examples. Basic assumed design and performance parameters for these rockets are listed in Table 3-4. Note how rapidly the curves in the figures increase as Ω approaches zero and how flat they become for Ω above about $\frac{1}{2}$. Although no maxima or minima exist in these curves—and thus no strict optimum values are obtainable—it seems evident that little improvement in vehicle weight for given performance is possible by increasing the reactor specific power per unit acceleration above about 1 $Mw/(lb)(g_0)$. On the other hand increasing reactor specific power greatly increases the difficulty of reactor design and construction. It is clear that an optimum value of Ω, in the practical sense, is one for which the vehicle gross weight–dead load ratio is not on the sharply rising portions of the curves in Figs. 3-22 and 3-23 and yet is as low as possible to minimize the problems of reactor design.

SYSTEM PRESSURE AND INITIAL ACCELERATION.   Analyses to determine optimum values of system pressure and vehicle acceleration are somewhat simpler than that just considered for reactor specific power output. Recall that the general vehicle weight and performance equations developed earlier in this section related the ratio of vehicle gross weight to dead load plus fixed weight to the velocity exponent ξ and the factors C_1 and C_2.   The complete expressions for C_1 and C_2 given in Tables 3-2 and

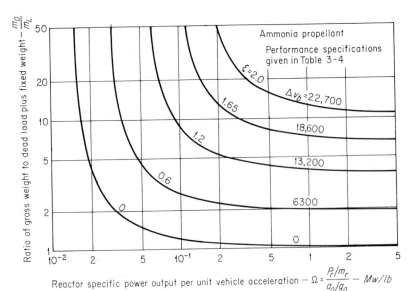

FIG. 3-23. Nuclear rocket performance as a function of reactor specific power.   Ammonia propellant.

3-3 show that C_2 is independent of both the initial acceleration and the reactor or pump-discharge operating pressure, while C_1 has terms which depend on both these parameters.   However, the full dependence of C_1 upon system pressure is not shown directly by its defining equation in Table 3-3, since both the propellant effective exhaust velocity and the temperature-averaged reactor-core heat-transfer coefficient are functions of reactor operating pressure.

The effective exhaust velocity becomes rather insensitive to pressure for system pressure above about 10 atm, provided that nozzles of sufficiently large exit–throat area ratio are used.   The reactor-core heat-transfer coefficient, however, is strongly dependent on pressure within the core over the entire practical range of pressures.   Equations developed in Chap. 4 show this dependence to be approximately proportional to the 0.8 power of the system pressure.   Incorporating this into the equation for C_1 and assuming the reactor-pressure-shell weight to be small compared to that of the core and reflector—which will generally be true—so that the effect of pressure on the shell-weight term can be neglected, the functional relationship of C_1, a_0, and P_c—which equals P_d for all practical purposes—can be written as

$$C_1 = 1 - F_1 a_0 P_d^{2/3} - F_2 a_0 P_c^{-1} - F_3 a_0 - F_4 a_0 P_c^{-0.8} \quad (3\text{-}61)$$

The F_i include the other factors entering into the defining equation for C_1 given in Table 3-3. The effect of system pressure on vehicle performance can then be determined by analyzing the effect of pressure on C_1, from Eq. (3-61), and using the results with the known effect of C_1 on performance as given by Eqs. (3-43) and (3-45) or Figs. 3-7 through 3-12.

A general solution for optimum pressure can be obtained relatively easily. It is obvious from Eq. (3-43) that the minimum value of m_0/m_L will result from a maximum value of C_1, for any given values of C_2 and ξ. Equation (3-61) shows that maximum C_1 results from a minimum value for the sum of the terms involving F_1, F_2, and F_4. Thus it is desired that

$$F_1 a_0 P_d^{2/3} + F_2 a_0 P_c^{-1} + F_4 a_0 P_c^{-0.8} = \Phi_1(P) \quad (3\text{-}62)$$

be a minimum for the optimum system operating pressure. Differentiating the terms in Eq. (3-62) and equating to zero leads to the relation

$$\frac{3}{2F_1 a_0} \frac{d\Phi_1}{dP} = P_d^{-0.33} - \frac{3F_2}{2F_1} P_c^{-2} - 1.2 \frac{F_4}{F_1} P_c^{-1.8} = 0 \quad (3\text{-}63)$$

for optimum P_c. This is almost an eighth-order equation in $P_c^{0.2}$, thus is not readily soluble. However, it can be rearranged as follows to permit easy numerical solution:

$$P_d^{1.67} = \frac{1.5F_2 + 1.2F_4 P_c^{0.2}}{F_1} \quad (3\text{-}64)$$

so that

$$P_d = \left(\frac{1.5F_2 + 1.2F_4 P_c^{0.2}}{F_1}\right)^{0.6} \quad (3\text{-}65)$$

Although this is an implicit equation, the value of the term involving $P_c^{0.2}$ is so insensitive to changes in P_c that rapid convergence is possible, and often only one iteration will be required for the determination of optimum P_c. The functional form of the factors F_1, F_2, and F_4 is evident by analogy between Eq. (3-61) and the defining equation for C_1 given in Table 3-3. These are

$$F_1 = A_4 \frac{\beta + \alpha_t}{\beta \rho_p v_e}$$

$$F_2 = A_{11} \frac{\epsilon}{g_0} \quad (3\text{-}66)$$

$$F_4 = P_{ref}^{0.8} \frac{\beta + \alpha_t}{\beta v_e} \left[\frac{0.678}{g_c}\left(\frac{v_{mi}}{10^3}\right)^2 + 1.055 \times 10^{-3} H_v\right]$$

$$\frac{\rho_c + 6\rho_{refl} t_{refl}/D_c + 4\rho_{sh} f_s P_c/\sigma_{sh}}{2.93 \times 10^{-7} A_{sp} \Delta T_{LM} (h_{cg}) P_{ref}}$$

where $(h_{cg})_{P_{ref}}$ is the average core heat-transfer coefficient at some arbitrarily chosen reference pressure P_{ref}. Substitution of values from Table 3-4 into Eqs. (3-65) and (3-66) shows that the optimum value of chamber pressure for the two assumed vehicles is about 1,600 and 3,740 lb/in.^{2} for the hydrogen- and ammonia-propellant vehicles respectively. Note that these differ from the assumed values; this shows that the original assumptions were not optimum.

Evaluation for optimum initial acceleration is a more cumbersome task, for the parameter a_0 appears in the velocity exponent ξ [Eq. (3-46)] as well as in the defining equation for C_1 [Eq. (3-61)]. Here, as similarly for the system pressure, minimum m_0/m_L results from a maximum value of the denominator of Eq. (3-43). Thus it is desired that

$$C_2 e^{-\xi} - (F_1 a_0 P_d^{2/3} + F_2 a_0 P_c^{-1} + F_4 a_0 P_c^{-0.8}) = \Phi_2(a_0) \qquad (3\text{-}67)$$

be a minimum for the optimum initial vehicle acceleration. Unfortunately, differentiation here (with respect to a_0) leads only to the implicit transcendental equation

$$C_2 \frac{g \sin \theta}{(1 - \mathcal{L})\chi} \frac{e^\xi - 1}{a_0^2} = F_1 P^{2/3} + F_2 P_c^{-1} + F_3 + F_4 P_c^{-0.8} \qquad (3\text{-}68)$$

for optimum a_0. Note that the exponent ξ is a function of both e^ξ (through m_p/m_0) and a_0. Analytical solution of this for a_0 is hopelessly impossible and recourse must be made to computing machines or manual numerical iterative methods.

Another way of arriving at the optimum acceleration is by a graphical numerical iterative process making use of the previously discussed general performance graphs. Here, as for system pressure, the effect of a_0 on C_1 can be obtained easily from Eq. (3-61). As previously mentioned, the effect of C_1 upon vehicle performance is shown in Figs. 3-7 through 3-12 or given by Eqs. (3-43) and (3-45).

Since it is only possible to generalize performance to the value of ξ, the mass-ratio-equation exponent, and since this is a function of both acceleration and burnout velocity, the vehicle burnout velocity will obviously vary together with the ratio of gross weight to dead load as initial acceleration is changed. Thus to compare vehicles of equal performance (i.e., equal burnout velocity) but with different initial accelerations it is necessary to compare these vehicles at different gross weight–dead load ratios and different velocity exponents simultaneously if Eqs. (3-43) and (3-45) or the graphs in Figs. 3-7 through 3-12 are to be used. Since such a comparison can only be made by use of vehicle burnout velocity, a specific dimensional parameter, it is necessary to know the drag, atmospheric, flight-path, and α and β factors for the vehicle. This clearly removes the last vestiges of generality from the procedure. The complications involved prohibit presentation of a specific example; however, it is possible to make some general remarks to serve as guideposts in this field. If C_1 alone is considered, it is obvious that optimum a_0 is also minimum a_0 [Eq. (3-62)]. For vertical (up) launching, a_0 must be greater than g_0 or the vehicle will not rise; this defines the minimum. From the equation for the mass-ratio exponent [Eq. (3-46)] it can be seen that the term involving a_0 is important only when it is comparable to the design vehicle burnout velocity. The importance of this term decreases inversely with increasing initial acceleration, so a definite incentive exists to increase a_0. However, for large long-range rockets the burnout velocity is usually greater than the term involving a_0, even for a_0 equal to g_0 (principally because long range implies a low value of $\sin \theta$) so that, to a first rough approximation, this term can be neglected for large rockets and the major performance dependence can be assumed through C_1 above. Results of many studies made by using automatic computing equipment indicate that initial accelerations between 1.2 and $2.0g_0$ are optimum for large rockets.

3-3. Limitations of System Analysis. The methods of system analysis outlined in this chapter are tools helpful in the examination of the idealized performance of rocket vehicles (or of any other system of interest) and in the investigation of the importance of or sensitivity to various parameters entering into the specification of system operation.

The results of a system analysis should not be accepted as a literal exposition of the predicted behavior of the system of interest, since such an analysis is only a computation of performance *on the assumption that everything works perfectly.* Practical considerations of the system reliability and of possible sources of failure are generally neglected in the comparison of performance of competing systems. Such factors are nearly always nonanalytic and thus cannot be handled satisfactorily by the mathematical methods outlined in this chapter. For example, in this connection, the vehicle performance comparisons presented in Sec. 3-2 do not include any estimation of the difficulties of reliable operation of multicomponent or multistage vehicles as compared to single-stage, thus are not a fair comparison of the over-all statistical performance of the nuclear vs. chemical systems considered.

Another weakness of system analysis lies in the fact that the output of a study (i.e., the results obtained) is often a very sensitive function of the input assumptions about system operating conditions. As an example of the sensitivity of the comparative results to these assumed operating conditions, calculations show that the gross weight of the nuclear hydrogen vehicle defined in Table 3-4 is always (for any range or burnout velocity) larger than that of the fluorine-hydrogen chemical rocket defined in Table 3-5, *if* the propellant tank pressure is chosen as

50 lb/in.^{2} for the hydrogen rocket, rather than 15 lb/in.^{2} as listed. This is a consequence of the large-volume tankage associated with the use of liquid hydrogen. Another example is shown by calculations of the comparative performance assuming the propellant gas in the nuclear rockets is heated to 6500°R rather than 5000°R as listed in Table 3-4. For this higher-temperature condition both the nuclear ammonia and hydrogen vehicles are superior, on a weight basis, to the chemical rockets presented (single- or multistaged) for all ranges and for dead loads above several thousand pounds.

In this situation it is clear that the ideal validity of a system study is almost totally dependent on the validity or reasonableness of the input assumptions. If optimistic values (relative to achievable reality) are chosen for exhaust velocity or motor weight, or any other parameter, then the results of a performance analysis will also be optimistic with respect to probable real performance. Here it should be noted that the performance curves and comparisons shown in Figs. 3-13 through 3-23 hold *only* for ideal operation at the conditions stated in Tables 3-4 and 3-5. These assumed operating conditions are not necessarily realistic; some are purely arbitrary, and others merely represent a selection of values most frequently cited in the reference literature. A different choice of values would lead to different performance capabilities and comparisons.

In conclusion it should be reemphasized that the methods of system analysis are tools for the exploration of idealized system behavior; system analysis is not an end in itself but can be very useful if its results are properly qualified and interpreted.

REFERENCES

1. Kooy, J. M. J., and J. W. H. Uytenbogaart: "Ballistics of the Future," chap. XI, secs. 3, 9, and 10, pp. 291–298 and 342–364, McGraw-Hill Book Company, Inc., New York, 1946.
2. Goddard, R. H.: "Rocket Development," Prentice-Hall, Inc., Englewood Cliffs, N.J., 1948.
3. Fischer, W. W., and R. H. Norris: Supersonic Convective Heat Transfer Correlation from Skin-temperature Measurements on a V-2 Rocket in Flight, *Trans. ASME*, vol. 71, no. 59, pp. 457–469, July, 1949.
4. Snodgrass, R. B.: Flight Measurements of Aerodynamic Heating and Boundary Layer Transition on the Viking 10 Nose Cone, *J. Am. Rocket Soc.*, vol. 25, no. 12, pp. 701–706, December, 1955.
5. a. Mulford, R. N., and J. P. Nigon: Heat Exchange between a Copper Surface and Liquid Hydrogen and Nitrogen, *LA*-1416, Los Alamos Scientific Laboratory, May 21, 1952.
   b. Haselden, G. G., and J. I. Peters: Heat Transfer to Boiling Liquid Oxygen and Liquid Nitrogen, *Trans. Inst. Chem. Engrs. (London)*, vol. 27, pp. 201–208, 1949.

6. McAdams, W. H.: "Heat Transmission," 2d ed., pp. 241–249, McGraw-Hill Series in Chemical Engineering, McGraw-Hill Book Company, Inc., New York, 1942.
7. Farber, E. A., and R. L. Scorah: Heat Transfer to Water Boiling under Pressure, *Trans. ASME*, vol. 70, no. 5, pp. 369–381, May, 1948.
8. *a*. Gatland, K. W., A. M. Kunesch, and A. E. Dixon: Minimum Satellite Vehicles, *J. Brit. Interplanet. Soc.*, vol. 10, no. 6, p. 288, November, 1951.
   b. Sutton, George P.: "Rocket Propulsion Elements," 2d ed., chap. 8, p. 300, John Wiley & Sons, Inc., New York, 1956.
9. Meghreblian, Robert V.: A Study of the Influence of Specific Impulse and Density on the Performance of Rocket Vehicles, pp. 14–15, 27, *Rept.* 1-31, Jet Propulsion Laboratory, California Institute of Technology, Pasadena, Calif., Dec. 29, 1950.
10. The Effect of Selected Parameters on the Design of Rocket Engine Pumping Plants, *Rept. SPD*-230, M. W. Kellogg Company, Jersey City, N.J., May 15, 1949.
11. Shepherd, L. R., and A. V. Cleaver: The Atomic Rocket—2, *J. Brit. Interplanet. Soc.*, vol. 7, no. 6, pp. 238–241, November, 1948.
12. Tsien, H. S.: "Rockets and Other Thermal Jets Using Nuclear Energy," in Clark Goodman (ed.), "The Science and Engineering of Nuclear Power," vol. II, chap. 11, pp. 183–184, 187–190, Addison-Wesley Publishing Company, Reading, Mass., 1949.
13. Cleaver, A. V.: Interplanetary Flight: Is the Rocket the Only Answer? *J. Brit. Interplanet. Soc.*, vol. 6, no. 5, pp. 143–146, June, 1947.
14. Sutton, George P.: "Rocket Propulsion Elements," 1st ed., table 4-3, p. 101, fig. 4-6, p. 104, John Wiley & Sons, Inc., New York, 1949.
15. Gordon, Sanford, and Vearl N. Huff: Theoretical Performance of Liquid Hydrogen and Liquid Fluorine as a Rocket Propellant, *NACA RM* E52L11, Feb. 6, 1953.

CHAPTER 4

HEAT TRANSFER AND FLUID FLOW

Since a nuclear reactor is, in the engineering sense, an unlimited heat source, the problem of core design reduces to the most efficient utilization of this source. For nuclear rockets, the goal is to heat a low-molecular-weight propellant to as high a temperature as practicable. Analysis and design to achieve this goal require an understanding of the heat-transfer processes and of the geometries that might be used to exploit these processes. In this chapter conventional approaches to the heat-transfer problem are presented. More exotic ideas for the utilization and exchange of fission energy are treated in Chap. 9. The discussion includes heat transfer by convection and conduction, with application to various geometries. In addition, material on core power density, fluid friction, pressure drop, and system flow stability is presented.

4-1. Convective Heat Transfer. As the subject of convective heat transfer has been treated in considerable detail by various authors,[1-3] no attempt will be made to develop the theory; instead a review and summary[4] will be presented on that portion of the theory applicable to nuclear rocket-reactor cores.

Convective heat transfer, like fluid friction, is considered a boundary-layer phenomenon, and it is held (1) that heat passes to or from the fluid by molecular conduction through a laminar layer which is always present immediately on the surface and (2) that the heat-transfer rate is proportional to the temperature difference between the surface and the ambient fluid. Thus the relationship for the convective heat transfer between a solid surface and a fluid is

$$\frac{q}{A} = -k \left(\frac{\partial T}{\partial y} \right)_{y=0} = h(T_w - T_b) \tag{4-1}$$

From Eq. (4-1) the heat-transfer coefficient may be defined as

$$h = -\frac{k(\partial T/\partial y)_{y=0}}{T_w - T_b} \tag{4-2}$$

where q/A = heat-transfer rate per unit area
k = thermal conductivity
T_w = wall temperature
T_b = fluid bulk static temperature
y = coordinate normal to fluid-surface interface

Heat-transfer data are conveniently correlated by use of dimensionless ratios. Following accepted practice, Eq. (4-2) is written in terms of the Nusselt number:

$$\mathbf{Nu} = \frac{hD}{k} = \frac{-(\partial T/\partial y)_{y=0}}{(T_w - T_b)/D} \tag{4-3}$$

where D is a length characteristic of the heat-exchanger geometry. By use of this definition of Nusselt number, and from the steady-flow energy equation of a fluid, it can be shown[5,6] that

$$\mathbf{Nu} = F_1\left(\mathbf{Re,Pr,M}, \frac{\Delta T_{ad}}{T_w - T_b}\right) \tag{4-4}$$

for a given system geometry where $\mathbf{Re} = \rho u_b D/\mu$ is the Reynolds number, $\mathbf{Pr} = \mu c_p/k$ is the Prandtl number, and $\mathbf{M} = u_b/a$ is the Mach number. Here ΔT_{ad} is total adiabatic stagnation-temperature rise, ρ is the fluid density, u_b is the fluid bulk velocity, μ is the absolute viscosity of the fluid, and a is the local speed of sound.

For heat transfer to low-velocity flows, the Mach number and the temperature ratio $\Delta T_{ad}/(T_w - T_b)$ are substantially zero, so that, of the five dimensionless variables in Eq. (4-4), only the first three, $\mathbf{Nu}$, $\mathbf{Re}$, and $\mathbf{Pr}$, normally appear. Consequently, the Nusselt number and in turn the heat-transfer coefficient h are independent of the temperature potential, which is a necessary requirement in order that Eq. (4-1) conveniently represent the rate of heat transfer. At high velocities, however, the temperature factor $\Delta T_{ad}/(T_w - T_b)$ in Eq. (4-4) is finite and the Nusselt number is dependent upon the temperature potential, thereby destroying the utility of Eq. (4-1). Clearly, what is needed is a heat-transfer equation in which the temperature potential and the heat-transfer coefficient are independent of each other for all velocities of flow.

It is postulated that the convective heat transfer with frictional heating can be expressed by

$$\frac{q}{A} = \bar{h}(T_w - T_{aw}) \tag{4-5}$$

where $\bar{h}$ is the heat-transfer coefficient with frictional heating and T_{aw} is the adiabatic wall temperature.

By imposing the boundary conditions of an insulated plate

$$T_w = T_{aw} \quad \text{and} \quad \left(\frac{\partial T}{\partial y}\right)_{y=0} = 0$$

and combining Eqs. (4-3) and (4-4), Eq. (4-4) reduces to

$$\frac{T_{aw} - T_b}{\Delta T_{ad}} = \frac{T_{aw} - T_b}{T_t - T_b} = \frac{T_{aw} - T_b}{u_b^2/2g_cJc_p} = F_2(\mathbf{Re,Pr,M}) \qquad (4\text{-}6)$$

where T_t is the total or stagnation temperature of the fluid.

Now if we define this temperature ratio as a "recovery factor" r, then

$$r = \frac{T_{aw} - T_b}{u_b^2/2g_cJc_p} = F_2(\mathbf{Re,Pr,M}) \qquad (4\text{-}7)$$

where g_c is the gravitational mass conversion factor [32.2 (lb mass/lb force)(ft/sec²)] and J is the mechanical equivalent of heat (778 ft-lb/Btu).

It is evident that, in order to determine the modified temperature potential $T_{aw} - T_b$, a knowledge of the recovery factor is required, and it is treated independently of the heat transfer.

Both theoretical analyses and experimental investigations[6–8] of laminar and turbulent flows have shown that the heat-transfer coefficient with friction $\bar{h}$ is independent of the modified temperature potential. Furthermore, it is identical with the coefficient for low-velocity flows when evaluated at the same Reynolds and Prandtl numbers, so that $h = \bar{h}$. Thus the forced-convection heat-transfer relationships become

$$\frac{q}{A} = h(T_w - T_{aw}) \qquad (4\text{-}8)$$

$$\mathbf{Nu} = \frac{hD}{k} = F_1(\mathbf{Re,Pr,M}) \qquad (4\text{-}9)$$

$$r = \frac{T_{aw} - T_b}{T_t - T_b} = F_2(\mathbf{Re,Pr,M}) \qquad (4\text{-}10)$$

What remains is the evaluation of Eqs. (4-9) and (4-10) for various geometries and flow conditions.

RECOVERY FACTORS. Though the necessity of using a recovery factor is less important in low subsonic flows of the type most interesting in heat-exchanger design, there are conditions in which it must be considered. While the recovery factor is defined in terms of the adiabatic wall temperatures by Eq. (4-10), there are occasions, depending upon the body geometry, where one or more recovery factors may be required. The most common one, generally referred to as simply the recovery factor, is the *local* recovery factor and is based on the local values of the fluid velocity and temperature at the edge of the boundary layer and on the local values of the adiabatic wall temperatures. If the upstream undisturbed free-stream fluid velocity, temperature, and the mean adiabatic surface temperature are used, the result is called an *over-all* recovery factor. A third type, based on upstream undisturbed fluid velocity and temperature and with the local adiabatic surface temperature, is referred to as the *local free-stream* recovery factor.

For laminar flow along the length of a flat plate the recovery factor has been evaluated[4] analytically and experimentally for values of Prandtl number from 0.72 to 1.2, Mach number from 0 to 10, and n, the temperature exponent for viscosity and thermal-conductivity variation, from 0.5 to 1.25. The results show that the recovery factor is independent of Reynolds number and Mach number and is well represented by the square root of the Prandtl number:

$$r = \frac{T_{aw} - T_b}{u_b{}^2/2g_cJc_p} = \mathbf{Pr}^{\frac{1}{2}} \qquad \text{laminar flow} \qquad (4\text{-}11)$$

The solutions, however, do not give the temperature upon which to evaluate the Prandtl number, since it was maintained as an independent parameter in the solutions.

For turbulent flow, the analytical solutions are not comparable to those for laminar boundary layers, but a good approximation to the recovery factor at large Reynolds numbers is given by the cube root of the Prandtl number:

$$r = \mathbf{Pr}^{\frac{1}{3}} \qquad \text{turbulent flow} \qquad (4\text{-}12)$$

Since the knowledge of recovery factor is also of great importance in the problem of aerodynamic heating, extensive theoretical and experimental investigations are being carried out for various types of flow and geometry. Consequently, for detailed use of recovery factors, reference to current literature should be made.

Boundary Layer. Since it has been postulated that convective heat transfer is considered a boundary-layer effect, a review of the boundary-layer equations and their significance is in order.

In flow systems where temperature differences bring about density changes, it is necessary to include buoyancy forces in the equations of motion of a viscous fluid and to treat them as impressed body forces. Introducing these forces into the Navier-Stokes equations of a steady compressible fluid, along with the continuity and energy equations we obtain:*

Continuity:

$$\frac{\partial(\rho u)}{\partial x} + \frac{\partial(\rho u)}{\partial y} + \frac{\partial(\rho w)}{\partial z} = 0 \qquad (4\text{-}13)$$

Navier-Stokes:

$$\rho \frac{Du}{Dt} = X - \frac{\partial p}{\partial x} + \rho g_x \beta \, \Delta T + \frac{\partial}{\partial x}\left[\mu\left(2\frac{\partial u}{\partial x} - \frac{2}{3}\operatorname{div}\omega\right)\right]$$
$$+ \frac{\partial}{\partial y}\left[\mu\left(\frac{\partial u}{\partial y} + \frac{\partial v}{\partial x}\right)\right] + \frac{\partial}{\partial z}\left[\mu\left(\frac{\partial w}{\partial x} + \frac{\partial u}{\partial z}\right)\right] \quad (4\text{-}14a)$$

* For derivation of these equations see H. Schlichting, "Boundary Layer Theory," McGraw-Hill Book Company, Inc., New York, 1955.

$$\rho \frac{Dv}{Dt} = Y - \frac{\partial p}{\partial y} + \rho g_y \beta \, \Delta T + \frac{\partial}{\partial y}\left[\mu\left(2\frac{\partial v}{\partial y} - \frac{2}{3}\operatorname{div}\omega\right)\right]$$
$$+ \frac{\partial}{\partial z}\left[\mu\left(\frac{\partial v}{\partial z} + \frac{\partial w}{\partial y}\right)\right] + \frac{\partial}{\partial x}\left[\mu\left(\frac{\partial u}{\partial y} + \frac{\partial v}{\partial x}\right)\right] \quad (4\text{-}14b)$$

$$\rho \frac{Dw}{Dt} = Z - \frac{\partial p}{\partial z} + \rho g_z \beta \, \Delta T + \frac{\partial}{\partial z}\left[\mu\left(2\frac{\partial w}{\partial z} - \frac{2}{3}\operatorname{div}\omega\right)\right]$$
$$+ \frac{\partial}{\partial x}\left[\mu\left(\frac{\partial w}{\partial x} + \frac{\partial u}{\partial z}\right)\right] + \frac{\partial}{\partial y}\left[\mu\left(\frac{\partial v}{\partial z} + \frac{\partial w}{\partial y}\right)\right] \quad (4\text{-}14c)$$

where $\rho g \beta \, \Delta T$ is the lift force per unit volume if ρ is the density before heating and g is the vector of gravitational acceleration with components $g_x g_y g_z$. The coefficient of expansion is β and $\Delta T = T - T_b$, the difference between the hotter fluid particle and the colder free-stream particle. With $\omega = iu + jv + kw$ being the velocity vector, and the total time derivative being

$$\frac{D}{Dt} = \frac{\partial}{\partial t} + u\frac{\partial}{\partial x} + v\frac{\partial}{\partial y} + w\frac{\partial}{\partial z}$$

the pressure is p, with X, Y, Z being the body forces.

Energy equation:

$$\rho g_c \frac{D}{Dt}(c_p T) = \frac{Dp}{Dt} + \left[\frac{\partial}{\partial x}\left(k\frac{\partial T}{\partial x}\right) + \frac{\partial}{\partial y}\left(k\frac{\partial T}{\partial y}\right) + \frac{\partial}{\partial z}\left(k\frac{\partial T}{\partial z}\right)\right] + \mu\Phi$$
$$(4\text{-}15)$$

where Φ is the dissipation function given by

$$\Phi = 2\left[\left(\frac{\partial u}{\partial x}\right)^2 + \left(\frac{\partial v}{\partial y}\right)^2 + \left(\frac{\partial w}{\partial z}\right)^2\right] + \left(\frac{\partial v}{\partial x} + \frac{\partial u}{\partial y}\right)^2$$
$$+ \left(\frac{\partial w}{\partial y} + \frac{\partial v}{\partial z}\right)^2 + \left(\frac{\partial u}{\partial z} + \frac{\partial w}{\partial x}\right)^2 - \frac{2}{3}\left(\frac{\partial u}{\partial x} + \frac{\partial v}{\partial y} + \frac{\partial w}{\partial z}\right)^2$$

In addition, for perfect gases the equation of state is

$$\frac{P}{\rho} = g_c \frac{R_u}{\mathfrak{M}} T \quad (4\text{-}16)$$

where R_u is the universal gas constant and $\mathfrak{M}$ is the molecular weight of the fluid.

For the cases where the properties of the gas are not constant and vary with temperature

$$\mu = \mu(T) \quad (4\text{-}17a)$$
$$c_p = c_p(T) \quad (4\text{-}17b)$$
$$k = k(T) \quad (4\text{-}17c)$$

After making the boundary-layer simplifications,[9] the system of equations for a steady two-dimensional compressible-fluid flow with properties as a function of temperature becomes

Continuity:

$$\frac{\partial(\rho u)}{\partial x} + \frac{\partial(\rho v)}{\partial y} = 0 \tag{4-18a}$$

Momentum:

$$\rho \left(u \frac{\partial u}{\partial x} + v \frac{\partial u}{\partial y} \right) = \frac{\partial}{\partial y} \left(u \frac{\partial u}{\partial y} \right) - \frac{dp}{dx} + \rho g_x \beta (T - T_b) \tag{4-18b}$$

Energy:

$$\rho g_c \left[u \frac{\partial}{\partial x} (c_p T) + v \frac{\partial}{\partial y} (c_p T) \right] = \frac{\partial}{\partial y} \left(k \frac{\partial T}{\partial y} \right) + \mu \left(\frac{\partial u}{\partial y} \right)^2 + u \frac{dp}{dx} \tag{4-18c}$$

State:

$$\frac{P}{\rho} = g_c \frac{R_u}{\mathfrak{M}} T \tag{4-18d}$$

Properties:

$$\mu = \mu(T) \tag{4-18e}$$
$$c_p = c_p(T) \tag{4-18f}$$
$$k = k(T) \tag{4-18g}$$

Within the framework of boundary-layer theory, the pressure may be considered as a given impressed force; therefore we have a system of seven simultaneous equations for the seven unknowns ρ, u, v, T, μ, c_p, and k. These equations, plus an appropriate set of boundary conditions, define the problem.

Solution of these equations under various assumptions regarding the physical properties of the fluid and the boundary conditions of the flow and a summary of the early investigations are given in Ref. 10. Since the literature is extensive on the theory of the boundary layer, the present discussion will be limited to the significant characteristics of the equations.

Examination of the momentum and energy equations (4-18b) and (4-18c), which describe the velocity and thermal boundary layers respectively, reveals a marked similarity in their structure differing only in the last two terms of each equation. Generally, this means that there is an interaction and interdependence between the velocity and temperature distributions. In the special case when buoyancy forces may be disregarded, mutual interaction ceases, and the velocity field no longer depends on the temperature field, although the converse dependence of the temperature field on the velocity field still persists. This condition exists when the temperature differences are small and the velocity and Reynolds number are large; such flows are described as being *forced*. The heat transfer occurring with this type of flow is called *forced convection*. Flows in which the buoyancy forces are dominant are called *natural* or *free*, and the respective heat transfer is known as *natural* or *free convection*. This condition results from large temperature differences and low velocities. Forced flows can be further divided into those with moderate and those with high velocities, depending on whether or not the heat due to friction and compression must be considered. In the case of moderate velocities, the heat due to friction and compression may be neglected, and the temperature velocity-field dependence is governed solely by the Prandtl number. However, at high velocities the work of friction and compression must be included; this condition exists when the temperature difference between the fluid and the body is comparable to the temperature rise due to friction and compression.

For most designs of nuclear rocket heat-exchanger cores, *forced-convection* heat transfer is the more applicable process, and is the one considered in further detail.

Laminar Flow. Experience has shown that, in forced-convection heat transfer, two types of flow can occur. In one case, say for flow through a straight tube, the fluid moves in an axial direction only, with the velocity remaining constant on cylindrical surfaces (stream tubes) which are concentric with the tube axis. For this condition, where the cylindrical laminae slide over each other, the flow is described as laminar. The second type occurs when the velocity increases and reaches a critical value, depending on the viscosity of the fluid and the conditions of the walls, and mixing of the fluid layers results from velocity components normal to the tube axis. In this case the flow is called turbulent.

Under laminar-shear flow conditions, the heat transfer is primarily due to molecular conduction between the fluid layers and Newton's law of cooling holds, together with the defining equation for viscosity. That is,

$$\frac{q}{A} = -k \frac{\partial T}{\partial y} \tag{4-19}$$

$$\tau = \mu \frac{\partial u}{\partial y} \tag{4-20}$$

where τ is the shear stress.

For laminar flow in a straight pipe, and at a reasonable distance from the entrance, it can be shown[9] from a balance of forces and the use of Eqs. (4-19) and (4-20) that the velocity distribution within the tube is parabolic over the radius, and the pressure drop along the tube is

$$p_1 - p_2 = 32\mu \frac{L}{D^2} \bar{u} \tag{4-21}$$

where $\bar{u} = 4Q/\pi D^2$ = mean velocity over cross section
L = tube length
Q = volumetric flow rate
D = tube diameter

Equation (4-21) is known as the Hagen-Poiseuille relation for laminar flow in a pipe.

The point at which the transition from laminar to turbulent flow takes place was investigated by Reynolds,[11] and it was determined that the transition occurred at a definite value of the Reynolds number. This critical Reynolds number depends in part upon the flow entrance conditions and, for a pipe with a sharp-edge entrance, is approximately

$$\mathbf{Re}_{crit} = \frac{\rho \bar{u} D}{\mu} \approx 2,300$$

Below this value, even strong disturbances will not cause the flow to become turbulent.

While laminar-flow heat exchangers appear to have a decided advantage from the pressure-drop standpoint, stability considerations indicate that, for the large propellant temperature changes necessary in a nuclear rocket-reactor core, laminar-flow systems tend toward flow instability, a characteristic that must be avoided in designing high-power-density reactor cores. Further discussion of flow stability is presented in Sec. 4-6.

Turbulent Flow. While many experimental investigations have been made to determine friction factors and heat-transfer coefficients for turbulent flow in tubes and parallel channels, the theoretical aspects of the mechanism of turbulent flow have received somewhat less attention. The first important contribution to a better understanding of heat transfer in turbulent flow was made by Reynolds,[11] in 1874, when he postulated the analogy between heat and momentum transfer in turbulent-shear flow. For turbulent-shear flow in tubes or parallel channels with velocity and temperature gradients predominant in the direction normal to the wall, the analogy can be expressed as

$$\frac{-q/A}{\rho c_p \, dT/dy} = \frac{\tau}{\rho \, du/dy} \tag{4-22}$$

where q/A is the rate of heat transfer per unit area normal to the wall and τ is the shearing stress. Since for laminar-shear flow $q/A = -k(dT/dy)$ and $\tau = \mu(du/dy)$, it is evident that Eq. (4-22) holds if, and only if, the Prandtl number is unity. Hence the Reynolds analogy is strictly correct for laminar-shear flow provided the fluid properties have a Prandtl number of 1. For most gases, whose Prandtl number is close to unity ($\mathbf{Pr} \approx 0.75$), the Reynolds analogy is sufficiently useful for engineering application, even though the flow is laminar close to the wall.

The extensions of the Reynolds analogy to fluids with Prandtl numbers different from unity were made by Taylor[12] in 1919, Prandtl[13] in 1928, and von Kármán[14,15] in 1934 and 1939. In his second paper, which has been so useful to those working in the heat-transfer field, von Kármán introduced a buffer layer between the laminar sublayer next to the wall and the turbulent core postulated by Taylor and Prandtl. In the thin laminar sublayer the transport processes were assumed purely molecular; in the turbulent core the Reynolds analogy was used; and in the buffer layer both molecular and turbulent transports were assumed, the first effect decreasing and the second increasing with distance from the wall. The Reynolds analogy was applied to the turbulent components of the transport terms within the buffer layer.

The differential equations resulting from the analyses have been developed by various authors.[16,17] The derivation presented here is essentially that of von Kármán.[15]

The shear stress τ occurring in an arbitrary plane perpendicular to the y axis is equal to the total momentum transferred by the molecular and turbulent exchange and is given by the sum of the laminar stress and the Reynolds stress:

$$\tau = \mu \frac{du}{dy} - \rho \overline{v'u'} \qquad (4\text{-}23)$$

where u' and v' are the velocity fluctuations parallel to the x and y axes, and $\overline{v'u'}$ is the time-averaged mean value of the turbulent fluctuation.

If the temperature T of the fluid varies along the y axis, the heat flow per unit area normal to the x axis can be similarly expressed, consisting of two parts: (1) the molecular heat conduction and (2) the turbulent heat transfer due to fluctuations of velocity and temperature.

$$\frac{q}{A} = -k \frac{dT}{dy} + c_p \rho \overline{v'T'} \qquad (4\text{-}24)$$

where $\overline{v'T'}$ is the time-averaged mean value of the velocity and temperature fluctuations.

The second term of Eq. (4-23) is called the contribution of the eddy viscosity, while the second term in Eq. (4-24) is the contribution of the eddy conductivity. If the mean value $\overline{v'u'}$ is expressed as $\epsilon \, du/dy$ and $\overline{v'T'}$ is equal to $\epsilon_h \, dT/dy$, where ϵ and ϵ_h are the eddy viscosity and eddy diffusivity respectively, by introducing the kinematic viscosity $\nu = \mu/\rho$ and the thermal diffusivity $\kappa = k/\rho c_p$, one obtains the fundamental equations

$$\frac{\tau}{\rho} = (\nu + \epsilon) \frac{du}{dy} \qquad (4\text{-}25a)$$

$$\frac{q}{A \rho c_p} = -(\kappa + \epsilon_h) \frac{\partial T}{dy} \qquad (4\text{-}25b)$$

Now by the use of the Reynolds analogy, it is proper to assume that, for flows where the molecular components are negligible, $\epsilon_h = \epsilon$. Following von Kármán, the same assumption will be made even when ν and κ are not negligible, resulting in

$$\frac{\tau}{\rho} = (\nu + \epsilon) \frac{du}{dy} \qquad (4\text{-}26a)$$

$$\frac{q}{\rho A c_p} = -(\kappa + \epsilon) \frac{dT}{dy} \qquad (4\text{-}26b)$$

From Eqs. (4-26) it can be seen that direct proportionality between shearing stress and heat transfer can be expected if:
1. ν and κ are negligible compared to ϵ.
2. ν and κ are numerically equal.

In the case of turbulent flow in pipes or channels, condition 1 is generally satisfied with the exception of a relatively narrow region near the solid walls, and Eqs. (4-26) can be applied in the fully developed turbulent core.

Condition 2 is approximately satisfied by gases, since the kinematic viscosity and the thermal diffusivity of gases are of the same order of magnitude. However, for liquids, ν is much larger than κ. The Prandtl number ($\mathbf{Pr} = \nu/\kappa$) is as high as 200 for some liquids. As a consequence, the Reynolds analogy cannot be applied directly to the heat transfer between solids and liquids.

Theoretical and experimental work has been done recently on the problem of heat transfer at the higher Prandtl numbers, and the reader is referred to the results of Deissler[16] and Rannie[17] on the solutions to Eqs. (4-25).

As for laminar flow, both experimental and theoretical analyses for turbulent flow are given extensively in the literature, and no attempt is made to include further work in this text. A selected number of semi-empirical equations are presented in a subsequent section for use in engineering design.

A consequence of Eqs. (4-26), under either assumption (1) or (2), which is of considerable assistance in correlating heat-transfer experiments is: For the case of ν and κ being numerically equal, this being the same as having a Prandtl number $\mathbf{Pr} = \mu c_p/k = \nu/\kappa$ of unity, Eqs. (4-26) become

$$\frac{\tau}{\rho} = (\nu + \epsilon) \frac{du}{dy} \qquad (4\text{-}27a)$$

$$\frac{q}{\rho A c_p} = (\nu + \epsilon) \frac{dT}{dy} \qquad (4\text{-}27b)$$

Now assuming τ and q/A are constant and letting u_w and T_w denote the wall velocity and temperature with u and T being the velocity at some arbitrary point in the fluid, it follows from the integration of Eqs. (4-27) that

$$u - u_w = \frac{\tau}{\rho} \int_0^y \frac{dy}{\nu + \epsilon} \tag{4-28a}$$

$$T - T_w = - \frac{q/A}{\rho c_p} \int_0^y \frac{dy}{\nu + \epsilon} \tag{4-28b}$$

This indicates that the distributions of velocity and temperature are similar if they are measured relative to the wall. This is also approximately so if q/A and τ are not constant, but vary in an approximately similar way. Now if U_m is taken as the mean velocity of the fluid relative to the wall, and for a mean temperature difference $T_w - T_m$, Eqs. (4-28) reduce to

$$\frac{U_m}{\tau/\rho} = \rho c_p \frac{T_w - T_m}{q/A} \tag{4-29}$$

Defining a friction coefficient as $C_f = \tau/(\rho/2)U_m^2$ and a heat-transfer coefficient $C_h = q/A \rho c_p U_m(T_w - T_m)$, the shearing-stress and heat-transfer equations become

$$\tau = \frac{C_f}{2} \rho U_m^2 \tag{4-30a}$$

$$\frac{q}{A} = C_h \rho U_m(T_w - T_m)c_p \tag{4-30b}$$

Substituting into Eq. (4-29) we obtain the important relationship that

$$\frac{C_f}{2} = C_h \tag{4-31}$$

This relation implies the following conclusions: (1) if the friction τ is proportional to the nth power of the velocity U_m, the heat transfer q/A is proportional to the power $n - 1$ and (2) roughness increases friction and heat transfer in the same ratio.

It should be noted that, because of the assumptions of a Prandtl number of unity and the similar laws of variation in shearing stress and heat flow, Eq. (4-31) is only approximate.

Extensions on the relationship between heat transfer and shearing stress have been made by various authors and are reviewed and summarized by Rubesin.[18]

Porous Flow. Since the desire in nuclear rocket cores is for designs which possess high power densities, the possibility of using porous construction to achieve efficient heat removal from a power-producing solid has always appeared attractive.[19] Such construction would have the advantage of high power density with small temperature differences in the solid and the coolant fluid. Studies[20] have been made to investigate the limiting case of heat removal from a porous wall by a gaseous coolant when the surface per unit volume of the porous structure is high enough that the temperature of the fluid at any point in its path may be considered the same as that of the adjacent solid. The analysis of Ref. 20, which is summarized below, treats the problems of both temperature distribution within the wall and flow resistance.

TEMPERATURE DISTRIBUTION. For this problem it is assumed that:

1. In the porous wall, the gas temperature and the solid temperature are approximately equal.

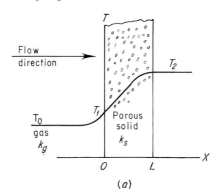

(a)

$$Gc_p T - k_s \frac{dT}{dx} \longrightarrow \boxed{Q\,dx} \longrightarrow Gc_p\left(T + \frac{dT}{dx}\,dx\right) - k_s\left(\frac{dT}{dx} + \frac{d^2T}{dx^2}\,dx\right)$$

|← dx →|

Unit area

(b)

FIG. 4-1. One-dimensional flow of gas through porous wall. (a) Temperature distribution; (b) heat balance on wall volume element.

2. The gas flow and heat flow are one-dimensional and steady. Convective effects, which are neglected, could alter the temperature of the approaching gas at low flow, but should not influence the conditions within the wall to any degree.

3. All heat conduction in the wall takes place in the solid.

4. The thermal conductivities of the gas and solid and the specific heat of the gas are constant.

Figure 4-1a shows the one-dimensional flow of a gas at a mass velocity G through a porous wall of thickness L. If the rate of heat generation per unit volume in the wall is Q, a heat balance (Fig. 4-1b) on an element of volume in the wall and gas yields the relationships

Wall: $$\frac{d^2T}{dx^2} - \frac{Gc_p}{k_s}\frac{dT}{dx} + \frac{Q}{k_s} = 0 \qquad (4\text{-}32)$$

Gas:
$$\frac{d^2T}{dx^2} - \frac{Gc_p}{k_g}\frac{dT}{dx} = 0 \qquad (4\text{-}33)$$

with the boundary conditions

At $x = -\infty$:	$T = T_0$	(4-34)
At $x = 0$:	$T = T_1$	(4-35)

with
$$\left(k_g \frac{dT}{dx}\right)_{\text{gas}} = \left(k_s \frac{dT}{dx}\right)_{\text{wall}} \qquad (4\text{-}36)$$

and

At $x = L$:
$$T = T_0 + \frac{QL}{Gc_p} = T_2 \qquad (4\text{-}37)$$

where T = temperature
$\quad G$ = mass velocity of gas
$\quad c_p$ = specific heat of gas
$\quad k_s$ = apparent (bulk) thermal conductivity of solid
$\quad k_g$ = thermal conductivity of gas
$\quad Q$ = rate of heat generation in wall
$\quad x$ = length variable
$\quad L$ = wall thickness
Units of measure are consistent.

For the above boundary conditions, solutions to Eqs. (4-32) and (4-33) are

Wall, with $0 \leq x \leq L$:
$$\frac{T - T_0}{QL/Gc_p} = \frac{x}{L} + \frac{1 - \exp\left[(-Gc_pL/k_s)(1 - x/L)\right]}{Gc_pL/k_s} \qquad (4\text{-}38)$$

Gas, with $-\infty < x < 0$:
$$\frac{T - T_0}{QL/Gc_p} = \frac{1 - \exp\left(-Gc_pL/k_s\right)}{Gc_pL/k_s}\exp\left(\frac{Gc_pL}{k_g}\frac{x}{L}\right) \qquad (4\text{-}39)$$

Examination of Eq. (4-38) reveals that uniformity in the wall temperature, which is desirable from a thermal-stress standpoint, is enhanced by a high thermal conductivity of the solid.

FLOW RESISTANCE. Experiments with porous metals[21] have shown that the pressure gradient in a perfect gas in steady, isothermal flow through a moderately fine-grained porous medium can be expressed by a quadratic relationship of the type

$$\frac{-d(p^2)}{dx} = \alpha(2bT\mu)G + \beta\frac{2bT}{g_c}G^2 \qquad (4\text{-}40)$$

where $b = R_u/\mathfrak{M}$ = specific gas constant
$\quad \mu$ = viscosity of gas
$\quad g_c$ = mass conversion constant

and α and β are length parameters characteristic of the structure of the porous material itself and are called the viscous- and inertial-resistance coefficients of the material, respectively. The viscous coefficient α, with dimensions L^{-2}, characterizes the flow resistance of the material in the regime of "creeping" flow, where inertia forces are negligible. The inertial coefficient β, of dimensions L^{-1}, provides a measure of the addi-

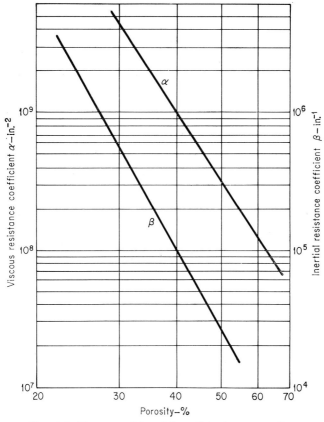

FIG. 4-2. Viscous and inertial coefficients vs. porosity.

tional resistance due to microscopic accelerations of the fluid within the interstices of the material. Figure 4-2 gives values of α and β for various material porosities.

To obtain a solution to the pressure-drop problem it is necessary to integrate Eq. (4-40) across the thickness of the heated wall, substituting at each point the proper gas temperature from Eq. (4-38) and the corresponding value of the viscosity of the gas, assuming for this procedure that the coefficients α and β are independent of temperature. Experimental data indicate that this latter assumption is justified.

The flow stability of porous systems is discussed in Sec. 4-6.

Experimental Correlation. As discussed in Sec. 4-1, the application of the theory of similarity to the differential equations of heat transfer by forced convection and of fluid flow yields for heat transfer from a solid to a fluid in similar systems the relationships of Eq. (4-9). That is,

$$\mathbf{Nu} = \frac{hL}{k} = F_1(\mathbf{Re,Pr,M}) \tag{4-41}$$

For the case of subsonic flows that are of general interest in nuclear-reactor heat-exchanger design, Eq. (4-41) reduces to

$$\mathbf{Nu} = \frac{hL}{k} = F_2(\mathbf{Re,Pr}) \tag{4-42}$$

Conventional practice in the field of convective heat transfer has led to correlation of experimental data by equations of the type

$$\mathbf{Nu} = C \ \mathbf{Re}^m \ \mathbf{Pr}^n \tag{4-43}$$

where C, m, and n are empirically determined constants.

In general, for specific geometries and design conditions, reference should always be made to the current technical literature to take advantage of advances being made in the heat-transfer field. However, many important cases have been thoroughly investigated and are well established. These include:

TURBULENT FLOW OF GASES IN SMOOTH TUBES. McAdams[1] has correlated the results of various investigators by the relationship

$$\mathbf{Nu} = 0.023 \ \mathbf{Re}^{0.8} \ \mathbf{Pr}^{\frac{1}{3}} \tag{4-44}$$

where the fluid properties are evaluated at a film temperature equal to the arithmetic mean of the mean surface and mean fluid bulk temperatures. Since it is necessary in many cases to designate a reference temperature for the fluid properties, Eq. (4-44) and those similar to it are written in the form

$$\frac{hD}{k_f} = 0.023 \left(\frac{DG}{\mu_f}\right)^{0.8} \left(\frac{c_{p_f}\mu_f}{k_f}\right)^{\frac{1}{3}} \tag{4-45}$$

where units are as previously defined and the subscript f indicates the fluid property evaluated at a film reference temperature $T_f = (T_w + T_b)/2$.

Equation (4-45) holds well for Reynolds numbers above 10,000 and Prandtl numbers of about 1 and greater, so that it can be used for gases, water, liquid hydrocarbons, and other nonmetallic liquids. Specifically, it applies only for "fully developed" flow, which occurs in long pipes or pipes with a preliminary "calming section" 50 or more diameters long.

Recent work[22,23] at high surface and fluid temperatures, utilizing various gases (air, hydrogen, and helium), has yielded results which were best correlated by an equation including the flow-channel length-diameter ratio. For this case the correlation relationship is

$$\frac{hD}{k_f} = 0.034 \left(\frac{\rho_f V_b D}{\mu_f}\right)^{0.8} \left(\frac{c_{p_f}\mu_f}{k_f}\right)^{0.4} \left(\frac{L}{D}\right)^{-0.1} \tag{4-46}$$

where $V_b = GT_b/\rho_f T_f$ is the bulk velocity and L is the tube length. The other symbols are identical to those of Eq. (4-45).

At times it becomes awkward to evaluate the various properties of the flow and the fluid at different temperatures, and consequently a correlation which lumps the effect of the temperature-dependent properties would be most useful for heat-exchanger design. This has been attempted[24] for gas flows in circular tubes with an abrupt contraction at the entrance, resulting in the following relationships for the cases given below.

Constant wall temperature:

$$\textbf{St Pr}^{2/3} = 0.020 \, \textbf{Re}^{-0.2} \left(\frac{T_w}{T_b}\right)^n \left(1 + \frac{6}{L/D}\right) \tag{4-47}$$

Constant heat input per unit of tube length or constant temperature difference in flow direction:

$$\textbf{St Pr}^{2/3} = 0.021 \, \textbf{Re}^{-0.2} \left(\frac{T_w}{T_b}\right)^n \left(1 + \frac{6}{L/D}\right) \tag{4-48}$$

with $n = -0.575$ for gas heating and -0.15 for gas cooling. Here $\textbf{St}$ is the Stanton number (h/Gc_p) and other symbols are as previously defined. Fluid properties should be evaluated at T_b.

Noncircular Flow Passages: While the above relationships are based on flow in circular tubes, they are valid for passages of noncircular shape if a proper *equivalent diameter* is used in evaluating the Reynolds number. Colburn's[25] investigations have shown this correct equivalent, or hydraulic, diameter to be

$$D_e = \frac{4A}{C} \tag{4-49}$$

where A is the cross-sectional flow area and C is the wetted perimeter.

LAMINAR FLOW OF FLUIDS OF MODERATE PRANDTL NUMBER. For laminar flow ($\textbf{Re} < 2{,}100$) of fluids with Prandtl numbers from about 0.5 to 300 in circular tubes at constant wall temperature, the following Colburn[25] equation has been found suitable:

$$\frac{h_a D}{k_b} = 1.62(1 + 0.015 \, \textbf{Gr}^{1/3}) \left(\frac{\mu_b}{\mu_f}\right)^{1/3} \left(\frac{4wc_{p_b}}{\pi k_b L}\right)^{1/3} \tag{4-50}$$

where $\textbf{Gr}$ is the Grashof number, used to correct for the effects of natural convection. This dimensionless modulus is defined by

$$\mathbf{Gr} = \frac{\beta \, \Delta T \, D^3 \rho_f g}{\mu_f{}^2} \tag{4-51}$$

where β = coefficient of thermal expansion ($1/T$ for a gas)

ΔT = average temperature difference between wall and fluid

g = acceleration due to gravity

In this correlation equation the heat-transfer coefficient h_a is defined by the relation

$$q = wc_{p_b}(T_2 - T_1) = h_a \pi DL \left(T_w - \frac{T_2 + T_1}{2} \right) \tag{4-52}$$

where w = fluid-weight flow rate

T_1 = average fluid temperature at entrance

T_2 = average fluid temperature at exit

and other symbols are as previously defined.

PACKED SPHERES. For flow through randomly packed spheres, the correlation equations must be employed with caution. As with the other heat-transfer relationships, the designer should be aware of the experimental conditions under which a particular correlation equation was determined. For packed spheres, it is customary to correlate heat-transfer results by means of a j factor which for the present case is defined as

$$j_h = \frac{h}{c_p G} \left(\frac{c_p \mu}{k} \right)_f^{2/3} \tag{4-53}$$

where the terms are similar to those used in previous equations.

In addition, a modified Reynolds number is used; it is based on the dry surface area for one packing unit A_p. That is,

$$\text{Modified Reynolds number} = \frac{G \sqrt{A_p}}{\mu} \tag{4-54}$$

where the effective diameter of a packing unit becomes

$$D_p = \sqrt{\frac{A_p}{\pi}} = 0.567 \sqrt{A_p} \tag{4-55}$$

With these definitions, one heat-transfer j factor[26] for packed spheres with modified Reynolds numbers $G \sqrt{A_p}/\mu$ above 620 is

$$j_h = 1.346 \left(\frac{G \sqrt{A_p}}{\mu} \right)^{-0.41} \tag{4-56}$$

which gives the heat-transfer equation

$$\mathbf{St} = \frac{h}{c_p G} = 1.346 \left(\frac{G \sqrt{A_p}}{\mu} \right)^{-0.41} \left(\frac{c_p \mu}{k} \right)_f^{-2/3} \tag{4-57}$$

Another correlation,[27] which is for experiments with a more deeply packed bed, is for Reynolds numbers from 200 to 2,000

$$\text{St} = 0.58 \left(\frac{GD_p}{\mu}\right)^{-0.30} \left(\frac{c_p\mu}{k}\right)^{-0.70} \tag{4-58}$$

when the properties are evaluated at the fluid bulk temperature.

FLOW OVER SURFACES WITH CONSTANT PRESSURE AND TEMPERATURE. Previous discussion has been primarily concerned with flows in tubes or channels; however, in many instances heat transfer to and from surfaces not associated with channel flow is desirable. The relations[28] given below permit calculations of friction and heat transfer from two-dimensional high-velocity flow to surfaces with locally constant pressure and temperature, considering both laminar and turbulent boundary layers. The calculation procedure utilizes constant-property equations and adapts them to conditions where properties vary in such a way that they are introduced into the equations at a properly defined reference temperature.

Laminar Boundary-layer Flow: The local wall-shearing stress is calculated from the relationship

$$\tau_w = C_f\rho \frac{V_s^2}{2} \tag{4-59}$$

where V_s is the velocity of the stream outside the boundary layer and the friction coefficient is given by

$$C_f = 0.664\,\text{Re}^{-\frac{1}{2}} \tag{4-60}$$

with the Reynolds number $\rho V_s x/\mu$, x being measured from the leading edge of the plate or surface.

The property values are introduced into both equations at the reference temperature

$$T^* = T_s + 0.50(T_w - T_s) + 0.22(T_{aw} - T_s) \tag{4-61}$$

where T_s, T_w, and T_{aw} are the temperatures just outside the boundary layer, the wall temperature, and the adiabatic wall temperature, respectively. The heat-transfer coefficients are defined by Eq. (4-8), that is

$$\frac{q}{A} = h(T_w - T_{aw})$$

with the adiabatic wall temperature determined from Eq. (4-7) and the recovery factor calculated by Eq. (4-11), and with the Prandtl number being evaluated at the reference temperature given by Eq. (4-61). The heat-transfer coefficient in Eq. (4-8) is calculated from the relationship for local Nusselt number

$$\text{Nu} = \frac{hx}{k} = 0.332\,\text{Re}^{\frac{1}{2}}\,\text{Pr}^{\frac{1}{3}} \tag{4-62}$$

with the properties evaluated at the reference temperature.

These relationships are for fluids with essentially constant specific heat. For variable-specific-heat cases, enthalpies instead of temperatures should be used, and the reader is referred to Ref. 28 for equations which are based on enthalpies.

Turbulent Boundary-layer Flow: The friction factor should be calculated from one of the constant-property relationships

$$C_f = 0.0296 \ \textbf{Re}^{-0.2} \qquad \text{Blasius} \qquad (4\text{-}63)$$
$$C_f = 0.370 \ (\log \textbf{Re})^{-2.584} \qquad \text{Schultz-Grunow} \qquad (4\text{-}64)$$
$$\bar{C}_f = 0.455 \ (\log \textbf{Re})^{-2.58} \qquad \text{Prandtl-Schlichting} \qquad (4\text{-}65)$$

where C_f is the local friction factor and $\bar{C}_f$ is the average friction factor. The Reynolds number is defined as in Eq. (4-60).

The recovery factor should be calculated from Eq. (4-12), where $r = \textbf{Pr}^{\frac{1}{3}}$, and the heat-transfer coefficient should be calculated from the Reynolds-analogy relationship for turbulent heat transfer and friction:

$$\textbf{St} = \frac{h}{\rho c_p V_s} = \frac{C_f}{2} \textbf{Pr}^{-\frac{2}{3}} \qquad (4\text{-}66)$$

with the property values being introduced into these equations at the reference temperature given by Eq. (4-61).

As in the laminar case, if the specific heat varies, enthalpies instead of temperatures should be used.

Mean Temperature Difference. In the design of a reactor-core heat exchanger, the gross heat transfer of the reactor is of interest. This is obtained by integration of the basic equation

$$dq = h \, dA \, \Delta T \qquad (4\text{-}67)$$

If the fluid-flow cross section is constant and the velocity of the fluid is fixed, the heat-transfer coefficient will depend on the physical properties of the fluid, and consequently upon the temperature. Since both temperature and temperature difference are related to total heat flow q by means of energy and material balances, h and ΔT depend on q. Therefore the geometric and thermal variables are separable and Eq. (4-67) can be written

$$\int \frac{dq}{h \, \Delta T} = \int dA \qquad (4\text{-}68)$$

In general, analytic integration of this expression is difficult, but solution in closed form is attainable in certain cases. However, in many heat-exchanger designs it is desirable to specify the entrance and exit conditions of the flows. For such a situation it is convenient to determine the over-all heat-transfer rate by an equation of the form

$$q_A = UA \, \Delta T_M \qquad (4\text{-}69)$$

where q_A is the over-all heat-transfer rate, U is an over-all heat-transfer coefficient, and ΔT_M is some mean temperature difference appropriate to the particular type of design. To evaluate this mean temperature difference consider a parallel- or counterflow heat exchanger (Fig. 4-3a) where two fluids are separated by a wall and heat is being transferred from the hotter to the colder fluid. Neglecting kinetic-energy changes

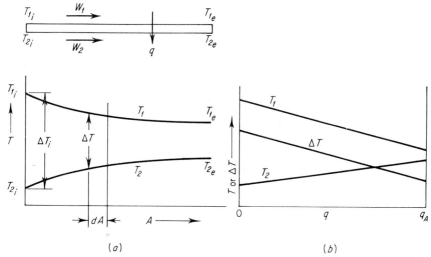

(a)   (b)

Fig. 4-3. Parallel-flow heat exchange

relative to enthalpy changes and assuming no heat losses from the system as a whole, the energy balance for the fluids is

$$dq = w_1 c_{p_1} dT_1 = \pm w_2 c_{p_2} dT_2 \qquad (4\text{-}70)$$

where w is the mass flow rate, with the positive sign applying to a counterflow and the negative sign to a parallel-flow heat exchanger.

If the specific heats are assumed constant, integration of the heat-balance equation shows that q is linear in each temperature. The temperature difference $\Delta T = T_1 - T_2$ is also linear in q (Fig. 4-3b). From Fig. 4-3b

$$\frac{d(\Delta T)}{dq} = \frac{\Delta T_e - \Delta T_i}{q_A} \qquad (4\text{-}71)$$

where the subscripts e and i refer to the heat-exchanger exit and inlet conditions, respectively. Using Eq. (4-71) with the over-all coefficient U and eliminating dq

$$\frac{d(\Delta T)}{U\,\Delta T} = \frac{(\Delta T_e - \Delta T_i)\,dA}{q_A} \qquad (4\text{-}72)$$

Assuming U constant, Eq. (4-72) can be integrated to give

$$\frac{1}{U} \int_{\Delta T_i}^{\Delta T_e} \frac{d(\Delta T)}{\Delta T} = \frac{(\Delta T_e - \Delta T_i)}{q_A} \int_0^A dA$$

$$\frac{1}{U} \ln \frac{\Delta T_e}{\Delta T_i} = \frac{(\Delta T_e - \Delta T_i)}{q_A} A \qquad (4\text{-}73)$$

Comparing this with Eq. (4-69) it is seen that

$$\Delta T_M = \frac{\Delta T_e - \Delta T_i}{\ln (\Delta T_e/\Delta T_i)} = \Delta T_{LM} \qquad (4\text{-}74)$$

and is called the logarithmic-mean temperature difference. Under the assumed conditions of constant U, constant specific heats, and no kinetic-energy changes, the log-mean temperature difference is applicable to parallel and counterflow operation of adiabatic systems. When one fluid is kept at a constant temperature, the direction of flow is immaterial and, for the case of one fluid passing next to a wall at a given temperature, the over-all heat-transfer coefficient U in Eq. (4-69) is replaced by h.

If U is not substantially constant, but varies with temperature, the integration of Eq. (4-72) must be carried out for the variation of interest. For a linear variation of U with temperature, Colburn found that Eq. (4-69) became

$$q_A = A \frac{U_i \Delta T_e - U_e \Delta T_i}{\ln (U_i \Delta T_e / U_e \Delta T_i)} \qquad (4\text{-}75)$$

Again, for the simple case of one fluid and a constant-temperature surface, Eq. (4-75) can be used, replacing U_i and U_e by h_i and h_e, respectively.

4-2. Conduction. As for fluid flow, literature on the theory of heat conduction is extensive[1-3] and is not repeated in this text. However, for completeness, the basic conduction equations and some useful methods of analysis are included.

In its most general form, conduction in a three-dimensional body, including nonsteady heat-generating processes, can be described by the well-known differential equation[*]

$$Q + \frac{\partial(k_x \, \partial T/\partial x)}{\partial x} + \frac{\partial(k_y \, \partial T/\partial y)}{\partial y} + \frac{\partial(k_z \, \partial T/\partial z)}{\partial z} = \rho c_p \frac{\partial T}{\partial t} \qquad (4\text{-}76a)$$

where k_i = thermal conductivity of material in ith direction
  ρ = density of conducting medium
  c_p = specific heat
  T = temperature
  t = time
  Q = rate of heat generation per unit volume

[*] For derivation of this equation see M. Jakob, "Heat Transfer," vol. 1, John Wiley & Sons, Inc., New York, 1949.

In the case where the thermal conductivity of the material is constant, we obtain the Fourier heat-conduction equation

$$\frac{\partial^2 T}{\partial x^2} + \frac{\partial^2 T}{\partial y^2} + \frac{\partial^2 T}{\partial z^2} = \frac{1}{a}\frac{\partial T}{\partial t} - \frac{Q}{\rho c_p} \tag{4-76b}$$

where $a = k/\rho c_p$ is called the thermal diffusivity.

The thermal diffusivity is a property of the material, and when there is no heat generated within the body, it is the only material property value which enters the heat-conduction equation. Therefore the rate at which the temperature reaches equilibrium within a non-heat-generating body depends only on the body's thermal diffusivity. Metals and gases have a higher value of thermal diffusivity than the nonmetals and liquids have.

Steady-state Conduction. For the case of steady-state heat conduction without internal heat generation and for constant physical properties, Eq. (4-76b) reduces to Laplace's equation

$$\nabla^2 T = \frac{\partial^2 T}{\partial x^2} + \frac{\partial^2 T}{\partial y^2} + \frac{\partial^2 T}{\partial z^2} = 0 \tag{4-77}$$

While analytical solutions to this equation have been determined for simple geometric shapes and boundary conditions, in most practical cases such solutions are difficult to achieve. The reader is referred to the cited references for a more detailed discussion of methods and analysis for handling Eq. (4-77).

Because of the symmetry desired for neutronic reasons in most nuclear rocket-reactor cores, many of the heat-conduction problems can be investigated on a one-dimensional basis. This is especially true in the preliminary phases of any design when it is desirable to investigate the effects of variation of many basic design parameters. In its simplest form the heat-flow equation is the defining equation for thermal conductivity k, where heat is not being generated but merely transmitted. This is

$$\frac{dq}{dA} = -k\frac{dT}{dx} \tag{4-78}$$

where q is the rate of heat flow and A is the area normal to the heat-flow path. If the temperature gradient dT/dx is constant over the heat-flow area A, Eq. (4-78) may be written as

$$\frac{q}{A} = -k\frac{dT}{dx} \tag{4-79}$$

and integrated as

$$\int_0^L \frac{q}{A}\,dx = -\int_{T_1}^{T_2} k\,dT \tag{4-80}$$

Equation (4-80) can be applied to several useful geometries such as:

HEAT FLOW THROUGH A SLAB WITHOUT HEAT GENERATION. The heat flow through a uniform slab with each face at a uniform temperature can be obtained directly by integration of Eq. (4-80). If A and k are constant, the result is

$$\frac{L}{A} = k \frac{T_1 - T_2}{q} \tag{4-81}$$

HEAT FLOW THROUGH THE WALL OF A CONCENTRICALLY HOLLOW CYL-INDER WITHOUT HEAT GENERATION. If $x = r$, then A can be expressed as a function of x, namely, $A = 2\pi r H$, where H is the cylinder height. Then Eq. (4-80) can be applied as

$$\int_{r_1}^{r_2} \frac{dr}{2\pi r H} = -\frac{1}{q} \int_{T_1}^{T_2} k \, dT \tag{4-82}$$

to yield
$$\frac{1}{2\pi H} \ln \frac{r_2}{r_1} = k \frac{T_1 - T_2}{q} \tag{4-83}$$

for k independent of temperature.

HEAT FLOW THROUGH A CONCENTRIC SPHERICAL SHELL WITHOUT HEAT GENERATION. Again if $x = r$, then $A = 4\pi r^2$ so that

$$\int_{r_1}^{r_2} \frac{dr}{4\pi r^2} = -\frac{1}{q} \int_{T_1}^{T_2} k \, dT \tag{4-84}$$

yielding for a k independent of temperature

$$\frac{1}{4\pi} \left(\frac{1}{r_1} - \frac{1}{r_2} \right) = k \frac{T_1 - T_2}{q} \tag{4-85}$$

While the above equations have some practical application in nuclear rocket reactors, in general, due to gamma and neutron heating, all components of the reactor, whether containing fissionable fuel or not, must be treated as heat-generating bodies. For these cases the general conduction equation (4-77) must be solved. Solutions for some of the simpler geometries include:

SLAB WITH INTERNAL HEAT GENERATION AND EQUAL COOLING ON BOTH FACES. Equation (4-77) reduces to the one-dimensional case and for steady-state and constant conductivity becomes

$$k \frac{d^2 T}{dx^2} + Q = 0 \tag{4-86}$$

Integrating, with Q assumed constant

$$T = -\frac{Q x^2}{2k} + C_1 x + C_2 \tag{4-87}$$

Assuming equal cooling on each face of the slab and measuring x from the midplane of the slab, the boundary conditions from which the constants C_1 and C_2 may be evaluated are

At $x = 0$: $$\frac{dT}{dx} = 0$$

At $x = L$: $$T = T_2$$

resulting in the solution

$$T - T_2 = \frac{Q}{2k} (L^2 - x^2) \tag{4-88}$$

SOLID CYLINDER WITH INTERNAL HEAT GENERATION. In cylindrical coordinates, Eq. (4-77) becomes

$$\frac{Q}{k} + \frac{\partial^2 T}{\partial r^2} + \frac{1}{r} \frac{\partial T}{\partial r} + \frac{\partial^2 T}{\partial z^2} = \frac{\rho c_p}{k} \frac{\partial T}{\partial t} \tag{4-89}$$

if the conductivity is a constant. For steady state and for the case of an infinite solid cylinder with internal heat generation this reduces to

$$\frac{d^2 T}{dr^2} + \frac{1}{r} \frac{dT}{dr} + \frac{Q}{k} = 0 \tag{4-90}$$

Proceeding as before, for constant heat generation the solution to this equation becomes

$$T - T_2 = \frac{Q}{4k} (r_2{}^2 - r^2) \tag{4-91}$$

For more complicated geometries and boundary conditions, the reader is referred to the literature previously cited.

Nonsteady Heat Conduction. When the temperature distribution within a conducting body varies with time, the basic conduction equation (4-76) must be solved and, depending on the geometry and boundary conditions, solutions are in general difficult to achieve. For example, take the simple case of:

SLAB WITH NO HEAT GENERATION, UNIFORM INITIAL TEMPERATURE, AND A FIXED SURFACE TEMPERATURE. For the one-dimensional, constant-property case, Eq. (4-76) reduces to

$$\frac{\partial T}{\partial t} = \frac{k}{\rho c_p} \frac{\partial^2 T}{\partial x^2} \tag{4-92}$$

For a uniform temperature T_0 at $t = 0$, at which time both walls are suddenly changed to T_w, the solution for T is an infinite-series expansion in x, the distance below the slab surface (here the solution is only valid for $0 \leq x \leq L/2$):

$$\frac{T_w - T}{T_w - T_0} = \frac{4}{\pi} \left(e^{-\beta} \sin \frac{\pi x}{L} + \frac{1}{3} e^{-9\beta} \sin \frac{3\pi x}{L} + \cdots \right) \tag{4-93}$$

where L is the slab thickness and $\beta = \dfrac{\pi^2 k t}{L^2 \rho c_p}$.

Other cases that are often of interest in reactor design include:

1. Infinite slab with known but nonuniform initial temperature distribution and a given fixed surface temperature.[25]

2. Infinite slab with uniform initial temperature in which, at $t = 0$, heat is transferred at a constant rate or at a rate which is linear with time.[25]

3. Infinite slab with uniform initial temperature suddenly bathed by a fluid at constant temperature and with a constant heat-transfer coefficient.[1]

4. Infinitely long cylinder with constant initial temperature and constant surface temperature or constant fluid temperature and heat-transfer coefficient.[1]

5. Sphere with constant initial temperature and constant surface temperature or constant fluid temperature and heat-transfer coefficient.[1]

Numerical Methods.   As previously mentioned, the determination of an analytical solution to the differential equation of heat conduction is a most difficult undertaking, except for the simplest geometric and boundary conditions.   On the other hand, approximate solutions for almost any case may be obtained by numerical, graphical, or experimental methods.   While the latter two methods leave a bit to be desired in the early stages of design, where shapes, materials, and boundary conditions are continually being revised, the numerical methods, though tedious, can be used to provide quite useful preliminary design information.   These methods are based on the relaxation techniques developed by Southwell for structural analysis and extended by Emmons[29] to problems of steady-state heat conduction.

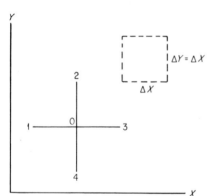

Fig. 4-4. Fictitious-rod arrangement for steady-state relaxation analysis.

For unsteady-state computations Dusinberre[30] has generalized the methods of Emmons.   Fundamentally the numerical and graphical methods are simply various ways of solving finite-difference equations based upon the analytically intractable differential equations.

RELAXATION METHOD FOR STEADY-STATE HEAT CONDUCTION.   Two-dimensional: For two-dimensional heat-conduction problems a cross section of the shape through which the heat is being transferred is first drawn.   Next a square grid is superimposed on the shape, with as many grid lines as possible coinciding with the principal bounding edges (physical edges or adiabatic surfaces) of the cross section.   The grid spacing should be such that the cross section is divided into a sufficient number of squares; about 50 is reasonable. Each grid intersection point represents the square of material surrounding it, and each line between two points represents the thermal resistance between the adjacent material elements.

Consider a pattern as shown in Fig. 4-4. Here heat is assumed to flow in the x and y directions only, through rods of equal length Δx and Δy. Each point represents a sink for the heat conducted to or from it by the rods meeting there. The conduction through any rod is assumed to be equal to the conduction in a square of side length Δx. Hence for a unit length in the z directions, the conductive heat flow to the point 0 becomes (for constant k)

$$q_0 = k(T_1 + T_2 + T_3 + T_4 - 4T_0) \qquad (4\text{-}94)$$

where k is the thermal conductivity of the conducting material and is assumed constant.

In the steady-state case without internal sources or sinks, $q_0 = 0$, which reduces Eq. (4-94) to

$$T_0 = \frac{T_1 + T_2 + T_3 + T_4}{4} \qquad (4\text{-}95)$$

Equation (4-95) shows that, for steady-state conduction, the temperature at any point inside the grid must equal the arithmetic average of the four points around it. Thus the method consists of first assigning a temperature at each point of the grid, after which the value at each point is changed by averaging it to the value of the points surrounding it. This is continued until the temperature at every point changes by less than some predetermined (desired) amount from one iteration to the next. When this condition has been achieved the problem is said to have converged. It is sometimes convenient to over- or underestimate the temperature of a point in the iteration process in order to reach the final temperature (achieve convergence) more rapidly, or to obtain the final temperature of key points by plotting the successive trial temperatures against the reciprocal of the number of the trial and extrapolating to $1/n = 0$.

After the final temperatures have been determined, the rate of heat transfer across any line between points is obtained by adding the temperature drops between all opposite pairs of points and multiplying by the thermal conductivity k and the thickness z. If the average width between points is less than a full space between adjacent points, the temperature difference must be weighted by the ratio of the average width to the point spacing. That is,

$$q = kz \sum \Delta T \frac{\text{avg width}}{\text{spacing}} \qquad (4\text{-}96)$$

For very irregular boundaries the reader is referred to the work of Dusinberre.[30] The following are some examples of modifications to the above method:

1. *Surface adjacent to fluid at a given temperature and with a fixed heat-transfer coefficient.* In this case the internal temperatures are determined as before. However, the surface temperatures are obtained by weighting the two other surface points by one-half, since the width of the heat-flow path is only half that of a unit width, and the fluid temperature by $h\,\Delta x/k$, where Δx is the spacing between points. Thus for a surface point

$$T_s = \frac{\dfrac{T_1}{2} + T_2 + \dfrac{T_3}{2} + \dfrac{h\,\Delta x}{k}\,T_f}{2 + \dfrac{h\,\Delta x}{k}} \tag{4-97}$$

where T_1 and T_3 are for adjacent surface points, T_2 is the adjacent interior point, and T_f is the fluid temperature.

2. *Fixed rate of heat transfer to or from a surface*

$$T_s = \frac{T_1 + 2T_2 + T_3}{4} \pm \frac{q}{A}\frac{\Delta x}{2k} \tag{4-98}$$

where the plus sign indicates a net heat flow from the fluid to the wall and the minus sign applies to the reverse situation.

3. *Heat generated within a solid.* For this case Eq. (4-94) applies, where q_0 is the rate of heat generated per unit thickness and may vary throughout the cross section, as in a nuclear-reactor core:

$$T_0 = \frac{T_1 + T_2 + T_3 + T_4}{4} + \frac{q_0}{4k} \tag{4-99}$$

4. *Cylindrical sections.* For cylindrical sections, in order to fit the boundaries, a cylindrical grid is more convenient. To get units of equal length and average widths (as in a square), the natural logarithm of successive radii must equal the angle in radians. The procedure is to decide on a desired number of concentric rings n; the radii of the concentric circles between R_1 and R_2 are then given by

$$r_m = R_1\left(\frac{R_2}{R_1}\right)^{m/n} \tag{4-100}$$

where m is an integer varying from 1 to $n-1$ and denoting the order of the cylindrical grid system. The angle γ between adjacent radial lines must be

$$\gamma = \frac{1}{n}\ln\frac{R_2}{R_1} \quad \text{radians}$$
$$= \frac{57.3}{n}\ln\frac{R_2}{R_1} \quad \text{deg} \tag{4-101}$$

The relaxation procedure is then similar to that for a square grid. If heat is being generated, Eq. (4-94) still holds, where q_0 is the heat generated per unit depth over the area represented by the point.

Three-dimensional: For three-dimensional steady-stage conduction, computations can be carried out by similar methods, except that all six temperatures around a point in a cubical grid must be averaged. The method is tedious, however, and is not frequently used by hand except

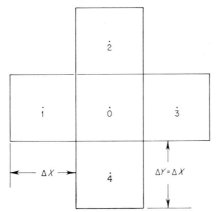

FIG. 4-5. Cubical blocks for unsteady-state relaxation analysis.

for check calculations of isolated points of interest. Such problems, as well as two-dimensional ones, are often solved most satisfactorily by large digital computing machines coded for the problems of interest.

RELAXATION METHOD FOR UNSTEADY-STATE HEAT CONDUCTION. In unsteady-state conduction the problem generally consists of finding the change in an initially given temperature distribution over a succession of uniform time increments chosen to provide the accuracy desired in the solution of the time-dependent difference equations. While the relaxation methods of steady-state conduction are applicable, some modifications must be made in the weighting procedure. In addition, the square two-dimensional grid is replaced by cubical blocks with the points of interest in the centers of the blocks. Consider an arrangement of cubical blocks of depth Δx as in Fig. 4-5 and further assume that:

1. Heat flows only in x and y directions.

2. The temperatures at points in the center of a cube are T_n at time t, and $T_{n,\Delta t}$ at a time interval Δt later than t.

3. The initial temperature gradient $(T_n - T_0)/\Delta x$ holds throughout the interval Δt.

4. The temperature at a point 0 is not affected by any changes at the outside of the blocks surrounding it.

5. The heat content (enthalpy) of block 0 can be computed, using the temperature at point 0.

6. Constant k and c_p for the conducting material.

A heat balance is found by equating the sum of the heat conducted from the outer blocks to the block 0 and the heat stored in this block, as follows:

$$k \frac{(\Delta x)^2}{\Delta x} (T_1 + T_2 + T_3 + T_4 - 4T_0) \Delta t = \rho c_p (\Delta x)^3 (T_{0,\Delta t} - T_0)$$

or

$$T_{0,\Delta t} = \frac{T_1 + T_2 + T_3 + T_4 + (M - 4)T_0}{M} \qquad (4\text{-}102)$$

where

$$M = \frac{\rho c_p (\Delta x)^2}{k \, \Delta t}$$

The greatest allowable change in T_0 would occur if $T_{0,\Delta t}$ assumed the average of the surrounding temperatures. Hence $M \geq 4$ and preferably 5.

For $M = 5$:

$$T_{0,\Delta t} = \frac{T_0 + T_1 + T_2 + T_3 + T_4}{5} \qquad (4\text{-}103)$$

For a time interval:

$$\Delta t = \frac{\rho c_p (\Delta x)^2}{5k}$$

The computing procedure is similar to that for the steady-state method, with heat generation and surface conditions being taken care of as before. Three-dimensional problems can be handled, but with considerably more effort.

Analog Methods. In addition to numerical solutions to the heat-conduction problems, various experimental methods utilizing "similarity phenomena" have been developed. The fundamental relation for heat flow by conduction in a homogeneous non-heat-generating substance is given by

$$\frac{\partial^2 T}{\partial x^2} + \frac{\partial^2 T}{\partial y^2} + \frac{\partial^2 T}{\partial z^2} = \frac{\rho c_p}{k} \frac{\partial T}{\partial t} \qquad (4\text{-}76b)$$

For the steady state this becomes

$$\frac{\partial^2 T}{\partial x^2} + \frac{\partial^2 T}{\partial y^2} + \frac{\partial^2 T}{\partial z^2} = 0 \qquad (4\text{-}77)$$

Equations (4-76b) and (4-77) are by no means restricted to heat flow; they apply to any diffusion process, whether diffusion of heat, fluids, or electrical current, for example. Since analytical solutions are in most cases difficult to achieve, attempts have been made to obtain solutions by making use of these analogous processes. In particular, electrical and hydraulic analogies have been developed by many investigators for use in the solution of heat-transfer problems, a summary of which has been made by Ramachandran.[31]   A few of the salient features of these analogies are as follows:

ELECTRICAL ANALOGY.   Steady-state Heat Conduction: By making use of the similarity between a heat-flow field and an electric-current-flow field, steady-state heat-conduction problems may be investigated.   The procedure usually calls for construction of a container shaped after the cross section of interest.   The sides of the container are electrodes and the interior is filled with an electrolyte, which takes the shape of the cross section.   The electrodes are then maintained at the desired voltages, and the thermal problem has been converted to an electrical problem of the same geometrical shape with temperatures replaced by voltages.   By means of an electric probe, isopotential lines, representing isothermal lines in the solid, can be established.   The current in the electrolyte corresponds to the heat flow, while the potential difference between electrodes represents the temperature difference.   Other and similar methods for solving conduction problems make use of thin metal sheets or special "resistance paper" cut to form the shape of the conducting medium of interest.

Transient Heat Conduction: The electrical analogy for transient or unsteady-state heat conduction is based on the similarity between an electric circuit and a thermal circuit, and not on construction of a model

TABLE 4-1. THERMAL-ELECTRICAL ANALOGS

Thermal circuit			Electrical circuit		
Quantity	Symbol	Unit	Quantity	Symbol	Unit
Temperature.........	T	°F	Potential........	V	volts
Rate of heat flow.....	q	Btu-hr	Current.........	I	amp
Thermal resistance....	$R_T = \dfrac{\Delta T}{q}$	°F-hr/Btu	Resistance.......	$R_e = \dfrac{\Delta V}{I}$	ohms
Thermal capacity.....	$C_T = \dfrac{Q_T}{\Delta T}$	Btu/°F	Capacitance.....	$C_e = \dfrac{Q_e}{\Delta V}$	μf
Heat content.........	Q_T	Btu	Charge..........	Q_e	amp-sec
Time...............	t	hr	Time...........	t	sec
Time constant........	$R_T C_T$		Time constant...	$R_e C_e$	

geometrically similar to the body under investigation.[3,32,33]   This is a result of the fact that the mathematical relationships expressing current flow in circuits having an even distribution of resistances and capacitances are identical with those expressing the flow of heat in a solid. Table 4-1 presents the analogous quantities between electrical and thermal systems.

MAGNETIC AND HYDRAULIC ANALOGIES.   As early as 1914, Jakob[3] developed a magnetic analog for solutions to the steady-state-conduction problem. By using cardboard, cut geometrically similar to the cross section of interest, covered with iron filings, and placed between electromagnetic poles also shaped to the cross section, he was able to determine thermal-flow lines by comparison with the magnetic-force lines.

Another analogy that has been employed is that between laminar flows of fluids and heat conduction. In heat transfer, one deals with heat flow, thermal resistance, temperature differences causing heat flow, and thermal storage. Hydrodynamically these correspond to potential difference, flow of material, resistance to flow, and capacity to store the flowing material.

The reader is referred to the extensive bibliography given in Ref. 31 for additional methods, details, and procedures.

4-3. Geometric Considerations. Since the weight-growth factor of missile systems is often extremely high, it is imperative that components of such systems be designed for minimum weight. In a nuclear rocket-motor heat-exchanger design, this requirement generally means compactness. A useful parameter for determining this compactness is the ratio of the core heat-transfer surface area to the core total volume:

$$\zeta = \frac{A_T}{V_c} \tag{4-104}$$

where A_T is the total heat-transfer surface area and V_c is the total volume of the core.

The larger this ratio, the greater the heat transfer per unit volume and hence per pound (in most systems) of heat-exchanger core. In conventional heat-exchanger design many schemes have been devised to obtain large heat-transfer areas, such as use of fins and dimpling; however, in nuclear systems, which require very high material temperatures, structural considerations generally rule out such refinements. For purposes of comparison, the ratio of heat-transfer area to total volume will be determined for geometries that might be applicable to nuclear rocket cores.

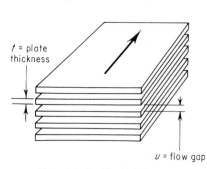

t = plate thickness

u = flow gap

Fig. 4-6. Stacked-plate core.

Stacked Plates. The stacked-plate configuration is one which offers many advantages in ease of fabrication and structural support along with certain latitude in obtaining variations in uranium loadings. For the arrangement of stacked plates of thickness t with flow gap u, shown in

Fig. 4-6, the ratio of heat-transfer surface area to volume is

$$\zeta = \frac{2}{t+u} = \frac{2}{u}\epsilon \qquad (4\text{-}105)$$

where $\epsilon = u/(t+u)$ is the void fraction.

Tubes. A core in which the flow is through the inside of long tubes offers the fabrication advantages of flat plates along with structural stability. However, hot spotting difficulties arising from variations in uranium loading are more severe than for plates, and the possibility of hot spots and complete failure due to tube plugging presents some disadvantages. For the arrangement shown in Fig. 4-7 the specific surface area is

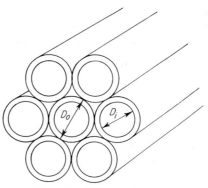

FIG. 4-7. Hollow-tube core.

$$\zeta = \frac{3\pi D_i/6}{\sqrt{3}\,D_0^2/2} = \frac{\pi D_i}{\sqrt{3}\,D_0^2} \qquad (4\text{-}106)$$

Solid Rods. A heat exchanger consisting of solid-rod fuel elements with the propellant flow parallel to the rod axes has fabrication advantages similar to those of the plate geometry without the severe plugging

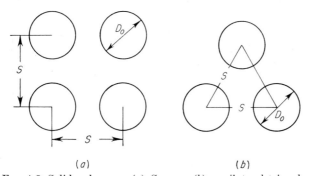

(a) (b)

FIG. 4-8. Solid-rod core. (a) Square; (b) equilateral triangle.

problem of the hollow-tube design. However, variations in uranium loading can lead to severe local temperature excursions, and the structural support of a rod core presents some difficulty. Figure 4-8 shows two arrangements of solid rods, with the ratio of heat-transfer surface area to total volume being

Square array: $$\zeta = \frac{\pi D_0}{S^2} \qquad (4\text{-}107)$$

Equilateral-triangular array: $\quad \zeta = \dfrac{2}{3}\dfrac{\pi D_0}{S^2}$ (4-108)

In addition to solid rods, the above ratios are also applicable to solid-block cores with flow through round holes, where D_0 is the hole diameter and S is the hole spacing.

Packed Spheres. Reactor cores consisting of packed spheres offer the advantage of requiring the fabrication of only a single type of fuel element while still retaining a capability for obtaining wide variations in the core fuel distributions. Core support, the possibility of hot spots, and severe thermal stresses are some of the disadvantages associated with such a

TABLE 4-2. GEOMETRIC RELATIONSHIPS AND POROSITY OF VARIOUS
SPHERE PACKINGS*

Square layers   Rhombic layers

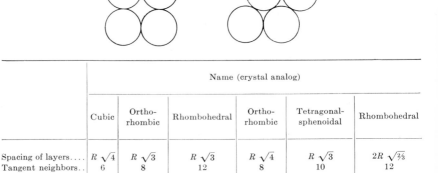

	Name (crystal analog)					
	Cubic	Ortho-rhombic	Rhombohedral	Ortho-rhombic	Tetragonal-sphenoidal	Rhombohedral
Spacing of layers....	$R\sqrt{4}$	$R\sqrt{3}$	$R\sqrt{3}$	$R\sqrt{4}$	$R\sqrt{3}$	$2R\sqrt{\frac{2}{3}}$
Tangent neighbors..	6	8	12	8	10	12
Face angles, deg....	90	90, 60-120	90, 60-120	90, 60-120	60-120 75°31'-104°29'	60-120
Interfacial angles, deg..............	90	90, 60-120	54°44'-125°16'	90, 60-120	90 63°26'-116°34'	70°32'-109°28'
Porosity, %........	47.64	39.54	25.95	39.54	30.19	25.95

* From L. Groton and H. Fraser, Systematic Packing of Spheres—with Particular Relation to Porosity and Permeability, *J. Geol.*, vol. 43, no. 8, pt. 1, pp. 785–909, November–December, 1935.

design. Table 4-2 contains the characteristics of a few of the many packing arrangements that are possible. It should be noted that some of these are extremely complicated. The ratio of core heat-transfer surface area to total core volume for packed spheres of any arrangement is

$$\zeta = \frac{6(1 - \epsilon)}{D_p} \qquad (4\text{-}109)$$

where ϵ is the external-void portion of the packing and D_p is the diameter of the spheres.

4-4. Power Density. As previously discussed, the ratio of heat-transfer surface to total volume is a means of comparing compact cores, but careful consideration must be given to the frictional losses within such cores. Since pump weights may be a considerable fraction of a nuclear rocket-motor system weight, the propellant pressure-drop requirements for particular heat-exchanger designs must be investigated before a true comparison can be made. Another factor arises from the possibility that the heat-transfer rates are not the same for the different configurations. Therefore it is convenient to make a comparison of cores of different geometry on the basis of bulk core power density. This is simply the ratio of the power output of the reactor to the total volume of the core:

$$\eta = \frac{P_r}{V_c} \qquad (4\text{-}110)$$

where P_r is the total power output of the reactor and V_c is the total volume of the core.

For preliminary-design purposes, it is reasonable to compute the overall heat transfer by the relationship

$$\frac{Q}{A_T} = h_a \, \Delta T_{LM} \qquad (4\text{-}111)$$

where Q = total heat transferred
h_a = average heat-transfer coefficient
A_T = total heat-transfer surface area
ΔT_{LM} = logarithmic-mean temperature difference
The reactor power in megawatts is related to the total heat transferred by

$$Q = K(1 - f_e)P_r \qquad (4\text{-}112)$$

where K is the conversion factor 3.413×10^6 Btu/Mwhr and f_e is the fraction of the fission energy escaping from the reactor in photons and fast neutrons. The analysis herein assumes that f_e is zero or that the reactor power used is only that given up to the cooling fluid (propellant). Under this assumption, substituting Eqs. (4-111) and (4-112) into Eq. (4-110) along with Eq. (4-104), the power density becomes

$$\eta = \frac{1}{K} h_a \frac{A_T}{V_c} \Delta T_{LM}$$
$$= \frac{1}{K} h_a \zeta \, \Delta T_{LM} \qquad (4\text{-}113)$$

with the average heat-transfer coefficients being obtained from Sec. 4-3 for particular geometries.

The consequences of high core power density in terms of core geometry are best demonstrated by an example. Consider a case where it is desired to design a 5,000-Mw nuclear rocket motor using hydrogen as the propellant with a core power density of 100 Mw/ft³ as in Ref. 19.

$$P_r = 5{,}000 \text{ Mw}$$
$$\eta = 100 \text{ Mw/ft}^3$$

The volume of the core must therefore be

$$V_c = 50 \text{ ft}^3$$

and the diameter and frontal area will be

$$D_c = \left(\frac{50 \times 4}{\pi}\right)^{\frac{1}{3}} = 4 \text{ ft}$$
$$A_c = 12.5 \text{ ft}^2$$

for a right-circular cylindrical geometry.

In Chap. 6 it is shown that the critical mass is heavily dependent upon the core-void fraction; therefore this must be kept to a minimum. For this example assume $\epsilon = 0.30$. The propellant flow area A_f then becomes

$$A_f = \epsilon A_c = 3.75 \text{ ft}^2$$

In order to obtain 5,000 Mw, with a peak hydrogen temperature of 5000°R, the propellant flow rate, as determined from the power–flow rate relationships shown in Fig. 2-25, must be

$$w = \frac{P_r}{20.8} = 240 \text{ lb/sec}$$

The specific mass flow rate for this particular core is thus

$$G = \frac{w}{A_f} = 2.30 \times 10^5 \text{ lb/(hr)(ft}^2)$$

For a constant wall temperature of 5500°R, a propellant inlet temperature of 500°R, and an exit temperature of 5000°R, Eq. (4-74) gives

$$\Delta T_{LM} = \frac{5000 - 500}{\ln (5000/500)} = 1950°R$$

and Eq. (4-113) yields

$$h_a \zeta = \frac{100 \times 3.413 \times 10^6}{1950} = 1.75 \times 10^5 \text{ Btu/(hr)(ft}^3)(°F) \qquad (4\text{-}114)$$

For a plate core the specific surface area is, from Eq. (4-105),

$$\zeta = \frac{2}{t + u} = \frac{2}{u}\epsilon$$

and for the assumed 30 per cent void

$$\zeta = \frac{0.60}{u} \qquad (4\text{-}115)$$

where u is the flow-gap width and t is the plate thickness.

Combining Eq. (4-115) with Eq. (4-114) gives a restrictive relation between the heat-transfer coefficient and the flow-passage width. This is

$$\frac{h}{u} = 2.92 \times 10^5 \tag{4-116}$$

Since for flow between parallel plates the hydraulic or equivalent diameter is $D_e = 2u$, then

$$h = 1.46 \times 10^5 D_e \tag{4-117}$$

Now by employing the correlation-relationship equation (4-45), it is possible to obtain the proper hydraulic diameter, since

$$h = 0.023 \frac{G^{0.8}}{D_e^{0.2}} \frac{k_f}{\mu_f^{0.8}} \left(\frac{c_{pf}\mu_f}{R_f}\right)^{\frac{1}{3}}$$

$$D_e^{1.2} = 15.75 \times 10^{-8} G^{0.8} \frac{k_f}{\mu_f^{0.8}} \left(\frac{c_{pf}\mu_f}{k_f}\right)^{\frac{1}{3}} \tag{4-118}$$

The mean film temperature needed to evaluate the physical properties of the propellant is assumed to be based on the logarithmic-mean temperature potential of 1950°R across the boundary layer, the inlet temperature of 500°R, and a plate-wall temperature of 5500°R, which from Eq. (4-45) becomes

$$T_f = \frac{2450 + 5500}{2} = 3975°R$$

For this temperature, Figs. 2-17, 2-18, and 2-20 show the following properties:

$\mu_f = 0.08$ lb/(hr)(ft) $k_f = 0.46$ Btu/(hr)(ft)(°F)

$$c_{pf} = 3.78 \text{ Btu/(lb)(°F)}$$

Using these properties and the mass flow rate per unit area,

$$G = 2.30 \times 10^5 \text{ lb/(hr)(ft}^2)$$

the required hydraulic diameter becomes, from Eq. (4-118),

$$D_e = 0.020 \text{ ft}$$

resulting in flow-gap and plate-thickness dimensions of

$$u = 0.010 \text{ ft} = 0.120 \text{ in.}$$
$$t = 0.0233 \text{ ft} = 0.280 \text{ in.}$$

Note that a tolerance of ±0.005 in. here can result in a 10 per cent variation in flow-gap width, with a consequent variation in flow from one channel to the next. These dimensions, which are typical, and their consequences show that the achievement of high power density requires extreme care in the detailed design and construction of the nuclear-reactor core.

4-5. Fluid Friction and Pressure Drop. Since the pressure drop across a nuclear rocket-reactor heat exchanger is often the major portion of the core structural design load, it is of utmost importance that accurate and detailed analysis be made of the effect of the flow and the core geometric characteristics on this pressure drop. The problem is not a simple one, because of the complicated nature of the differential equations that govern frictional flow with heat addition in a compressible fluid. The classical Rayleigh line[34,39] considers heat addition in the absence of friction, while the classical Fanno line[34] considers fluid friction in the absence of heat transfer. Various investigators[35,36] have considered the problem of combined heat transfer, using average fluid properties or average heat-transfer and friction coefficients. Thompson[37] has considered the case of combined heat transfer with variable area and either the Mach number or the entropy held constant. Valerino[38] has combined constant-area heat transfer and friction for the case of constant wall temperature and has obtained solutions in terms of the average friction coefficient for the channel.

In this section, pressure-drop relations for the case of a constant-area channel with and without heat addition will be developed.

Pressure Drop Due to Friction in Tubes. If one postulates that, for an incompressible fluid, the pressure drop in a smooth tube is proportional to the length and that the quantity $\Delta P/L$ depends upon the diameter of the tube D, the mean velocity V_m, the fluid density ρ, and the absolute viscosity μ of the fluid, then a dimensional equation relating these variables can be written as

$$\frac{\Delta P}{L} = C D^\alpha V_m{}^\beta \rho^\gamma \mu^\delta \tag{4-119}$$

By dimensional analysis,[3] Eq. (4-119) reduces to a general expression for the pressure drop in a smooth tube, whether the flow be laminar or turbulent. This is

$$\frac{\Delta P}{\rho V_m{}^2/2} = 2C \frac{L}{D} \left(\frac{V_m D \rho}{\mu} \right)^{\alpha+1} \tag{4-120}$$

For laminar flow, a balance-of-forces consideration results in $\alpha = -2$, and Eq. (4-120) becomes

$$\frac{\Delta P}{\rho V_m{}^2/2} = 64 \frac{L}{D} \frac{\mu}{V_m D \rho} = \frac{64}{\mathbf{Re}} \frac{L}{D} \tag{4-121}$$

This is well known as Poiseuille's law.

In general, the exponents as well as the constant C must be determined by experiment. For turbulent flow in a smooth tube, for Reynolds numbers from 5,000 to 200,000, it has been found that Eq. (4-121) becomes

$$\frac{\Delta P}{\rho V_m{}^2/2} = \frac{0.184}{\mathbf{Re}^{0.2}} \frac{L}{D} \tag{4-122}$$

When the Reynolds numbers become larger or the tubes are no longer smooth, it becomes convenient to write the pressure-drop equation in the form

$$\frac{\Delta P}{\rho V_m/2} = 4f \frac{L}{D} \tag{4-123}$$

where f is a nondimensional friction factor defined as

$$f = \frac{\tau_0}{\rho V^2/2} \tag{4-124}$$

Here τ_0 is the surface shearing stress.

For smooth tubes, from Eqs. (4-121) and (4-122),

$$f = \frac{16}{\mathbf{Re}} \quad \text{for laminar flow} \tag{4-125}$$

and

$$f = \frac{0.046}{(\mathbf{Re})^{0.2}} \quad \text{for turbulent flow} \tag{4-126}$$

when $5{,}000 < \mathbf{Re} < 200{,}000$.

For the case of higher Reynolds numbers, the Kármán-Nikuradse relation between friction and Reynolds number correlates the experimental data for incompressible turbulent flow and is given by

$$\frac{1}{\sqrt{f}} = 4.0 \log (\mathbf{Re} \sqrt{f}) - 0.40 \tag{4-127}$$

NONCIRCULAR CROSS SECTIONS. As discussed on page 101 for cross sections other than circular tubes the equivalent diameter may be used. That is,

$$D_e = \frac{4A}{C} \tag{4-49}$$

where A is the cross-sectional area of the duct and C is the wetted perimeter of the duct. The pressure-drop equation then can be rewritten, after Jakob,[3] in the form

$$\frac{\Delta P}{\rho V_m/2} = N \frac{L}{D_e} \frac{\mu}{\rho D_e V_m} \tag{4-128}$$

The values of N and D_e for various cross sections are given in Table 4-3.

Plenum Effects. In addition to the frictional pressure losses, losses due to sudden contraction or expansion of the flow passages must be considered. Since the end effects are peculiar to a specific design, the details of each heat-exchanger plenum must be investigated individually. However, for rough estimates the following relationships can be utilized.

For contraction:

$$\Delta p = p_0 - p_1 = \rho_a \frac{V_1{}^2 - V_0{}^2}{2g_c} + \rho_a \frac{K_c V_1{}^2}{2g_c} \tag{4-129}$$

For enlargement:

$$\Delta p = p_0 - p_1 = \rho_a \frac{V_1{}^2 - V_0{}^2}{2g_c} + \rho_a \frac{(V_0 - V_1)^2}{2g_c} \qquad (4\text{-}130)$$

where subscript 0 denotes upstream and subscript 1 downstream conditions, ρ_a is the average fluid density, and K_c is the contraction coefficient. This coefficient varies roughly as shown in Fig. 4-9.

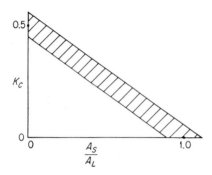

FIG. 4-9. Contraction coefficient vs. area ratio.

Pressure-Temperature Relation for a Constant-area Flow with Heat Transfer and Friction. While the foregoing analysis presented the pressure-drop relations due to friction for an incompressible fluid, it cannot accurately predict the pressure-temperature behavior of a nuclear rocket heat-transfer core through which a compressible fluid is flowing with heat being added. For such flows, consideration must be taken of density changes in the process as well as the effect of heat transfer through the boundary layer. The equations that describe this process for a constant-area flow channel in the x direction are the one-dimensional

TABLE 4-3. EQUIVALENT DIAMETER D_e AND CONSTANT $N*$

Shape of cross-section area	$\dfrac{2b}{2a}$	$\dfrac{D_e}{2b}$	N
Circle (diameter $D = 2b$)...........................	.....	1	64
Ellipse (major axis $2a$, minor axis $2b$)................	0.7	1.17	65
	0.5	1.30	68
	0.3	1.44	73
	0.2	1.50	76
	0.1	1.55	78
Rectangle (long side $2a$, short side $2b$)................	0.5	1.30	62
	0.333	1.50	69
	0.25	1.50	73
	0.2	1.67	76
	0.1	1.82	85
	0	2.0	96
Equilateral triangle (side length $2b$)..................	.....	0.58	53
Square (side length $2b$)............................	.....	1	57
Annular ring (width $2b$)............................	.....	2	96

* From M. Jakob, "Heat Transfer," vol. I, John Wiley & Sons, Inc., New York, 1949.

forms of Eqs. (4-8) and (4-18) along with Eqs. (4-20) and (4-124). They are

Energy:

$$dq = wc_p \, dT_t = hC(T_w - T_{aw}) \, dx \qquad (4\text{-}131)$$

where C is the wetted perimeter.

Continuity:

$$\rho V = \frac{G}{g_c} \qquad (4\text{-}132)$$

Momentum:

$$dP = -\rho V \, dV - \frac{4f}{D}\frac{1}{2}\rho V^2 \, dx \qquad (4\text{-}133)$$

where D is the hydraulic diameter; $D = 4A/C$.

Equation of state for an ideal gas:

$$\rho = \frac{P\mathfrak{M}}{g_c R_u T} \qquad (4\text{-}134)$$

Combining Eqs. (4-131) to (4-134) results in

$$\left(\frac{g_c P^2 \mathfrak{M}}{G^2 R_u T} - 1\right)\frac{dP}{P} = -\frac{dT}{T} - \frac{f/2}{h/Gc_p}\frac{dT_t}{T_w - T_{aw}} \qquad (4\text{-}135)$$

Differentiating Eqs. (4-132) and (4-134) and combining gives

$$\frac{dP}{P} = \frac{dT}{T} - \frac{dV}{V} \qquad (4\text{-}136)$$

The relation between local velocity V, Mach number $\mathbf{M}$, and temperature is

$$V = \mathbf{M}\sqrt{\gamma g_c \frac{R_u T}{\mathfrak{M}}} \qquad (4\text{-}137)$$

where γ is the ratio of specific heats of the fluid, from which

$$\frac{dV}{V} = \frac{d\mathbf{M}}{\mathbf{M}} + \frac{dT}{2T} \qquad (4\text{-}138)$$

Combining Eqs. (4-136) and (4-138),

$$\frac{dP}{P} = \frac{dT}{2T} - \frac{d\mathbf{M}}{\mathbf{M}} \qquad (4\text{-}139)$$

Now the relations[40] for static-stagnation pressure and static-stagnation temperature as a function of Mach number are

$$T_t = T\left(1 + \frac{\gamma - 1}{2}\mathbf{M}^2\right) \qquad (4\text{-}140)$$

$$\frac{dT}{T} = \frac{dT_t}{T_t} - \frac{(\gamma - 1)\mathbf{M}^2}{1 + \dfrac{\gamma - 1}{2}\mathbf{M}^2}\frac{d\mathbf{M}}{\mathbf{M}} \qquad (4\text{-}141)$$

$$P_t = P\left(1 + \frac{\gamma - 1}{2}\,\mathbf{M}^2\right)^{\gamma/(\gamma-1)} \tag{4-142}$$

with subscript t denoting stagnation conditions.

Assuming the value of the "temperature recovery" factor from Eq. (4-10) to be

$$r = \frac{T_{aw} - T}{T_t - T} \approx 0.9 \qquad \text{for turbulent gas flows} \tag{4-143}$$

and defining two temperature parameters as

$$\varepsilon_t = \frac{T_t}{T_{t_i}} \qquad \text{and} \qquad \alpha = \frac{T_w}{T_{t_i}} \tag{4-144}$$

where the subscript i refers to inlet conditions, and with a friction-heat-transfer Reynolds analogy parameter[18] of

$$\lambda = \frac{f/2}{h/Gc_p} \approx \mathbf{Pr}^{2/3} \qquad \text{for gas flows} \tag{4-145}$$

Eqs. (4-135) through (4-144) combine to a single differential equation which describes the flow process:

$$\left[\frac{1 - \mathbf{M}^2}{\gamma \mathbf{M}^3\left(1 + \dfrac{\gamma - 1}{2}\,\mathbf{M}^2\right)}\right] d\mathbf{M} = \left(\frac{1 + \gamma\,\mathbf{M}^2}{2\gamma\,\mathbf{M}^2}\right)\frac{d\varepsilon_t}{\varepsilon_t}$$

$$+ \frac{\lambda\, d\varepsilon_t}{\alpha - \varepsilon_t \dfrac{1 + 0.9\dfrac{\gamma - 1}{2}\,\mathbf{M}^2}{1 + \dfrac{\gamma - 1}{2}\,\mathbf{M}^2}} \tag{4-146}$$

Since Eq. (4-146) is a nonlinear differential equation and not amenable to analytical solution in its present form, it becomes necessary to make linearizing assumptions or to utilize digital methods in order to obtain a useful result. Such a digital solution to this equation has been made[41] for a constant wall temperature, a γ of 1.3, and λ of 0.8, and some of the generalized results are given in Figs. 4-10 and 4-11. These curves are recommended for use in preliminary design calculations for cases where the inlet Mach numbers and inlet temperatures are low ($\mathbf{M}_i \leq 0.10$, $T_i \approx 600°\text{R}$).

4-6. System Stability. The problem of heat-exchanger stability is one of extreme importance to the nuclear rocket designer. This stems from the desirability for high power density, which, if coupled with flow or heat-removal instabilities, could result in hot spots and reactor-core failure. Typically, stability criteria are difficult to establish, since most analytical treatments require many limiting assumptions in regard to the

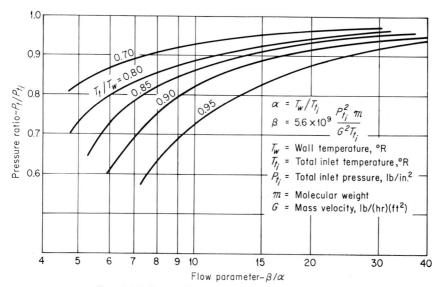

Fig. 4-10. Stagnation pressure vs. flow parameter.

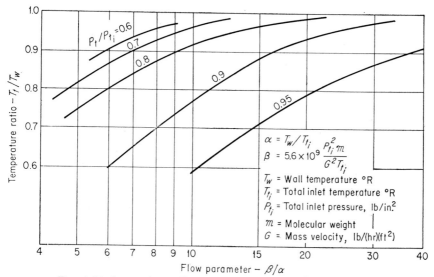

Fig. 4-11. Stagnation-wall temperature ratio vs. flow parameter.

physical model being investigated. On the other hand, model testing can provide some of the answers, but this is complicated by the necessity of duplicating the fission power distribution within the model. In general, other than testing the final device, the best approach is to examine simplified models which are amenable to analysis, then apply the results to the actual case. In many instances this procedure requires considerable engineering judgment and faith.

*Laminar-Turbulent Flow.** The case of laminar flow in a capillary is an example of the use of a simplified model. If the velocity of flow is constant, and neglecting heat conduction in the direction of flow, the equations describing the system, in nondimensional form, are

$$w(t) = -\frac{1}{T^{n+1}} \frac{\partial p(x,t)}{\partial x} \tag{4-147}$$

$$q_0 = \frac{\partial T(x,t)}{\partial t} + w(t) \frac{\partial T}{\partial x} \tag{4-148}$$

$$\mu = T^n \tag{4-149}$$

where $w(t)$ = mass flow

T = temperature with the entry temperature normalized as unity

p = pressure

t = time

q_0 = heat source per unit length normalized to unity

x = position and ranges from zero to one

μ = absolute viscosity

Equation (4-147) is a form of the well-known Hagen-Poiseuille equation for laminar flow in a pipe. Its derivation can be found in Ref. 9. Equation (4-148) is the heat-conduction equation of a flowing gas and is derived in Ref. 3.

To examine the stability of a system of two or more capillaries in parallel, consider first the steady-state solutions. If all the quantities are independent of time, and are so designated by the subscript zero, Eq. (4-148) yields

$$T_0 = 1 + \frac{x}{w_0} \tag{4-150}$$

Using this result, Eq. (4-147) can be integrated:

$$\Delta p_0 = -\int_0^1 \frac{\partial p_0}{\partial x} dx = w_0 \int_0^1 \left(1 + \frac{x}{w_0}\right)^{n+1} dx$$

$$= \frac{w_0^2}{n+2} \left[\left(1 + \frac{1}{w_0}\right)^{n+2} - 1\right] \tag{4-151}$$

Now for small flows

$$\Delta p_0 \approx \frac{1}{(n+2)w_0^n} \tag{4-152}$$

while for large flows

$$\Delta p_0 \approx w_0 \tag{4-153}$$

---

* Based on some unpublished analyses by C. Longmire and G. Birkhoff of the Los Alamos Scientific Laboratory.

Since n, the exponent of the temperature in the viscosity-temperature relationship, is greater than zero, Fig. 4-12 represents Δp_0 as a function of w_0.

If Δp_0 is large enough, there are two solutions for w_0, and from Eq. (4-150) the smaller w_0 has the higher exit temperature.   Figure 4-12 also shows that, for the solution with low flows, the capillary presents a "negative" resistance.   It then appears likely that, if two or more capillaries are connected in parallel, one capillary will take more flow and the other less, with the smaller flow having the higher temperature. This is an unstable condition, and it is possible to show, by examining time-dependent equations in the vicinity of the steady solutions, that it is indeed true that the low-flow case is unstable and the larger flow is stable.   This analysis is not presented herein.   Instead, the problem of laminar flow vs. turbulent

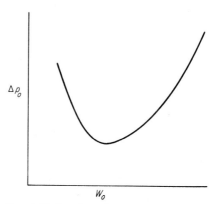

Fig. 4-12. Laminar-flow pressure drop vs. flow rate.

flow for conditions that might be expected in a nuclear rocket-reactor heat exchanger will be examined.

Consider a gas flowing in a constant-area duct of length L from an inlet pressure p_i and temperature T_i to an exit pressure and temperature p_e and T_e, respectively.   If it is assumed that the pressure ratio p_i/p_e is near unity and the heat absorption is at a constant rate q per unit length and time, then Eq. (4-148) in the following form will describe the heat addition for the steady-state condition with constant specific heat:

$$\frac{dT}{dx} = \frac{aq}{w} = \frac{bq}{\rho V} \quad \text{for } w = \rho V A \text{ constant} \qquad (4\text{-}154)$$

where a and b are constants independent of x, q, and w; ρ is density; and V is gas velocity.   Using a proportionality simplification, Eq. (4-154) becomes

$$\frac{dT}{dx} \propto \frac{q}{w} \propto \frac{q}{\rho V} \qquad (4\text{-}155)$$

For a constant-length duct, this proportionality can be extended to the integrated form of Eq. (4-155), that is,

$$T_e - T_i \propto \frac{qL}{w} \propto \frac{q}{w} \qquad (4\text{-}156)$$

Introducing a dimensionless temperature parameter φ by dividing by the inlet temperature T_i, Eq. (4-156) becomes

$$\varphi = \frac{T_e}{T_i} - 1 \propto \frac{q}{wT_i} \tag{4-157}$$

For a nuclear rocket heat exchanger, φ must attain values of the order of 10 for interesting performance. For a single duct, Eq. (4-157) indicates that this ratio can be controlled by the flow rate w for any q and T_i.

However, if p_i, T_i, and p_e are stabilized at some steady-state value, the situation might be such that the heat transfer could become unstable in the following way. A rise in temperature would tend to increase the gas viscosity μ and decrease its density ρ; in turn these factors would diminish the mass flow rate w, and hence the capacity of the duct for heat absorption q. Mathematically this means that, for sufficiently large φ, q may be a *decreasing* function of φ for fixed p_i, T_i, and p_e. Such an instability could lead to a failure of the duct by excessive heating.

A quantitative analysis of this instability is obtained if one considers friction as the major source of pressure drop within the constant-area duct. Then the pressure gradient along the duct will satisfy the approximate relationship of page 122:

$$-\frac{dp}{dx} = B\mu^\beta \rho^{1-\beta} V^{2-\beta}$$
$$-\frac{dp}{dx} \propto \frac{\mu^\beta w^{2-\beta}}{\rho} \tag{4-158}$$

where B is a constant and β is unity for laminar (Poiseuille) flow, is approximately 0.20 for turbulent flow for Reynolds numbers between 3,000 and 150,000, and decreases toward zero for very large Reynolds numbers.

If it is assumed that the gas is at nearly constant pressure, $p \approx p_i$, then the density-temperature relationship is approximated by

$$\rho \propto \frac{1}{T} \tag{4-159}$$

and taking the viscosity-temperature relationship to be

$$\mu \propto T^{1/2} \tag{4-160}$$

Eq. (4-158) then becomes

$$-\frac{dp}{dx} \propto w^{2-\beta} T^{1+\beta/2} \tag{4-161}$$

From Eq. (4-156), the heat equation, and Eq. (4-157), the nondimensional relationship, it is implied that

$$dx \propto T_i \frac{dT}{\varphi} \tag{4-162}$$

and for a given T_i

$$dx \propto \frac{dT}{\varphi} \tag{4-163}$$

Substituting this relationship into Eq. (4-161) gives

$$-dp \propto \frac{w^{2-\beta}}{\varphi} T^{1+\beta/2} dT \tag{4-164}$$

Integration results in

$$p_i - p_e \propto w^{2-\beta}\varphi^{-1}(T_e^{2+\beta/2} - T_i^{2+\beta/2}) \tag{4-165}$$

But by Eq. (4-157) for a fixed T_i, $w \propto q/\varphi$ so from the definition of φ

$$p_i - p_e \propto q^{2-\beta}\varphi^{\beta-3}[(1 + \varphi)^{2+\beta/2} - 1] \tag{4-166}$$

From this relation, and for a fixed p_i, T_i, and p_e,

$$q^{2-\beta} \propto \frac{\varphi^{3-\beta}}{(1 + \varphi)^{2+\beta/2} - 1} = Q(\varphi) \tag{4-167}$$

where

$$\varphi = \frac{T_e}{T_i} - 1$$

To determine the associated zones of stability and instability, first define as a matter of convenience the function

$$G(\varphi) = \frac{1}{Q(\varphi)} \tag{4-168}$$

It has been determined that, for stability, q must be an increasing function of φ, which in turn means that $Q(\varphi)$ must also be an increasing function of φ. But as a consequence of Eq. (4-168), $G(\varphi)$ must be a decreasing function of φ. If Eq. (4-168) is differentiated with respect to φ, we obtain

$$\frac{dG(\varphi)}{d\varphi} = \frac{(1 + \varphi)^{1+\beta/2}}{\varphi^{4-\beta}} \left[(\tfrac{3}{2}\beta - 1)\varphi - (3 - \beta) + \frac{3 - \beta}{(1 + \varphi)^{1+\beta/2}} \right] \tag{4-169}$$

Since φ is positive, the criterion for stability is for the quantity within the bracket to be less than zero, thereby making $G'(\varphi)$ negative and $Q(\varphi)$ an increasing function of φ. That is,

$$(\tfrac{3}{2}\beta - 1)\varphi - (3 - \beta) + \frac{3 - \beta}{(1 + \varphi)^{1+\beta/2}} < 0$$

or

$$\frac{1}{(1 + \varphi)^{1+\beta/2}} < 1 - \frac{3\beta - 2}{6 - 2\beta} \varphi \tag{4-170}$$

For the laminar-flow case, $\beta = 1$ and the inequality reduces to

$$\frac{1}{(1 + \varphi)^{3/2}} < 1 - \frac{\varphi}{4} \tag{4-171}$$

and is satisfied by approximately $\varphi < 3.6$. For values of $\varphi > 3.6$ the flow will be unstable.

In the turbulent-flow case where β is approximately 0.20, and more generally where $0 < \beta < \tfrac{2}{3}$, the left side of Eq. (4-170) is less than unity, while the right side is greater than unity, always resulting in stable flow.

Based on these two simplified models and within the limits of the assumptions, it appears that, to avoid flow and heat-transfer instabilities, it is important that the flow within a nuclear rocket heat exchanger be kept turbulent.

Porous Flow. The question of the temperature stability of a porous heat source can be examined in a manner similar to the laminar (Poiseuille) flow case, in which it was possible to obtain two flow rates for a particular pressure drop. This can be demonstrated[20] by determining the relationship between power required in pumping the fluid, the power removed as thermal energy, the mass velocity, and the temperature. It should be noted that the ratio of pumping power to power removed as thermal energy is normally utilized as a figure of merit when comparing heat exchangers.

The pumping power required to force a perfect gas through the porous wall shown in Fig. 4-1 is

$$W = -G \int_{p_1}^{p_2} \frac{dp}{\rho} = \frac{R_u}{\mathfrak{M}} T_a G \ln \frac{p_1}{p_2} \tag{4-172}$$

and the heat-removal rate is

$$Q = G c_p (T_2 - T_0) \tag{4-173}$$

where the variables are as defined for Eq. (4-37).

Here T_a is defined by

$$T_a = \frac{1}{L} \int_0^L T \, dx \tag{4-174}$$

and may be determined by utilizing Eq. (4-38). This temperature can be expressed in the form

$$\frac{T_a - T_0}{\dfrac{qL}{G c_p}} = \frac{1}{2} + \frac{\dfrac{G c_p L}{k_s} - 1 + \exp\left(-\dfrac{G c_p L}{k_s}\right)}{\left(\dfrac{G c_p L}{k_s}\right)^2} \tag{4-175}$$

which gives a figure-of-merit ratio of

$$\frac{W}{Q} = \frac{\dfrac{R_u}{\mathfrak{M}} T_a}{c_p (T_2 - T_0)} \ln \frac{p_1}{p_2} \tag{4-176}$$

or for small pressure drops relative to the average absolute pressure

$$\frac{W}{Q} = \frac{\dfrac{R_u}{\mathfrak{M}} T_a}{c_p (T_2 - T_0)} \frac{p_1 - p_2}{p_{\text{avg}}} \tag{4-177}$$

This ratio has been computed[20] for particular materials and boundary conditions and is plotted in Fig. 4-13. Examination of these curves suggests operation of a porous heater at the point of minimum W/Q. However, because of the temperature dependence of the gas viscosity, instability of the wall temperature may occur. If a hot spot within the wall

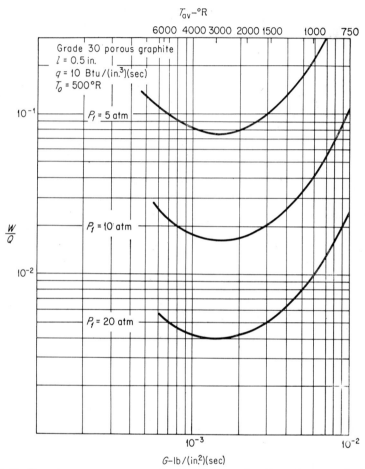

FIG. 4-13. Pumping power–power output ratio as a function of mass velocity for different inlet conditions.

exists because of some inhomogeneity of the porous material, the increased viscosity would tend to reduce the flow, which in turn would result in increase in temperature, continuing in this manner until failure. On the other hand, stability might be promoted by high thermal conductivity of the wall material, high heat capacity in the gas, and a high flow rate. In fact, stability considerations might require operation on the high-flow side of the optimum point, where the flow resistance is dominated by the quadratic nonviscous term of Eq. (4-40).

Choking. For the flow of a compressible fluid in a constant-area passage with heat transfer and friction—which is an interesting case in nuclear rocket-reactor core design—a flow phenomenon referred to as "choking" must be guarded against. This condition can best be illustrated by examining the relationship of local Mach number $\mathbf{M}$ to flow-passage length x in the form[40]

$$\frac{d\mathbf{M}^2}{dx} = \frac{\phi(x)}{1 - \mathbf{M}^2} \qquad (4\text{-}178)$$

where for the case of constant-area channel and constant specific heat and molecular weight

$$\phi(x) = \mathbf{M}^2\left(1 + \frac{\gamma - 1}{2}\mathbf{M}^2\right)\left[(1 + \gamma\mathbf{M}^2)\frac{d(\ln T_t)}{dx} + \gamma\mathbf{M}^2\,4\,\frac{f}{D}\right]$$

$$(4\text{-}179)$$

For our case x is positive, and ϕ is also positive for the situation of flow through a constant-area channel with heat addition and friction. Here, it is impossible for the flow to pass continually through $\mathbf{M} = 1$. This can be proved by assuming that the flow is initially subsonic and that the Mach number unity is reached at some point in the channel where $x = x_0$. Now assume that the flow subsequently became supersonic. This would mean, according to Eq. (4-178), that at a point $x_0 + \Delta x$, where Δx is positive, $d\mathbf{M}^2/dx$ would be negative. This contradicts the assumption that the flow became supersonic, for if $\mathbf{M}^2$ at $x_0 + \Delta x$ is greater than unity, $d\mathbf{M}^2/dx$ in the interval between x_0 and $x_0 + \Delta x$ must be positive. Accordingly, it is impossible for the flow to become supersonic if it is initially subsonic. At the choking point, $d\mathbf{M}^2/dx$ is infinite, and most of the fluid properties change at an infinite rate.

If choking actually occurs within a passage, it will not be possible to maintain steady-state flow. After a transient period of readjustment, a new steady-state condition for which choking will not occur will be established. Such a readjustment usually involves a reduction in the initial Mach number, the appearance of shock waves, or both. This is not a desirable condition to have existing within a high-power-density heat exchanger.

Two-phase Flow. Another serious situation that may arise, and is severe in a highly stressed reactor core, is the extreme pressure fluctuations resulting from a flow condition that might be described as "chugging." If a liquid propellant is introduced into a core heat exchanger at below the critical pressure and temperature during some stage of the heating process, some of the propellant will have been vaporized while the remainder will still be a liquid; in other words, the flow will be two-phased. The heat-transfer rates and the flow conditions existing during two-phase flow are in most cases extremely unstable, causing fluctuations in pressure and temperature. While it is beyond the scope of this text to treat the problem of two-phase flow, it is a problem that must be considered in nuclear rocket core design. It might be pointed out that, if the pressure and temperature of the liquid propellants are maintained above their critical value (see Table 2-1), large changes in density can take place, but two-phase flow as such does not exist.

REFERENCES

1. McAdams, W. H.: "Heat Transmission," 3d ed., McGraw-Hill Series in Chemical Engineering, McGraw-Hill Book Company, Inc., New York, 1954.
2. Eckert, E. R. G.: "Introduction to the Transfer of Heat and Mass," McGraw-Hill Book Company, Inc., New York, 1950.
3. Jakob, M.: "Heat Transfer," vol. I, John Wiley & Sons, Inc., New York, 1949.
4. Johnson, H. A., and M. W. Rubesin: Aerodynamic Heating and Convective Heat Transfer—Summary of Literature Survey, *Trans. ASME*, vol. 71, pp. 447–456, July, 1949.
5. Eckert, E. R. G., and W. Weise: The Temperature of the Unheated Bodies in a High-speed Gas Stream, *NACA TM* 1000, January–February, 1941.
6. Eckert, E. R. G.: Heat Transmission of Bodies in Rapidly Flowing Gases, Intelligence T-2 Documents Office, Foreign Exploitation Section, Wright Field, Dayton, Ohio, 1946.
7. Eckert, E. R. G., and O. Drewitz: Heat Transfer to a Plate in Flow at High Speed, *NACA TM* 1045, May–June, 1945.
8. Crocco, L.: Transmission of Heat from a Plate to a Fluid at a High Velocity, *NACA TM* 690, February, 1932.
9. Schlichting, H.: "Boundary Layer Theory," McGraw-Hill Book Company, Inc., New York, 1955.
10. Rubesin, M. W., and H. A. Johnson: A Critical Review of Skin Friction and Heat Transfer Solutions of the Laminar Boundary Layer of a Flat Plate, *Trans. ASME*, vol. 71, no. 4, pp. 383–388, May, 1949.
11. Reynolds, O.: "Collected Papers," vol. I, pp. 81–85.
12. Taylor, G. I.: *ARC R and M* 272, 1919.
13. Prandtl, L.: Bemerkung über den Warmenbergang im Rohr, *Physik. Z.*, vol. 29, pp. 487–489, 1928.
14. von Kármán, T.: Some Aspects of the Turbulence Problem, pp. 54–91, *Proc. Intern. Congr. Appl. Mechanics, 4th Congr.*, 1934.
15. von Kármán, T.: Analogy between Fluid Friction and Heat Transfer, *Trans. ASME*, vol. 61, pp. 705–710, 1939.
16. Deissler, R. G.: Analysis of Turbulent Heat Transfer, Mass Transfer and Friction in Smooth Tubes at High Prandtl and Schmidt Numbers, *NACA Rept.* 1210, 1955.
17. Rannie, W. D.: Heat Transfer in Turbulent Shear Flow, *J. Aeronaut. Sci.*, vol. 23, no. 5, pp. 485–489, May, 1956.
18. Rubesin, M. W.: A Modified Reynolds Analogy for the Compressible Turbulent Boundary Layer on a Flat Plate, *NACA TN* 2917, 1953.

19. Tsien, H. S.: "Rockets and Other Thermal Jets Using Nuclear Energy," in Clark Goodman (ed.), "The Science and Engineering of Nuclear Power," vol. II, chap. 11, p. 124, Addison-Wesley Publishing Company, Reading, Mass.

20. Green, L., Jr.: Gas Cooling of Porous Heat Source, *J. Appl. Mechanics*, vol. 19, p. 173, 1952.

21. Green, L., Jr., and P. Duwez: Fluid Flow through Porous Metals, *J. Appl. Mechanics*, vol. 18, p. 39, 1951.

22. Durham, F. P., R. C. Neal, and H. J. Newman: High Temperature Heat Transfer to a Gas Flowing in Heat Generating Tubes with High Heat Flux, *Proc. Reacior Heat Transfer Conference*, Nov. 2, 1956. Distributed by Nuclear Development Corporation of America.

23. Humble, L. V., W. H. Lowdermilk, and L. G. Desmon: Measurements of Average Heat Transfer and Friction Coefficients for Subsonic Flow of Air in Smooth Tubes at High Surface and Fluid Temperatures, *NACA Rept.* 1020, 1951.

24. Kays, W. M., and A. L. London: A Summary of Experimental and Analysis for Gas Flow Heat Transfer and Friction in Circular Tubes, *Tech. Rept.* 22, Contract N-6-onr-251 Task Order 6 (NR-090-104), Stanford University, June, 1954.

25. Bonilla, C. F.: An Up-to-date Review of the Principles of Heat Transfer, with Particular Application to Nuclear Power, *U.S. AEC M*-4476, 1949.

26. Gamson, B. W., George Thodos, and O. A. Hougen: Heat, Mass and Momentum Transfer in the Flow of Gases through Granular Solids, *Trans. AIChE*, vol. 39, no. 1, pp. 1–32, 1943.

27. Denton, W. H., C. H. Robinson, and R. S. Tibbs: The Heat Transfer and Pressure Loss in Fluid Flow through Randomly Packed Spheres, vol. I, *U.S. AEC, HPC*-35, June, 1949.

28. Eckert, E. R. G.: Engineering Relations for Heat Transfer and Friction in High Velocity Laminar and Turbulent Boundary-layer Flow over Surfaces with Constant Pressure and Temperature, *Trans. ASME*, vol. 78, no. 6, pp. 1273–1284, August, 1956.

29. Emmons, H. W.: The Numerical Solution of Heat Conduction Problems, *Trans. ASME*, vol. 65, p. 608, August, 1943. The Numerical Solution of Partial Differential Equations, *Quart. Appl. Math.*, vol. 2, p. 173, October, 1944.

30. Dusinberre, G. M.: "Numerical Analysis of Heat Flow," McGraw-Hill Book Company, Inc., New York, 1949.

31. Ramachandran, A.: Analogic Experimental Methods in Heat Transfer, *Electrotechnics*, no. 23, pp. 110–115, March, 1951.

32. Paschkis, V.: Electric Methods for the Solution of Laplace's Equation, *Exp. Stress Analysis*, vol. 2, no. 2, p. 39, 1944.

33. Paschkis, V., and H. D. Baker: A Method of Determining Unsteady State Heat Transfer by Means of an Electrical Analogy, *Trans. ASME*, vol. 64, pp. 105–110, 1942.

34. Shapiro, A. H., and W. R. Hawthorne: The Mechanics and Thermodynamics of Steady One-dimensional Gas Flow, *J. Appl. Mechanics*, vol. 14, no. 4, pp. A317–A336, December, 1947.

35. Hall, N.: "Thermodynamics of Fluid Flow," Prentice-Hall, Inc., Englewood Cliffs, N.J., 1951.

36. Sibulkin, M., and W. K. Koffel: Chart for Simplifying Calculations of Pressure Drop of a High-speed Compressible Fluid under Simultaneous Action of Friction and Heat Transfer, *NACA TN* 2067, March, 1950.

37. Thompson, A. S.: Flow of Heated Gases, *NAA-SR*-18, North American Aviation, Inc., Downey, Calif., 1947.

38. Valerino, M. F.: Generalized Charts for Determination of Pressure Drop of a High-speed Compressible Fluid in Heat Exchanger Passages, *J. Aeronaut. Sci.*, vol. 16, no. 5, pp. 311–315, May, 1949.

39. Foa, J. V., and G. Rudinger: On the Addition of Heat to a Gas Flowing in a Pipe at Subsonic Speeds, *J. Aeronaut. Sci.*, vol. 16, no. 2, pp. 84–94, February, 1949.

40. Shapiro, A. H.: "The Dynamics and Thermodynamics of Compressible Fluid Flow," vol. I, The Ronald Press Company, New York, 1953.

41. Durham, F. P.: unpublished calculations made at the Los Alamos Scientific Laboratory, 1956.

CHAPTER 5

MATERIALS

The peak performance of a heat-exchanger type of rocket reactor is fixed by limitations on the reactor component structures. Maximum performance results from a design in which all component parts are pushed as close to their material limits as possible. In order to do this the designer must be aware of the major problems to be overcome in each section of the reactor and must know the properties and capabilities of the materials of interest. These are discussed in this chapter, with particular emphasis on thermal stress and strain, radiation damage, and corrosion and erosion, problems which are especially severe in high-power-density nuclear rocket reactors.

5-1. Basic Requirements. In order to assess the worth of any material for use in a nuclear reactor it is necessary to know the requirements for different reactor structures and to understand the reasons underlying these requirements. For rocket reactors the four major subdivisions of interest in discussing these requirements are fuel elements, moderators, control elements, and structural materials.

Fuel Elements. To achieve high performance in the reactor core, fuel elements must heat the coolant-propellant gas to a very high temperature. In addition, because of the inherent characteristics of the flow of a fluid over surfaces (Chap. 4) the fuel elements must withstand loads due to pressure differences arising from the coolant flow. Still other requirements are imposed by the condition of operation in a radiation field. Here, since the fission power may be generated throughout the fuel-element volume and since energy deposition by gamma-ray absorption occurs throughout the material, the fuel element will be subjected to internal temperature gradients resulting in thermal stresses. At the high power density required to produce a flyable rocket motor it will often be found that these internal temperature gradients, as well as the heat-removal rates, will be extreme. For such operation it is generally necessary to rely on creep of the fuel element to relieve thermal stresses. Another requirement is that, for successful use of a rocket power plant, the reactor must be capable of heating up to full temperature and power in a time of the order of seconds. Thus if creep relief is to take place, the fuel-element material must have extremely high creep rates at stresses lower than the rupture strength at high temperature.

By definition, a fuel element contains or carries the fissionable material which supplies power to the reactor when operated at the critical nuclear condition. Because of this it is desirable that the fuel-element base material not compete strongly with the fissionable material for neutrons. Such competition or nonproductive neutron absorption can result in striking increases in fissionable-material requirements for reactor criticality. Furthermore, it is desirable that the base material aid in the slowing down of neutrons and thus help to reduce the size and weight of the complete reactor assembly.

Another consideration is the effect the propellant has on the fuel-element base material. All propellant gases of interest contain hydrogen, and it is because they contain hydrogen that they are interesting as propellants. Unfortunately, hydrogen is sometimes a bad actor at high temperature, for it embrittles some materials, hydrides others, and forms volatile hydrogen compounds with still others. A successful fuel-element material must, then, be capable of withstanding the assault of high-temperature hydrogen without structural damage or significant loss of fissionable fuel.

In summary, a good fuel element should have high strength at high temperature as well as at room temperature; it should have high conductivity to reduce internal temperature gradients; it should be a poor absorber of neutrons but a good neutron moderator; and it should be proof against attack by hot propellant gases. Obviously a fuel-element base material which has all or most of these characteristics is worthless if it loses them with the addition of fissionable material. Consequently first and foremost, a fuel-element material must be able to contain fissionable fuel.

Moderators and Reflectors. In homogeneous core-moderated reactors the neutron thermalization is accomplished primarily by the core material, hence by the fuel-element material. For this type of reactor the moderator must clearly be capable of operation at high temperature under the same conditions as those imposed on the fuel elements, above. However, many of the reactor design configurations that exist do not require core fuel-element moderation. The two general types in this category are matrix-geometry cores moderated by material between bundles of fuel elements, and externally reflected cores moderated by thermalizing material surrounding or enclosing the reactor core. For these latter applications the high-temperature-stability requirements of homogeneous-core fuel-element-moderated reactors do not apply. By definition, moderator materials must have low atomic weights and low neutron-absorption cross sections if neutron thermalization is to be accomplished without excessive loss by absorption of neutrons.

The energy of fission neutrons is lost to a moderating material by collisions with the nuclei of the moderator. In addition, gamma-ray absorption deposits energy throughout the volume of the moderator. For use in matrix-geometry or externally reflected cores the moderator material, if solid, must be capable of operation at a temperature sufficiently high to permit the removal of this neutron and gamma heat energy by a liquid or gaseous coolant. Here, as for the fuel elements, internal temperature gradients will be built up, thus giving rise to thermal stresses in the moderator material. Since it is often convenient to use the incoming propellant as the coolant for removal of the neutron and gamma heat, the moderator must also be chemically compatible with the propellant in its liquid state and as a low-temperature gas.

Depending on the particular reactor design, it is often the lot of the moderator to carry a large part of the core pressure-drop load and transmit it to the outer pressure shell. For this application the moderator must have reasonable tensile and compressive strength.

In summary, a good moderator must have a low atomic weight; low neutron-absorption cross section; high conductivity, but not so important here as for fuel elements; fair strength at moderate temperatures if used in heterogeneous matrix or reflector-moderated geometries; and must be compatible with its coolant, which may be the incoming liquid propellant.

Control Elements. Proper reactor operation requires that "power" reactors must have some mechanical means of control or reactivity to permit safe start-up, operation, and shutdown. This control is often best accomplished by use of neutron poisons capable of being moved into or out of the reactor core, reflector, or other regions of high neutron flux. The primary requirement of such a control material is that it have a high neutron-capture cross section. Now, in capturing a neutron generally, an alpha particle, beta particle (electron), or gamma photon is emitted in the course of the nuclear reaction, so that all control-rod materials become, in a sense, volume heat sources by neutron absorption. In addition to this heat load, gamma radiation from the fissions taking place in the core will be absorbed by the control-rod material, in roughly direct proportion to the material density. To minimize the rod-heating problem, then, a desirable control-rod material either should not emit radiative energy upon neutron capture or should emit very penetrating radiation such as gamma rays, and it should have a low density for less gamma heating and a high thermal conductivity for heat removal. If a solid, it is desirable that the rod material be capable of operation at moderate temperatures ($\sim$1500°R) in order to facilitate heat removal.

Generally, control rods and control materials do not carry external loads, thus need not have strength characteristics above those required for proper cooling and structural integrity during operation.

Structural Components. The two principal structural components of any rocket reactor are the external pressure shell and the internal core-support structure. The pressure shell can generally be thermally insulated from the hot fissioning core, thus need not be capable of withstanding high temperature. However, energy is deposited directly in the shell by gamma absorption, causing internal heating and thermal stresses in the material and thus requiring a shell-cooling system. Since it is generally convenient to cool the shell with the incoming liquid propellant, one requirement for shell material is that of compatibility with the liquid propellant. Obviously the shell-material strength-density ratio should be as high as possible to permit use of minimum-weight pressure shells. In operation the shell is loaded circumferentially by the reactor-core gas pressure and is loaded axially by internal pressure and the axial rocket-motor thrust. Joints in the shell such as break flanges or the point of nozzle attachment can be points of local high stressing, principally because of the thermal stresses set up by gamma heating in these thicker-than-normal sections. Local points of high loading can also occur where the core structure is connected to the shell and is transmitting the core pressure-drop load through structural elements to the shell.

This internal core-support structure poses the most difficult problems in the reactor structural design. It must live in an environment of very hot, corrosive propellant gas, and it must carry the pressure drop and any differential-expansion loads of the core. It must itself be cooled sufficiently to remove the internally deposited gamma heat energy, and must not be so distorted by the various thermal gradients and loads imposed on it that the fuel-element design geometry is changed in any significant way. This is a difficult requirement, since total core loads can be extremely high in some specific designs. For example, a pressure drop of 200 lb/in.^{2} across a 3-ft-diameter cylindrical reactor core yields a total load of about 100 tons which must be transmitted by the core-support structure to the outer pressure shell.

Fortunately, there are generally no specific nuclear characteristics required of the support structure or pressure shell, so that choice of materials for these functions is not hampered by nuclear considerations.

In summary, structural-component materials should have high strength-density ratios and high thermal conductivity and be chemically compatible with the propellant as either a liquid or a hot gas, depending upon its state when used as a structure coolant.

5-2. Properties. Having discussed the basic requirements for the components of high-temperature rocket reactors, it is now pertinent to examine the characteristics of the various potentially useful materials in order to gain a feeling for the range of applicability and consequences of use of these materials. The emphasis in this section, as throughout the text, is on those characteristics of most interest and pertinence to the rocket-reactor application of the material under discussion. The discussion presented herein is thus far from exhaustive, and the reader is referred to the more "standard" sources[1] for general background and further specific information.

Physical Properties. FUEL ELEMENTS. The requirement of operability above 4500°R, or so, severely restricts the choice of fuel-element base materials. Of the pure elements only graphite, C; tungsten, W; tantalum, Ta; molybdenum, Mo; niobium, Nb; and rhenium, Re, have

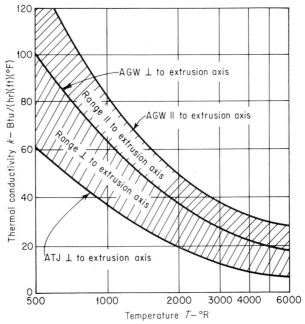

FIG. 5-1. Thermal conductivity of various graphites.

sufficiently high melting or sublimation temperatures to permit their consideration. Although hundreds of thousands of chemical compounds are known, it appears that the only compounds of potential value for rocket-reactor fuel elements are the simple metallic carbides, nitrides, and borides of tungsten, tantalum, niobium, and zirconium. Unfortunately, not enough is known about the high-temperature physical properties of many of these materials to permit sound assessment of their value and realistic comparison with graphite, the one material for which many high-temperature data are available. Furthermore, the effects of addition of fissionable material (for example, U^{235}) to the fuel-element base material are generally not readily obtainable; hence the rocket-reactor designer is forced to pursue a course of action based upon data on nonloaded materials coupled with a parallel program of experimental study of the effects of fuel loading.

Graphite is an extremely variable material whose characteristics depend to a large extent on the particular batch process and raw materials used in its manufacture; thus it is not correct to speak of the properties of graphite as though they applied to all grades and types of this material.

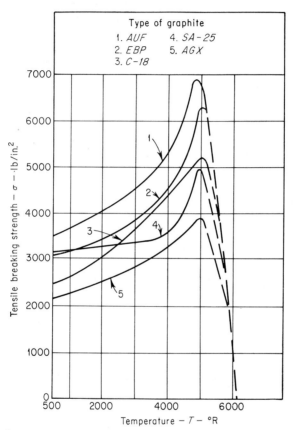

FIG. 5-2. Tensile strength of various graphites. (*Data from "The Reactor Handbook," vol. 3, sec. 1, AECD-3647, March, 1955.*)

For our purposes, however, it is convenient to speak of general properties and to consider typical values for strength, conductivity, and the other properties of interest. Although not useful for purposes of detail design, such information is adequate to guide the engineer in preliminary design work. Any final design must necessarily be based on the results of experiments on the graphite of interest.

The thermal conductivity of normal graphite is high [~50 Btu/(hr)(ft) (°F)] at room temperature but drops rapidly with increasing temperature.

Typical values of conductivity at about 5000°R are given in Table 5-1, and the variation of conductivity with temperature is shown in Fig. 5-1 for several grades of graphite. The shaded area in the figure marks the range of variation of experimental determinations of thermal conductivity. In general, the strength of graphite increases up to about 5000°R and then decreases rapidly above this temperature to nearly zero strength at about 5800 to 6000°R, as shown in Fig. 5-2. Although graphite exhibits high creep rates under stress at high temperatures, structural

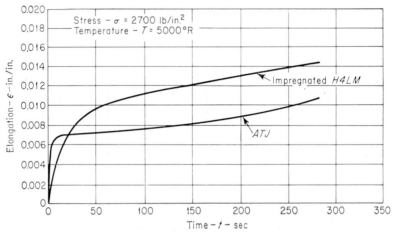

FIG. 5-3. Typical creep curves for graphite. (*Private communication from P. J. Wagner, April, 1957.*)

failure at these temperatures as well as at room temperature seems to be by brittle fracture, in both tension and compression.[2] Typical elongation-vs.-time curves are shown in Fig. 5-3 for two types of graphite at one temperature-and-stress condition. The Young's modulus of graphite is lower than that of "normal" materials like steel and varies only slightly with temperature as compared with the variation in thermal conductivity. The thermal-expansion coefficient is comparable to that for low-expansion steels, increases by a factor of about 2 with temperature up to 5000°R, and differs by about a factor of 2 between the axis normal to grain orientation and that parallel to the grains. Graphite can be loaded with uranium in the form of UC_2, either by direct loading or by carburization of a uranium salt impregnate which decomposes at high temperature.

Tungsten has been in high-temperature use for many years as the base material for lamp filaments. In pure form it is not suited for high-temperature service, for continued grain growth at high temperature results in a very weak, brittle material with large crystalline grains. Inhibition of grain growth is accomplished in filament manufacture by the addition of small quantities of ThO_2 to the metal before swaging into

TABLE 5-1. PHYSICAL PROPERTIES OF SOME FUEL-ELEMENT BASE MATERIALS

Material	Melting point T_m, °R	Sp gr at room temperature, ρ/ρ_{water}	Short-time tensile strength, lb/in.² σ_a	°R	Young's modulus, 10^6 lb/in.² E	°R	Mean-linear-expansion coefficient, 10^{-6} °F⁻¹ α	°R	Thermal conductivity, Btu/(hr)(ft)(°F) k	°R	Poisson's ratio ν	Thermal-stress parameter[a] $\bar\sigma_1 = \frac{\sigma_{th}}{\sigma_a} 10^4$; $q\Psi_2$ — $\bar\sigma_1$	°R
Graphite, C	7000[b]	1.65–1.85	2,000–4,000; 3,000–6,000	500; 5000	0.4⊥,[c] 1.2∥; 0.8⊥, 1.6∥	500	3⊥,[c] 1∥; 7⊥, 4.5∥	500; 5000	7–18⊥[c]; 15–30∥	5000; 500	0.2–0.3	1.42	5000
Tungsten, W	6600	19.1	60,000–140,000; 5,000–9,000	2000; 5000	50	500	2.6; 4.0	500; 4000	110; 70; 60	500; 2000; 3500	[d]	7.8	5000
Rhenium, Re	6200	20.5	90,000–130,000; 4,000–6,000	2000; 5000	65–72; 54; 27	500; 2200	3.6; 3.8	500; 2200	……		[d]	14.3	5000
Tantalum, Ta	5850	16.6	50,000–70,000; 1,000–6,000	2000; 5000	……	500	3.4; 4.5	500; 5000	31; 49	500; 4000	[d]	21.1	5000
Molybdenum, Mo	5150	10.2	30,000–50,000; 500–1,000	2000; 5000	48; 40	500; 2000	2.8; 4.0	500; 4000	75; 60; 40	500; 2000; 3200	[d]	87	5000
Niobium, Nb	4800	8.6	30,000	2000			4.0	500	25[e]; 20[e]	500; 2200	[d]		
Niobium carbide, NbC	7500	7.8			49	500							
Tantalum carbide: TaC	7450	14.5	2,000–4,000	500	41	500	4.5	500	8.2	500		85	500
Ta₂C	6600	15.1											
Zirconium carbide, ZrC	6250	6.8	14,000; 16,000	2200; 2700					12	500			
Tungsten carbide: WC	5100	15.6	50,000	500	102	500	2.9, a;[f] 4.1, c	500				18.5	500
W₂C	5600	17.2			60	500	0.7, a; 6.3, c	500					500

[a] $\dfrac{\sigma_{th}}{\sigma_a} = q\Psi_2 \dfrac{\alpha E}{\sigma_a k(1 - \nu)}$; see Eq. (5-3).

[b] Sublimes.

[c] ⊥ and ∥ indicate properties perpendicular and parallel to grain orientation, respectively.

[d] No data available, but values for most metals lie between 0.25 and 0.35.

[e] Estimated values.

[f] Values along a and c axes, as indicated.

145

wire form.   The ThO₂ effectively stops migration across grain boundaries
and prevents the "connecting-up" of smaller grains.   For reactor application this technique seems plausible for use with UO_2 rather than ThO_2,
thus introducing fuel into the base fuel-element material.   Tungsten
metal has a high thermal conductivity which changes only slightly as
compared with that of graphite over the temperature range from room
temperature to about 5000°R.   Little is known about the strength of
tungsten above about 4000°R; however, if it follows the behavior of
other metals as they approach their softening or melting points, the

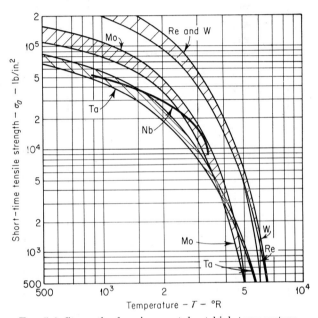

FIG. 5-4. Strength of various metals at high temperature.

strength should drop markedly above 4000°R.   Figure 5-4 gives some
data on the short-time tensile strength of tungsten as a function of temperature.   The properties of tungsten are isotropic unless the material
has been grain-oriented in extreme swaging.   Typical values for some of
these properties at 5000°R are given in Table 5-1.

   Molybdenum is another metal which may be useful for high-tempera-
ture-reactor fuel elements.   Since its melting point (Table 5-1) is more
than 1000°R below that of tungsten, it is not capable of operation under
load at temperatures much above 4000°R.   Molybdenum has problems
of grain growth similar to those of tungsten; presumably they too can
be solved by grain inhibition with ThO₂ or UO₂.   The known tensile-
strength data for molybdenum are shown in Fig. 5-4.   Note the sharp
decrease in strength at about two-thirds of the melting-point temperature.

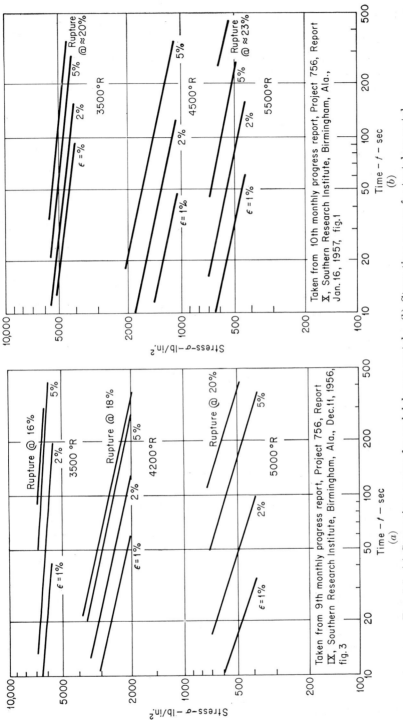

FIG. 5-5. (a) Stress-time curves for molybdenum metal.   (b) Stress-time curves for tantalum metal.

147

The thermal conductivity is less than that of tungsten but greater than that of graphite at 5000°R. Data on the creep of molybdenum are shown in Fig. 5-5a.

The state of knowledge about *tantalum, niobium,* and *rhenium* is generally less complete than for the previously discussed materials. Rhenium is distinguished principally by its high melting point and by its scarcity, at present. As discussed on page 179, tantalum forms a hydride between 2000 and 4000°R when in contact with hydrogenous gases. The effect of this on structural stability of tantalum fuel elements is not known but is likely to be severe since the hydride is very brittle at moderate temperatures. Grain growth at high temperature in tantalum is a problem, as before, but is soluble with inhibitors such as UO_2 or ThO_2. The short-time breaking strength of tantalum and niobium as a function of temperature is shown in Fig. 5-4. Figure 5-5b shows data on the creep of tantalum as a function of time and temperature for several different values of stress. Typical values of some of the physical properties of these three metals are given in Table 5-1.

The nitrides of W, Ta, Zr, and Nb are generally characterized by extreme brittleness at temperatures below 3000°R and tend to decompose or carburize in the presence of carbon above about 4500°R. In general the nitrides have lower mechanical strength and are less stable at elevated temperatures than are the metallic carbides, and are more difficult to fabricate than the carbides.

Very little information is available on the strength, stability, and other physical characteristics of the refractory borides. What information is available indicates that the borides of W and Zr are stable at least up to 5000°R and can be used as low-strength structural materials (primarily in compression) at this temperature. However, natural boron contains an appreciable fraction of B^{10}, which has an extremely high thermal-neutron-capture cross section; thus refractory borides using natural boron are not suitable for use as reactor-core materials (fuel elements and support structure).

Because of the paucity of data and the unpromising picture outlined by the meager available information, no further consideration is given to the metallic refractory nitrides or borides.

The metallic carbides of W, Ta, Zr, and Nb all appear to have good thermal-shock-resistance characteristics above 4000°R (indicating some ductility) and are relatively stable at high temperature in a hydrogenous reducing atmosphere. The melting points of these materials are above 5600°R with the exception of tungsten carbide, which melts below 5000°R. In particular, NbC has a sufficiently high melting point to be considered for use at or above 6300°R. The effects of addition of fissionable fuel, as UC_2, to these carbides is not known; however, information on the base materials alone suffices for preliminary design purposes, particularly in systems which can be made critical with low relative loadings of fissionable fuel. Pertinent available data on the strength, conductivity, and other physical properties of these materials are summarized in Table 5-1.

MODERATORS AND REFLECTORS. The physical characteristics of some materials useful as moderators are summarized in Table 5-2. For reasons given in the following section the most practical moderator materials are C, Be, or BeO, or one of the many stable compounds of hydrogen and/or deuterium. The physical characteristics of graphite have been summarized in the preceding section and are not repeated here.

Both Be and BeO are good reflector and moderator materials; they are distinguished by differences in density and thermal conductivity. At moderate temperatures ($< 2000°R$), BeO is rather brittle and a relatively poor conductor of heat, like most oxides, while Be metal is fairly ductile and is a better conductor than nickel. These differences become important when considering the problems of removing the heat generated within the moderating material by neutron slowing down and gamma absorption. A simple comparison of moderator materials for use in thermal-stress, heat-removal conditions is possible by use of a parameter $\bar{\sigma}_1$ derived from standard elastic-thermal-stress equations [Eq. (5-3)]. This parameter is listed in Table 5-2 for each material considered. Low values of this parameter indicate good resistance to thermal shock (elastic deformation only). The problem of creep under thermal loading is more fully discussed later in this chapter.

The use of liquid compounds of hydrogen or deuterium, such as hydrocarbons, alcohols, and water, is attractive because no thermal stresses are possible in the liquid and moderator cooling is relatively simple compared to the problems of cooling solid moderators. Use of H_2O or D_2O is hampered by the low liquid boiling point and by the dissociation and recombination which takes place under ionizing radiation (see page 185). High-boiling-point hydrocarbons can be used as moderators, but they suffer radiation damage under prolonged exposure to neutron and gamma fluxes. In general, use of liquid moderators for high-power rocket reactors is most practical in a through-flowing system where the moderator may be the propellant itself. For such use the moderator-propellant must have a sufficiently high heat capacity and heat of vaporization to assure its existence in the liquid state through most of the moderator region. The properties of several potentially useful liquid moderators are given in Table 5-2.

The use of solid moderators implies operation at temperatures sufficiently high to permit the removal of neutron- and gamma-generated heat and requires that the moderator be stable (in respect to radiation damage)

TABLE 5-2. PHYSICAL PROPERTIES OF SOME MODERATOR MATERIALS

Material	Melting point T_m, °R	Boiling point T_b, °R	Sp gr at room temp ρ/ρ_{water}	Short-time tensile strength, lb/in.² σ_a	°R	Young's modulus, 10⁶ lb/in.² E	°R	Mean linear-expansion coef, 10⁶ °F⁻¹ α	°R	Thermal conductivity, Btu/(hr)(ft)(°F) k	°R	Poisson's ratio ν	Thermal-stress parameter[a] $\bar\sigma_1 = \dfrac{\sigma_{th}\,10^4}{\sigma_a q \Psi_2}$ $\bar\sigma_1$	°R
Beryllium, Be	2800	5800	1.85	65,000 30,000 6,000	500 1200 2000	40–43 34–37	500 2000	6 11	500 2000	85 54	500 1500	0.01–0.10	0.48 13.5	500 2000
Beryllium oxide, BeO	5050	8150	2.7	15,000 7,000–13,000 2,000–8,000 1,000–4,000	500 2000 2500 2700	40 30 10	500 2500 2700	3 6	500 2400	53 21 8.5	500 1500 3000	0.35	2.32 18.5	500 2000
Graphite, C	7000[b]		1.65–1.85	2,000–4,000 2,500–5,000	500 2000	0.4⊥,[c] 1.2∥ 0.5⊥, 1.3∥	500 2000	3⊥,[c] 1∥ 4⊥, 2∥	500 2000	18–36∥,[c] 30–50⊥	2000	0.2–0.3	0.067 0.31	500 2000
Zirconium hydride, ZrH₂	…[d]		5.6											
Heavy water, D₂O	460	670	1.10							0.35	500			
Cyclohexane,[e] C₆H₁₂	470	610	0.78							0.08–0.12	500			
Ammonia, NH₃	350	430	0.68[f]							0.29	500			

[a] $\dfrac{\sigma_{th}}{\sigma_a} = q\Psi_2 \dfrac{\alpha E}{\sigma_a k(1 - \nu)}$; see Eq. (5-3).

[b] Sublimes.

[c] ⊥ and ∥ indicate properties perpendicular and parallel to grain orientation, respectively.

[d] Decomposes; see Fig. 5-6.

[e] Values given are typical of liquid hydrocarbons with gross composition of $(CH_2)_n$.

[f] Density at 430°R; see Fig. 2-14.

in a radiation field. For these reasons solid hydrocarbons do not seem attractive as moderating materials. However the metallic hydrides of Ce and Zr are potentially suitable for use at moderately high temperature, especially under high overpressure of hydrogen gas as will be the case in nearly all useful rocket reactors. These metallic hydrides tend to decompose, losing hydrogen at temperatures above 1500°R, thus becoming less and less useful as moderators with increasing temperature. The hydro-

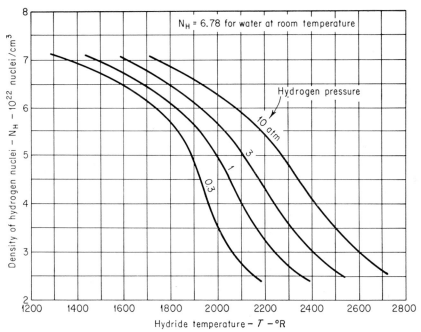

FIG. 5-6. Hydrogen density in zirconium hydride.

gen content of zirconium hydride is shown in Fig. 5-6 as a function of temperature and hydrogen overpressure.[3] The chief disadvantage of these metallic hydrides is their high density—compared to C, Be, or D_2O, for example—resulting in heavier reactors for the same degree of neutron thermalization.

CONTROL ELEMENTS. Since the principal requirement for reactor control materials is that they be good neutron absorbers, the choice of these materials is determined primarily by nuclear considerations. Compounds of B, Cd, Gd, and Eu are of major interest. Boron is available as a metal, a carbide, in alloyed form with other metals such as copper, and in dispersed-carbide form with aluminum as Boral sheet and plate. The carbide, B_4C, can be formed into various shapes from powder by hot pressing and sintering operations. It possesses good dimensional stability up to at least 3500°R and has a fair thermal conductivity. Cadmium is historically interesting because it was used to control the world's first fission reactor, in 1942, at the University of Chicago. It has often been used as the pure metal, but offers promise for use in solid or liquid compounds such as cadmium borotungstate and dimethyl-cadmium. Gadolinium and europium are chiefly available as oxides; as such they can be formed into reactor control rods by metal cladding, using swaging techniques to produce a tight compact such as is commercially produced in the manufacture of electric-resistance heating elements used in present-day electric ranges. The physical characteristics of some of these materials are given in Table 5-3.

TABLE 5-3. PHYSICAL PROPERTIES OF SOME CONTROL-ELEMENT MATERIALS

Material	Melting point T_m, °R	Sp gr at room temp ρ/ρ_{water}	Short-time tensile strength, lb/in.²		Young's modulus, 10⁶ lb/in.²		Mean linear-expansion coef, 10^{-6} °F⁻¹		Thermal conductivity, Btu/(hr)(ft)(°F)		Poisson's ratio ν
			σ_a	°R	E	°R	α	°R	k	°R	
Boron, B.......	4100–4600	2.3	36,000*	500	....	...	4.6	1800			
Boron carbide, B₄C	4700–4950	2.5	10,000	500	....	...	2.6	1900	70	500	
			22,500	2250					54	1250	
									35	2000	
Cadmium, Cd..	1050	8.65	7,000–12,000	500	7–10	500	17.7	600	53	500	0.3
									27	1250	
Gadolinium oxide, Gd₂O₃	....	7.4									
Hafnium, Hf...	4300	13.4	70,000	500	14	500	3.3	2250			
			43,000	1100							

* Compressive strength only.

STRUCTURE COMPONENTS. Some materials for use as high-temperature structural components have already been discussed for use as fuel-element base materials. Structural metals suitable for use at low temperatures (<1000°R) or when cooled in a high-temperature environment are of more direct interest here. Aside from simple strength considerations, the choice of a structural material for pressure-shell or other low-temperature reactor-component use must consider the gamma-heating and heat-removal problem. The volumetric rate of heating in a given gamma flux is roughly directly proportional to the material density. The internal temperature difference is proportional to the volume heat-generation rate and the square of some characteristic thickness (heat-removal path) of the component divided by the thermal conductivity of the material. For the pressure shell and many other structures this thickness is inversely proportional to the material yield strength. Combining these dependencies, an expression for internal temperature difference induced in a gamma field can be obtained as proportional to the ratio of material density to thermal conductivity, all divided by the square of the strength. The induced elastic thermal stress is proportional to the product of Young's modulus, the expansion coefficient of the material, and the induced internal temperature difference. Using this, a general parameter $\bar{\sigma}_2$ for comparison of structural materials on a thermal-stress basis for use in a gamma-radiation field can be obtained as

$$\frac{\sigma_{th}}{\sigma_y} \propto \frac{\alpha E \rho}{(1 - \nu)k\sigma_y{}^3} = \frac{\bar{\sigma}_2}{10^{11}} \qquad (5\text{-}1)$$

where σ_{th} = induced thermal stress
σ_y = material yield strength
α = coefficient of thermal expansion
E = Young's modulus
k = conductivity
ρ = density
ν = Poisson's ratio for the material

Low values of this parameter indicate desirable behavior in a gamma-radiation field. Table 5-4 tabulates values of this parameter together with various pertinent physical properties of several potentially useful structural metals. Note from the table that high-strength, high-conductivity aluminum alloys are superior to such conventional high-temperature materials as alloy steels or Inconel X for use at low temperatures, as would prevail in liquid-propellant-cooled structures. Note also that the high-strength titanium alloy shown in Table 5-4 is superior to all the other materials for structural applications up to 1000°R in a gamma-radiation field.

Nuclear Characteristics. FUEL ELEMENTS. For predominantly thermal reactors the thermal-neutron-capture cross sections of fuel-element base materials are of importance in comparing different materials for such use. Values of the microscopic and macroscopic (at normal material density) thermal-absorption cross section are given in Table 5-5 for a variety of fuel-element materials which appear interesting on the basis of the physical-properties evaluation of the preceding section. Note that the macroscopic thermal-absorption cross section of tungsten is about 3,000 times that for graphite. Also important, especially for thermal reactors, is the resonance-absorption probability or cross section for neutrons slowing down from fission energy to thermal. This cross section is an "effective" cross section suitable for use in two-group reactor neutronic calculations for estimation of the probability that a fission neutron will be captured before being thermalized (also see Chap. 6).

TABLE 5-4. PHYSICAL PROPERTIES OF SOME STRUCTURAL MATERIALS

Material	Melting point T_m, °R	Sp gr at room temp ρ/ρ_{water}	Short-time tensile strength, lb/in.² σ_a	°R	Yield strength, lb/in.² σ_y	°R	Stress for 1% creep in 10^4 hr, lb/in.² σ_c	°R	Young's modulus, 10^6 lb/in.² E	°R	Mean linear-expansion coef, 10^{-6} °F⁻¹ α	°R	Thermal conductivity, Btu/(hr)(ft)(°F) k	°R	Poisson's ratio ν	Thermal-stress parameter for gamma-heated structures* $\bar\sigma_2$	°R
Aluminum, 2S0	1650	2.71	13,000 7,000 3,000	500 850 1050	5,000 3,000 1,800	500 850 1050	3,000– 4,000†	850	10 8	500 1000	11 14	500 1000	128 122	500 1000	0.33	175 2,700	500 1000
Aluminum, 17S-T4	1400	2.79	60,000 24,000 7,500	500 850 1050	50,000 17,500 5,000	500 850 1050	18,000†	850	10.5 8.4	500 1000	11 14	500 1000	70 84	500 1000	0.33	0.34 100	500 1000
Stainless steel, type 316	2950	7.92	76,000 71,000 25,000	500 1350 2000	31,000 22,000 17,000	500 1350 2000	24,000– 3,000	1500 2000	29 24.5 21.3	500 1350 2000	8.9 9.6 10.9	650 1550 2250	8.5 12.1	650 1350	0.29	72 95	500 1000
Stainless steel, type 430	3100	7.70	67,000 48,500 6,000	500 1350 2000	35,000 28,500 2,000– 3,000	500 1350 2000	7,000– 800	1500 2000	29 25 18	500 1350 2000	5.6 5.8 6.7	650 1550 2250	13.8 14.7	650 1350	0.29	18 29	500 1000
Titanium, Ti-150A	3350	4.64	152,000 93,000 40,000	500 1000 1500	140,000 69,000 26,000	500 1000 1500	50,000– 70,000 10,000– 20,000	850 1250	16 11	500 1500	4.7–5	500–2000	8.2–9.9	500	‡	0.14 0.94	500 1000
Inconel X	2900–3050	8.3	164,000 136,000 64,000	500 1500 2000	102,000 84,000 54,000	500 1500 2000	35,000– 13,000	1800 2000	 11		7.5 9.2	500 2000	8.3–9.4 20	500 2000	‡	1.8 1.7	500 1000
Inconel	3000	8.5	90,000 80,000 18,000	500 1500 2000	36,500 27,500 11,000	500 1500 2000	57,000 19,000– 1,000– 2,000	1250 1500 2000	31 25 15	500 1500 2000	6.4	650	8.7–9.4 13	500 2000	‡	34 47	500 1000

* $\dfrac{\sigma_{th}}{\sigma_y} \propto \dfrac{\alpha E \rho}{\sigma_y{}^3 k (1-\nu)} = \dfrac{\bar\sigma_2}{10^{11}}$; see Eq. (5-1).

† Creep strength for 1 per cent creep in 10^3 hr.

‡ No data available, but values for most metals lie between 0.25 and 0.35.

TABLE 5-5. NUCLEAR PROPERTIES OF SOME FUEL-ELEMENT BASE MATERIALS

Material	Density at room temp ρ, gm/cm³	Atomic or molecular weight A	Atomic or molecular density N, atoms/cm³ or molecules/cm³	Microscopic thermal-absorption cross section σ_a, barns/atom or barns/molecule	Macroscopic thermal-absorption cross section Σ_a, cm⁻¹	Approximate resonance-absorption integral σ_{RI}, *† barns/atom or barns/molecule	Effective microscopic resonance-absorption cross section σ_{ra},‡ barns/atom or barns/molecule	Macroscopic resonance-absorption cross section Σ_{ra},‡ cm⁻¹
Graphite, C	1.65	12.0	0.083×10^{24}	4.5×10^{-3}	3.7×10^{-4}	0	0	0
Tungsten, W	19.1	183.9	0.0625×10^{24}	19	1.19	450	31	1.94
Rhenium, Re	20.5	186.3	0.0662×10^{24}	84	0.56	650	45	2.97
Tantalum, Ta	16.6	180.9	0.0552×10^{24}	21	1.16	500	35	1.93
Molybdenum, Mo	10.2	96	0.064×10^{24}	2.4	0.15	16	1.1	0.07
Niobium, Nb	8.6	92.9	0.0556×10^{24}	1.1	0.061	4	0.28	0.016
Niobium carbide, NbC	7.8	104.9	0.0448×10^{24}	1.1	0.049	4	0.28	0.013
Tantalum carbide:								
TaC	14.5	192.9	0.0453×10^{24}	21	0.95	500	35	1.59
Ta₂C	15.1	373.8	0.0243×10^{24}	42	1.02	1,000	70	1.70
Zirconium carbide, ZrC	6.8	103.2	0.0396×10^{24}	0.185	7.3×10^{-3}	3	0.2	0.008
Tungsten carbide:								
WC	15.6	195.9	0.0479×10^{24}	19	0.91	450	31	1.48
W₂C	17.2	379.8	0.0273×10^{24}	38	1.04	900	62	1.69

* The resonance-absorption integral given is defined by $\sigma_{RI} = \int_{u_0}^{u} \sigma_a(u)\,du = \sigma_{ra}(u - u_0)$.

† See also R. A. Charpie et al. (eds.), "Physics and Mathematics," chap. 6 (R. L. Macklin and H. S. Pomerance, Resonance Capture Integrals), McGraw-Hill Progress in Nuclear Energy Series, ser. I, vol. 1, McGraw-Hill Book Company, Inc., New York, 1956.

‡ Averaged over the energy range from 0.5 ev to 1.0 Mev ($u - u_0 = 14.5$).

Both W and Ta have a large number of resonances in the epithermal regions, resulting in high values of resonance-absorption cross section for both materials. These are tabulated in Table 5-5. Since, in both cases, the resonance-absorption cross section is quite a bit higher than the thermal-absorption cross section, it is not practical to consider the use of W or Ta as semihomogeneously distributed fuel materials. In fact, from a neutron standpoint, efficient use of either of these materials as fuel elements requires lumping of structure in a moderator matrix so that thermalization of neutrons can take place with very little epithermal resonance absorption by the fuel-element base material. Here we see that the choice of fuel-element material cannot be made independently of reactor geometry, and vice versa, for W and Ta are best suited for use in moderated matrix cores while C, which has a low atomic weight and is thus a good moderator, can be used either homogeneously or in a matrix geometry. The thermal- and resonance-absorption cross sections of Nb and Zr are low compared to those of W and Ta. As a consequence, these metals can be used in rather large quantities in reactor cores without undue neutron-poisoning effects. Neither Nb nor Zr is useful for a fuel element as a pure metal, but both elements form high-melting-point carbides which are capable of neutron moderation.

MODERATORS AND REFLECTORS. Among the elements only H and its isotopes, He, Li, Be, B, and C are low enough in atomic weight to be considered as moderators. Of these few, Li and B are ruled out because of excessive neutron absorption and He is not practical because of its low density. Thus the choice of moderators is reduced to C, Be or BeO, or one of the many stable compounds of hydrogen or deuterium.

Carbon is only a mediocre reflector or moderator; it is required in about twice as great a thickness as beryllium for neutron thermalization. However, graphite has good strength and thermal-conductivity characteristics at high temperatures and thus can be used as a moderating fuel carrier up to about 5000°R. Be and BeO are both good reflectors and good moderators, entirely because of the low atomic weight of Be. The oxygen in the BeO neither contributes to nor detracts from neutron thermalization and conservation, since the O atom is too heavy to moderate very well and has such a low absorption cross section that few neutrons are lost by oxygen capture. The Be density in BeO is less than that of metallic Be; therefore BeO is not as good a moderator on a volume-and-weight basis as is Be metal. D_2O is also a good moderator and reflector material, being about intermediate between BeO and Be metal in thermalization per unit thickness. Deuterium is particularly good because of its very low neutron-absorption cross section. Because of its single-proton mass, hydrogen is an excellent moderator, but is a poor neutron reflector because of the high *forward scattering* taking place in neutron-proton collisons. This forward scattering results in a preferential motion of the scattered neutron in the direction it was following before collision with the H proton, resulting in a high transport of neutrons away from the reactor core when H is used as a reflector. Hydrogen also has a rather high thermal-neutron-absorption cross section, relative to the other moderators of prime interest, which makes it suitable for use only in sections thick enough to thermalize but not absorb neutrons.

Liquid hydrogen, whose H density is only slightly less than that of water, is an obvious candidate for consideration as a moderator. At its low temperature the thermal-neutron-scattering cross section is much larger than at room temperature (following roughly a $1/v$ law); hence scattering collisions take place more frequently, thus shortening the thermal diffusion length to absorption from about one centimeter to a few millimeters. This results in neutron absorption at almost the same point in the liquid as that at which the neutron reached thermal (liquid) energy. Thus fast neutrons being thermalized in liquid hydrogen never escape but are absorbed by the hydrogen itself. This phenomenon is called *thermal trapping* of neutrons and is obviously very undesirable. For this reason liquid hydrogen alone is a poor choice for a moderator.

As one of the hydrogen compounds, H_2O (light water) is of interest as a moderator, but it is inferior to D_2O (heavy water) by virtue of the high absorption and forward scattering associated with the use of H. Many hydrocarbons, both solid and liquid, exist and can be used as moderators. As previously mentioned, obvious choices are those which are potential liquid propellants, such as C_3H_8, C_8H_{18}, and $(CH_2)_n$. Most of these compounds have hydrogen densities somewhat less than that of water but have an additional moderating capability due to the C present in the molecule. Also of interest are the alcohols, which differ only slightly from hydrocarbons in moderating ability because the addition of oxygen to the molecule has little effect on neutron slowing down or capture. The potential propellants NH_3 and N_2H_4 can also be considered as moderators. The hydrogen density in each of these compounds is comparable to that in the liquid hydrocarbons mentioned above, but unfortunately the high thermal-absorption cross section of N^{14} will about triple neutron absorption in the moderator material, resulting in increased critical mass over that attainable in a hydrocarbon-moderated system.

Other hydrogen compounds, such as the metallic hydrides of Zr and Ce, are valuable as moderators only in proportion to their hydrogen density. For this reason careful analysis of the decomposition of these compounds with increasing temperature is extremely important if they are to be used as cooled structural moderators operating at a moderate temperature in a high-temperature reactor core.

Two simple parameters which are useful in comparing materials for

TABLE 5-6. NUCLEAR PROPERTIES OF SOME MODERATOR MATERIALS

Material	Density at room temp ρ, gm/cm^3	Atomic or molecular weight A	Average log energy change per scattering collision ξ	Atomic or molecular density N, atoms/cm^3 or molecules/cm^3	Microscopic epithermal scattering cross section $\sigma_{s,epi}$, barns/atom or barns/molecule	Microscopic thermal-absorption cross section $\sigma_{a,th}$, barns/atom or barns/molecule	Macroscopic epithermal scattering cross section $\Sigma_{s,epi}$, cm^{-1}	Macroscopic thermal-absorption cross section $\Sigma_{a,th}$, cm^{-1}	Slowing-down power $\xi\Sigma_{s,epi}$, cm^{-1}	Moderating ratio $\xi\Sigma_{s,epi}/\Sigma_{a,th}$
Beryllium, Be	1.85	9.0	0.208	0.124×10^{24}	6.0	0.009	0.74	1.1×10^{-3}	0.155	141
Beryllium oxide, BeO	2.70	25.0	0.172	0.065×10^{24}	9.8	0.0092	0.64	6.0×10^{-4}	0.11	183
Graphite, C	1.65	12.0	0.158	0.083×10^{24}	4.8	0.0045	0.40	3.7×10^{-4}	0.063	170
Zirconium hydride, ZrH_2	5.63	93.2	0.88	0.0364×10^{24}	50.3	0.84	1.83	3.1×10^{-2}	1.61	52
Heavy water, D_2O (0.25% H_2O)	1.10	20.0	0.51	0.0331×10^{24}	10.6	0.0026	0.35	8.6×10^{-5}	0.18	2,090
Cyclohexane, C_6H_{12}	0.78	84.2	0.92	0.00557×10^{24}	293	3.99	1.63	2.2×10^{-2}	1.50	68
Ammonia, NH_3	0.68	17.0	0.90	0.0241×10^{24}	76	2.77	1.83	6.7×10^{-2}	1.65	24.6

use as moderators are the *slowing-down power* and the *moderating ratio*. The first of these is a measure of the fractional neutron energy loss per unit path length occurring in scattering collisions in the epithermal energy range. This is also inversely proportional to the total random-walk distance a neutron must travel from birth at fission energies to thermal, given by the product of the number of collisions required to thermalize and the mean free path per scattering collision. The second parameter is the ratio of the slowing-down power to the absorption probability per collision. This is useful in comparing materials on the basis of relative probabilities that a fission neutron will ever reach thermal in an infinite medium of the material of interest. These parameters, as well as other pertinent information, are tabulated in Table 5-6.

CONTROL ELEMENTS. The control materials of prime interest, B, Cd, Gd, and Eu, all have high thermal-neutron-capture cross sections. This alone does not describe them sufficiently to indicate the problems or advantages associated with their use as neutron-control materials in high-temperature reactor cores. Since a nuclear rocket reactor must be capable of critical operation at room temperature and at high temperature (5000°R), it is necessary to examine the *variation* of capture and fission cross sections of the materials within the reactor over this possible wide variation in neutron thermal base (0.025 to 0.25 ev). Of course, in cooled matrix-geometry, hydrogen-moderated cores the neutron temperature will not change significantly over the complete temperature operating range of the lumped fuel elements; hence cross-section changes with varying neutron energy are of little importance. However, in a homogeneous, core-moderated reactor the neutron temperature will closely follow the core fuel-element temperature, and cross-section variations become important. The U^{235} fission and capture cross sections fall slightly faster than $1/\sqrt{T}$ up to about 0.2 ev, then go through a slight resonance to about 0.3 ev and continue falling up to a few electron volts or so. This variation in monoenergetic U^{235} fission and absorption cross sections is shown in Fig. 5-7. Also shown is the variation in the ratio of capture to fission cross sections for monoenergetic neutrons. Thermal neutrons are not monoenergetic, however, but are distributed approximately in a Maxwell-Boltzmann distribution; thus cross sections for use with thermal-neutron groups must be averaged over such a distribution. Figure 5-8 shows such Maxwellian-averaged fission and absorption cross sections. Unfortunately the absorption cross sections of many other core materials such as C, W, and Nb do not decrease as rapidly with increasing neutron temperature as does that of U^{235}. This fact ensures that a cold critical reactor core will become less and less critical as the neutron thermal-base energy is increased. In order to compensate for this change in large,

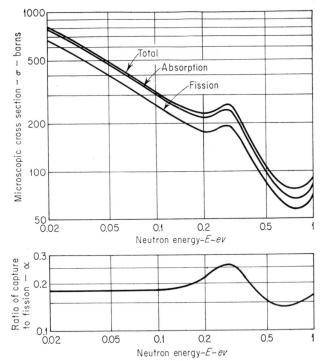

FIG. 5-7. Cross sections of U^{235} for monoenergetic neutrons.

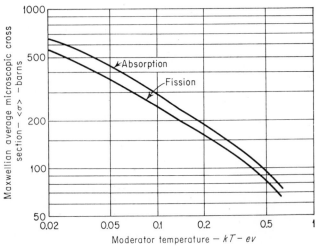

FIG. 5-8. Maxwell-average cross sections of U^{235} for neutrons in thermal equilibrium with moderator material.

highly thermal reactors, it would be desirable to load the core with a material whose absorption cross section fell off more rapidly with temperature than does that of U^{235}. Gd and Eu are such materials and thus appear potentially useful as reactivity-temperature *shims* to permit the operation of homogeneous, core-moderated reactors over a wide temperature range without use of excessively large movable control rods.

For control rods it is desirable that the neutron-absorption characteristics of the rod material be relatively insensitive to neutron temperature, so that the rod has the same total control "worth" at any condition of core operation. For this reason Gd and Eu are not as attractive for control-rod materials as are B and Cd, whose absorption characteristics vary less widely with neutron temperature. Despite this variation, the high total-capture cross sections of Gd and Eu at temperatures below 5000°R indicate that they could be used to make very effective small, lightweight control rods. The monoenergetic-capture cross sections of Gd, Eu, B, and Cd are shown in Fig. 5-9 as a function of neutron thermal base temperature (energy). Proper control-rod design requires use of cross sections averaged over the Maxwellian distribution of thermal neutron energies.

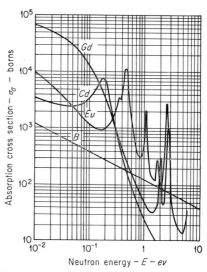

FIG. 5-9. Absorption cross section of various control elements for monoenergetic neutrons.

Thermal-neutron absorption in boron, where B^{10} is the principal absorber, results in the formation of a Li^7 nucleus and an α particle (He nucleus) for each neutron absorbed. Experiments have shown that almost all of the He produced in this fashion is retained, trapped in the boron itself for low burnup irradiation of boron control rods.[4] Thus, although boron "fissions" by neutron capture and produces a gaseous product, it is mechanically as stable under neutron irradiation as are the other absorbers mentioned, all of which produce nongaseous β or γ emitters. For high burnup (greater than a few per cent) boron carbide spalls and disintegrates, while boron steels become embrittled. (See page 186 for further discussion.)

From the standpoint of control-rod heating it is better to use a poison which yields γ emitters than one which produces β or α emitters. Alpha particles, massive and charged, lose their energy by charge interaction in the material immediately surrounding the point of their birth. Beta rays (electrons) also lose most of their energy close to the point of production, but are somewhat more penetrating than alpha particles. On the other hand, gamma rays are extremely penetrating and spread their energy out over many cubic centimeters of volume away from their birthplace. For this reason γ-emitting neutron absorbers are easier to cool when used as control-rod materials than are α or β emitters.

STRUCTURAL COMPONENTS. The nuclear characteristics of interest for structural materials are the gamma-absorption coefficients and the neutron-capture or -activation cross sections. Gamma-absorption coefficients are needed to estimate gamma heating in structural materials and are given in Chap. 6, together with a detailed discussion of methods of analysis of gamma- and neutron-heating problems. Neutron-capture cross sections are required for the estimation of neutron activation of structural materials such as those used in the pressure shell, nozzle, flanges, etc. Material activation will always be primarily by thermal-neutron-capture production of an unstable heavier nuclide. Thermal-neutron-capture cross sections are given in the Chart of the Nuclides (Fig. A-1), together with the decay characteristics of the various radioactive nuclei produced by such capture. Calculation of the activation of alloys, such as stainless steel or Inconel, shows that important residual activity often results from neutron capture by an alloying constituent which is present only in a small amount in the alloy. Further information on materials for use in test stands, missile frames, and other structures external to the reactor pressure shell is given in Chap. 8.

Interaction Effects. It is evident that not all of the possible combinations of propellant, materials, and geometry are equally compatible. Therefore, to achieve an optimum system the choice of any single characteristic cannot really be made without consideration of its effect on the other elements of the reactor system.

Because of their low boiling points and heats of vaporization, the primary cryogenic propellants, H_2 and CH_4, present difficult problems for use as liquid moderators, thus restricting their use to coolants for solid-moderator systems. The problems of solid-moderator coolant-system design are more easily and surely solved if the moderator is in large block volumes; thus it is concluded that the cryogenic propellants are not well suited for use in heterogeneous matrix cores but could best be used in solid-reflector-moderated systems. On the other hand the room-temperature hydrocarbons, ammonia, and hydrazine are well suited for use in liquid-hydrogenous-moderator systems, but because of their absorption characteristics could be used best as such only in heterogeneous-core geometries.

The choice of geometry and materials fixes reactor critical mass and determines the nonuniformities in fuel loading required to flatten the fission density distribution normal to the coolant flow (Chap. 6). These, in turn, determine the maximum fuel concentration required, which may be a limiting characteristic of the fuel-element material previously chosen. Reflected homogeneous cylindrical cores may require higher critical mass than hydrogenous matrices, but the maximum uranium concentration needed for fission density flattening could be higher in the matrix geometry. This results from the potentially greater fuel-loading nonuniformities associated with heterogeneous matrices than for homogeneous cores.

From the practical standpoint the choice of fuel-element material will influence the choice of "best" core geometry. The epithermal-capture cross sections of W and Ta indicate they are most useful in a core-moderated, matrix-geometry, lumped-metal-fuel-element system. Moderation in such a heterogeneous core can most easily be accomplished by use of a room-temperature hydrogenous propellant; thus metal fuel elements naturally lead toward use of liquid-propellant moderators and matrix-geometry, lumped-fuel cores.

Graphite can be used in either homogeneous or heterogeneous systems. It is a sufficiently good moderator so that nearly entirely self-moderating thermal cores are possible in large reactor sizes such as those with core diameters of 4 ft or larger. For use in smaller, lower-power systems, graphite fuel elements may require appreciable external moderation to achieve criticality without excessively high fuel loadings.

The choice of core geometry and flow scheme also has a profound effect on the physical dimensions and heat-transfer characteristics of the fuel elements. Axial flow systems with full-core-length passages lead to relatively high Reynolds number flows and result in large flow-path widths. Heterogeneous geometries with radial flow through the fuel elements are characterized by short flow paths, low Reynolds number flows, and small passage widths.

High Reynolds number flows result in relatively high pressure drops and large wall-to-gas temperature differences. Both the pressure drop and required temperature potential decrease with decreasing Reynolds number, assuming core structure is increased or varied in such a way as to retain a roughly constant heat-transfer rate per unit core volume. Design in the lowest range of flow, the laminar regime, can result in insignificant fuel-element pressure drops and required temperature potentials. For such systems the inlet- and outlet-header flow design becomes of great importance to assure the proper distribution of coolant to each section of fuel element. Investigations of the characteristics of laminar flow with heat addition have concluded that such flow has inherent instabilities under certain temperature and flow-rate conditions; however, stability may be achieved by use of flow resistances properly located in the flow path. Turbulent flow with heat addition appears to be inherently stable. A more thorough discussion of the stability problem is given in Chap. 4. From the fabrication standpoint large fuel-element dimensions are more desirable than small, since larger fabrication errors can be tolerated for a given allowable resultant nonuniformity in flow.

As discussed in Chap. 6, it is considerably easier to calculate the fission distribution in a homogeneous core with uniform fuel and material densities than in a reactor which utilizes fuel-density variations to achieve some desired fission distribution. Therefore, in principle, it would seem easier to match the coolant flow and fission heat generation in a homogeneous core by adjusting only the coolant flow, which is under the complete control of the designer (e.g., by means of orifices, coolant-passage sizes, etc.). The fallacy in this argument is that the adjustment of coolant flow to match the simply computed fission distribution, by the use of cooling holes of different diameters at different radii in a cylindrical core, for example, will generally require variations in local material density and probably also in fuel density distribution throughout the reactor. The calculation of fission distribution in such a core is at least as complex and difficult, and probably more so, as a calculation made for a core with uniform material density with a varying fuel distribution, as is required for variation of fission distribution by means of varying fuel density. For this reason it is almost always simpler to design for a combination of uniform coolant flow and uniform fission density distribution, resulting in the use of coolant passages of constant size distributed evenly over the reactor core. The practical advantages in construction of such a reactor over one requiring varying coolant-passage dimensions are evident.

5-3. Special Problems. The general requirements for fuel elements, moderators, control elements, and structural components have been outlined in the preceding sections. In addition, tables and figures showing some physical and nuclear characteristics of many potentially useful materials have been given. In this section the three most important problems unique to nuclear rocket-reactor structures are considered and discussed at some length. In order of importance these three problems are thermal strain and stress, corrosion and erosion, and radiation effects on materials.

Thermal Strain and Stress. The structures comprising a nuclear reactor act as volume heat sources whether or not the fissionable fuel is loaded uniformly through the core-fuel-element base material. This is the result of volumetric absorption of energy from γ and β rays and fast neutrons produced in the fission process. Practically speaking, the fissionable fuel is most often distributed through the fuel-element volume, thus assuring that the reactor fuel elements themselves operate at the highest volumetric power-generation rate. If the reactor is not to melt, energy deposited in the volume of a structure must be removed by coolant flowing over the structure surfaces. Heat flow through the solid volume is by conduction; thus reactor structures will have temperature gradients induced internally. These temperature gradients give rise to differential expansions of adjacent parts of the same structure, causing distortions or strains. A material under forced distortion of this sort is in a state of stress. In addition to differential distortion within single structures, it will often develop that separate structures within the same reactor will of necessity operate at different average temperatures and hence will expand differentially, resulting in stresses due to mutual interference and constraint. An example of this latter difficulty is exhibited by a reactor designed so that a relatively cold (e.g., 2000°R) cylindrical reflector must contain a very hot (e.g., 5000°R) core. If the core reflector assembly is "tight" at room temperature, when the reactor is assembled, much mutual interference and stressing will result when operation is at design temperature. On the other hand, if the design is such that no interference occurs at high temperature, then the core will be loose and tend to rattle around inside the reflector at room temperature. Mechanical expedients such as spring supports and flexible containers can be used to alleviate the difficulties of the example cited; however, it will often be found impossible to provide free movement for all reactor component parts over their entire temperature operating range. Thus "thermal" stresses arise.

When computed on an elastic basis, the magnitude of such stresses, especially for the fuel elements of a high-power-density reactor core, is often much greater than the allowable "breaking" strength of the material of interest. For such a condition the piece will either break or relieve the induced stress by plastic flow or creep. The structural analysis of a reactor core or core fuel element thus becomes an analysis of a time-varying, stress-strain situation which changes with the changing conditions of reactor operation during start-up, steady-state operation, and shutdown. It is evident that there are as many different possible stress-strain conditions for a given design as there are possible time variations in reactor operating conditions, and thus no valid general analysis is possible. Rather, it is useful first to examine several isolated idealized-structure geometries to determine the elastic stress-strain conditions which would prevail in the absence of creep, and second to study the effects of temperature and material deformation on the relief of the thermally induced stresses. It should be noted that, for instantaneous thermal loading of plastic materials, the resulting stresses should be computed from elastic theory.

In the design of rocket reactors it will be found that structure stresses pass through a peak value at some time for any given reactor operating sequence. Past this time the stresses in the piece of interest decrease and will not reach or exceed the previous peak value until the operating sequence is reversed or repeated. In general, in a single cycle of thermal straining, the piece will fail only if the peak combined thermal and load stresses on the piece exceed the breaking or rupture strength somewhere within the volume or on the surface of the piece. For repeated cycling the situation is quite different; failure in such a case is most often by a kind of fatigue cracking of the material due to repeated, reversed plastic flow. The limitations on design for repeated cycling are much less clear and well founded, at the present time, than are those for single-cycle operation. Much work has been done in connection with thermal fatigue for hundreds and thousands of cycles, as might occur in the rotating machinery or the refuelable reactor of a ground-based nuclear power plant. Roughly, this work indicates that allowable material strains for repeated cyclic straining are of the order of one-fourth to one-half of those allowable for single-cycle operation as outlined above.[5]

Of necessity, the designers of ground-based power plants lean heavily to conservatism, principally for reasons of economics and assured long operating life. Such considerations do not play strong roles in rocket-reactor design, where technical performance is of prime importance and all else is secondary. Clearly, a flight-type reactor will be flown only once, since it will destroy itself by decay heat after in-flight shutdown, and thus can be designed by single-cycle thermal-stresss-and-strain criteria. However, a test reactor may be required to operate over many cycles and many different types of operating sequence and so must be designed more conservatively than by the single-cycle criteria. Paradoxically it is more difficult to design test- than flight-type rocket reactors. It has been found that this paradox generally holds for other nonrocket types of reactors, for in a reactor development program it is often harder to design the component tests to prove the reactor design than it is to design the reactor itself. In any event, design for repeated reactor operation need consider only some 20 to 40 cycles, at most, for rocket test-reactor purposes. In view of the number of cycles and the paucity of data on thermal fatigue failure under few cycles at high temperature, it is suggested that the designer be guided by the criteria of failure for single-cycle operation tempered by the experimental observation that a reduction of 2 to 4 in allowable strain is required for successful cyclic operation. For clarity these criteria are repeated here:

1. In single-cycle use, a reactor component piece will fail if the combined load stress and peak (in time) thermally induced stress exceeds the rupture strength of the material somewhere within the piece, *or* if the total peak local distortion (strain) exceeds the allowable elongation to failure at the temperature of interest.

2. For cyclic duty, the allowable maximum strain is from one-fourth to one-half of that permitted for single-cycle use as described above, and the allowable internal stresses are correspondingly reduced.

Much excellent work on this subject has appeared in the literature in recent years and should be consulted for a more thorough and illuminating discussion of the present problems and confusion in this field. The work of Shanley[6] and Higgins[7] and that of Dorn and Shepard,[8] as well as the text by Freudenthal,[9] provide a particularly valuable picture of stress-strain-time relations for materials subjected to high temperatures and large internal temperature gradients.

The structures which make up a reactor core are often unsymmetrical and complex in shape and not subject to simple mathematical analyses for heat conduction, temperature and stress distribution, and load and thermal distortion conditions. However it is generally possible to predict the approximate behavior of such structures by study of the characteristics of spheres, rods, tubes, or plates, or some combination of these joined by equipotential surfaces, such as isothermal, isostress, or isostrain surfaces, under similar environmental conditions. A summary of previous analyses of this type[10,11] is presented, but no attempt is made to demonstrate the mathematical manipulations required to obtain the formulas given. In every case it is assumed that energy is deposited uniformly throughout the volume of the solid, is conducted to the cooled surface, and is transferred to the external coolant. The thermal conductivity, coefficient of expansion, and modulus of elasticity of the material are assumed constant throughout the solid volume. For these conditions it is found that the temperature distribution can be expressed by an equation of the form

$$\Delta T = T - T_s = \Psi_1 \frac{q}{k} \tag{5-2}$$

where q = volume rate of heat generation
k = thermal conductivity
T_s = surface temperature
and Ψ_1 is a function only of the geometry of interest. Similarly the elastic or "zero time" thermal stress is given by

$$\sigma_{th} = \Psi_2 \frac{\alpha E}{1 - \nu} \frac{q}{k} = \frac{q\Psi_2}{10^4} \sigma_a \bar{\sigma}_1 \tag{5-3}$$

where α = coefficient of expansion
E = Young's modulus
ν = Poisson's ratio
σ_a = short-time tensile strength of the material
$\bar{\sigma}_1$ = thermal-stress parameter useful in material evaluation (see Tables 5-1 and 5-2)
and Ψ_2 is a function only of the system geometry. For convenience, the

equations for Ψ_1 and Ψ_2 are given for each case of interest. For reference purposes, curves showing the variation of Ψ_2, normalized to the length parameter pertinent to the system, are presented for some cases in Figs. 5-10 to 5-15. Here, negative stress indicates compression; positive is tension. These curves are simply dimensionless representations of the stress distributions in the particular systems of interest.

SPHERES. Consider a solid sphere of outer radius b and a hollow sphere of outer radius b and inner radius a cooled only on the outer surface. The geometrical parameters are

$$\Psi_{1_s} = \frac{b^2 - r^2}{6} \quad \text{for solid sphere} \tag{5-4}$$

$$\Psi_{1_h} = \frac{b^2 - r^2}{6} - \frac{a^3}{3}\left(\frac{1}{r} - \frac{1}{b}\right) \quad \text{for hollow sphere} \tag{5-5}$$

$$\Psi_{2_s} = \frac{r^2 - b^2}{15} \quad \text{for radial stress in solid sphere} \tag{5-6a}$$

$$\Psi_{2_s} = \frac{2r^2 - b^2}{15} \quad \text{for tangential stress in solid sphere} \tag{5-6b}$$

$$\Psi_{2_h} = \frac{2(r^3 - a^3)}{3r^3(b^3 - a^3)}\left(\frac{b^5}{15} - \frac{a^3 b^2}{3} + \frac{3a^5}{5} - \frac{a^6}{3b}\right) - \frac{2}{3r^3}\left(\frac{r^3 b^2}{6} - \frac{r^5}{10}\right.$$
$$\left. + \frac{a^3 r^3}{3b} - \frac{a^3 r^2}{2} - \frac{a^3 b^2}{6} + \frac{3a^5}{5} - \frac{a^6}{3b}\right) \quad \begin{array}{l}\text{for radial stress in}\\ \text{hollow sphere}\end{array} \tag{5-7a}$$

$$\Psi_{2_h} = \frac{2r^3 + a^3}{3r^3(b^3 - a^3)}\left(\frac{b^5}{15} - \frac{a^3 b^2}{3} + \frac{3a^5}{5} - \frac{a^6}{3b}\right) + \frac{1}{3r^3}\left(\frac{r^3 b^2}{6} - \frac{r^5}{10}\right.$$
$$\left. + \frac{a^3 r^3}{3b} - \frac{a^3 r^2}{2} - \frac{a^3 b^2}{6} - \frac{3a^5}{5} - \frac{a^6}{3b}\right) - \frac{1}{3}\left[\frac{b^2 - r^2}{2}\right.$$
$$\left. - a^3\left(\frac{1}{r} - \frac{1}{b}\right)\right] \quad \text{for tangential stress in hollow sphere} \tag{5-7b}$$

RODS. Consider an infinitely long solid rod of radius b. Then

$$\Psi_1 = \frac{b^2 - r^2}{4} \tag{5-8}$$

$$\Psi_2 = \frac{r^2 - b^2}{16} \quad \text{for radial stress} \tag{5-9a}$$

$$\Psi_2 = \frac{3r^2 - b^2}{16} \quad \text{for tangential stress} \tag{5-9b}$$

$$\Psi_2 = \frac{2r^2 - b^2}{8} \quad \text{for axial stress} \tag{5-9c}$$

TUBES. First consider an infinitely long thick-walled tube of inner radius a, outer radius b, cooled internally only. This model can be used to approximate the cooling of a solid body by equilaterally spaced parallel passages carrying a constant-temperature coolant. Such a situation might exist in the moderator, reflector, pressure shell, or other non-fissioning structures of a nuclear rocket reactor. It is also of interest in connection with reactor-core designs utilizing drilled fuel blocks or bundles of cylindrical fuel tubes through which coolant or propellant is

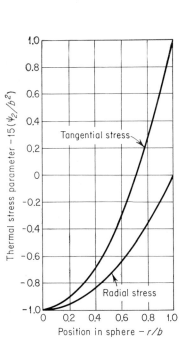

FIG. 5-10. Stresses in solid spheres. (*J. C. Carter, Temperature and Stress Distribution in Spheres, Rods, Tubes, and Plates in Which the Heat Source Is within the Boundaries of the Solids, ANL-4690, Argonne National Laboratory, Chicago, Ill., Sept. 7, 1951.*)

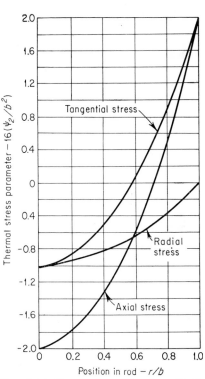

FIG. 5-11. Stresses in solid rods. (*J. C. Carter, Temperature and Stress Distribution in Spheres, Rods, Tubes, and Plates in Which the Heat Source Is within the Boundaries of the Solids, ANL-4690, Argonne National Laboratory, Chicago, Ill., Sept. 7, 1951.*)

made to flow. For equilateral cooling-hole spacing the center-to-center spacing s is related to the outer radius b of the "equivalent" tube by

$$2b = 1.05s \qquad (5\text{-}10)$$

The pertinent geometrical parameters are

$$\Psi_1 = \frac{b^2}{2} \ln \frac{r}{a} - \frac{r^2 - a^2}{2} \qquad (5\text{-}11)$$

$$\Psi_2 = \frac{r^2 - a^2}{16r^2(b^2 - a^2)} \left(4b^4 \ln \frac{b}{a} - 3b^4 + 4a^2b^2 - a^4 \right)$$
$$+ \frac{b^2}{8} \left(1 - 2 \ln \frac{r}{a} \right) - \frac{a^2}{8r^2} (b^2 + r^2) + \frac{r^4 + a^4}{16r^2} \qquad \text{for radial stress}$$

$$\text{(5-12a)}$$

$$\Psi_2 = \frac{r^2 + a^2}{16r^2(b^2 - a^2)} \left(4b^4 \ln \frac{b}{a} - 3b^4 + 4a^2b^2 - a^4 \right)$$
$$- \frac{b^2}{8} \left(1 + 2 \ln \frac{r}{a} \right) + \frac{a^2}{8r^2} (b^2 - r^2) + \frac{3r^4 - a^4}{16r^2} \qquad \text{for tangential stress}$$

$$\text{(5-12b)}$$

$$\Psi_2 = - \frac{b^2}{2} \ln \frac{r}{a} + \frac{r^2}{4} - \frac{a^2}{4} + \frac{1}{8(b^2 - a^2)} \left(4b^4 \ln \frac{b}{a} - 3b^4 \right.$$
$$\left. + 4a^2b^2 - a^4 \right) \qquad \text{for axial stress} \quad \text{(5-12c)}$$

For heat removed from the outer tube surface only, the equations become

$$\Psi_1 = \frac{b^2 - r^2}{4} - \frac{a^2}{2} \ln \frac{b}{r} \qquad\qquad\qquad \text{(5-13)}$$

$$\Psi_2 = \frac{r^2 - a^2}{16r^2(b^2 - a^2)} \left(b^4 - 4a^2b^2 + 3a^4 + 4a^4 \ln \frac{b}{a} \right)$$
$$- \frac{1}{16r^2} \left(2r^2b^2 - r^4 - 4a^2r^2 \ln \frac{b}{r} - 2a^2r^2 - 2a^2b^2 \right.$$
$$\left. + 3a^4 + 8a^4 \ln \frac{b}{a} \right) \qquad \text{for radial stress} \quad \text{(5-14a)}$$

$$\Psi_2 = \frac{r^2 + a^2}{16r^2(b^2 - a^2)} \left(b^4 - 4a^2b^2 + 3a^4 + 4a^4 \ln \frac{b}{a} \right)$$
$$- \frac{1}{16r^2} \left(2r^2b^2 - r^4 - 4a^2r^2 \ln \frac{b}{r} - 2a^2r^2 - 2a^2b^2 + 3a^4 \right.$$
$$\left. + 4a^4 \ln \frac{b}{a} \right) - \left(\frac{b^2}{4} - \frac{r^2}{4} - \frac{a^2}{2} \ln \frac{b}{r} \right) \qquad \text{for tangential stress} \quad \text{(5-14b)}$$

$$\Psi_2 = - \frac{b^2}{4} + \frac{r^2}{4} + \frac{a^2}{2} \ln \frac{b}{r} + \frac{1}{8(b^2 - a^2)} \left(b^4 - 4a^2b^2 + 3a^4 \right.$$
$$\left. + 4a^4 \ln \frac{b}{a} \right) \qquad \text{for axial stress} \quad \text{(5-14c)}$$

FLAT PLATES. Consider a semi-infinite flat plate of thickness t, cooled equally on both surfaces. For this case, of great interest in reactor-core design, the parameters are

$$\Psi_1 = \frac{t^2}{8} - \frac{x^2}{2} \qquad\qquad\qquad \text{(5-15)}$$

$$\Psi_2 = \frac{x^2}{2} - \frac{t^2}{24} \qquad \text{for longitudinal stress} \quad \text{(5-16)}$$

where x is the distance from the plate center plane to any point within the plate.

Note from the figures that the peak axial and tangential stresses are often reached at the inner or outer surfaces of the heat-generating structure. This fact can be important in considerations of structural corrosion and erosion at high temperature (see page 179).

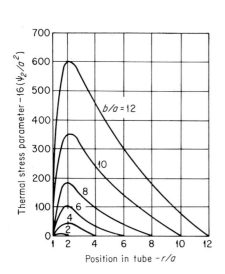

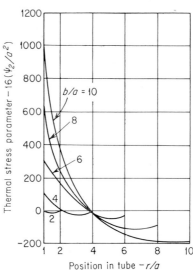

FIG. 5-12. Radial stress in tubes. Heat is removed from inside surface. (*J. C. Carter, Temperature and Stress Distribution in Spheres, Rods, Tubes, and Plates in Which the Heat Source Is within the Boundaries of the Solids, ANL-4690, Argonne National Laboratory, Chicago, Ill., Sept. 7, 1951.*)

FIG. 5-13. Tangential stress in tubes· Heat is removed from inside surface. (*J. C. Carter, Temperature and Stress Distribution in Spheres, Rods, Tubes, and Plates in Which the Heat Source Is within the Boundaries of the Solids, ANL-4690, Argonne National Laboratory, Chicago, Ill., Sept. 7, 1951.*)

From Eqs. (5-2) and (5-3) it is evident that the maximum value of internal temperature difference, for a given geometry, is directly proportional to the reactor structural power density and that the maximum elastic stresses can thus be related directly to this power density. It will be helpful at this point to introduce a parameter Ψ_3, useful later in transient-stress analysis, defined by the equation

$$\Psi_3 = \frac{1 - \nu}{\alpha E} \frac{\sigma_{max}}{\Delta T_{max}} \tag{5-17}$$

This parameter is given by the value of Ψ_2 for the maximum value of the stress of interest, divided by the value of Ψ_1 for the maximum temperature difference in the particular system geometry. Values of Ψ_3 thus determined are given, following, for the case of solid spheres, rods, and plates, and for tubes with internal heat removal only.

SPHERES.   Maximum radial compressive stress equals maximum tangential compressive stress, and both occur at the sphere center.   Maximum tangential tensile stress, at sphere surface, is of equal magnitude but opposite sign.   The parameter

$$\Psi_3 = \pm \tfrac{2}{5} \tag{5-18}$$

RODS.   Maximum axial compressive stress, along the rod center line, is of equal magnitude but opposite sign to the maximum axial and tan-

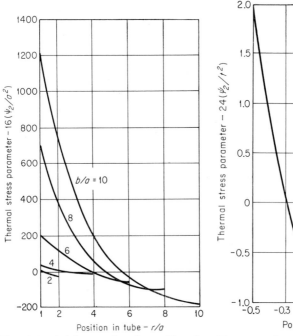
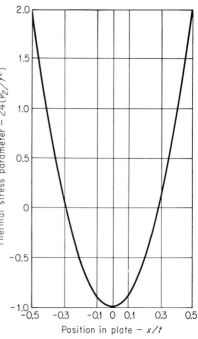

FIG. 5-14. Axial stress in tubes.   Heat is removed from inside surface.   (*J. C. Carter, Temperature and Stress Distribution in Spheres, Rods, Tubes, and Plates in Which the Heat Source Is within the Boundaries of the Solids, ANL-4690, Argonne National Laboratory, Chicago, Ill., Sept. 7, 1951.*)

FIG. 5-15. Longitudinal stress in plates.

gential tensile stresses occurring on the rod surface.   Maximum radial stress (compressive) is only half as high as peak axial or tangential stresses.   Here

$$\Psi_3 = \pm \tfrac{1}{2} \tag{5-19}$$

TUBES.   For internal heat removal the axial and tangential stresses reach a maximum, in tension, at the inner hole surface.   Peak radial stress, which is tensile, is only about one-third as high as peak axial and tangential stresses. For this case

$$\Psi_3 = \frac{\dfrac{b^4}{b^2 - a^2}\ln\left(\dfrac{b}{a}\right)^2 - \dfrac{3b^2 - a^2}{2}}{b^2\ln\left(\dfrac{b}{a}\right)^2 - b^2 + a^2} \qquad (5\text{-}20)$$

FLAT PLATES. The maximum longitudinal stress is tensile and occurs at the plate surface. Its value is twice that of the peak compressive stress, which occurs in the plate center plane. For this condition we have

$$\Psi_3 = \tfrac{2}{3} \qquad (5\text{-}21)$$

As previously discussed, the elastic strains and stresses computed from the foregoing equations will not actually be obtained in a reactor structure at high temperature. Plastic flow or creep of the material itself

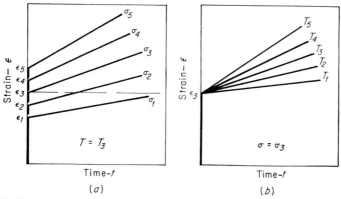

FIG. 5-16. Idealized elongation-time diagrams. (a) Effect of σ at constant T; (b) effect of T at constant σ.

will tend to reduce the thermal stresses as they are built up. However, if the rate of input strain due to rapid thermal loading is sufficiently high that creep cannot keep up with it without reaching stresses above the rupture strength, then the part will fail, generally in tension. How, then, can we estimate the time dependence of stress? First consider a material which has an idealized elongation-time diagram as shown in Fig. 5-16 for one set of constant-stress and/or constant-temperature conditions. Initial zero-time build-up of strain, by extremely rapid differential expansion due to internal temperature gradients, for example, to values ϵ_1, ϵ_2, etc., is followed by creep relaxation of the initially "elastic" stress σ_1, σ_2, etc., to lower stresses, found by traversing a constant elongation line (shown dashed) in time. In a one-dimensional system with zero external load the total strain at any time is the sum of the elastic strain computed by

$$\epsilon_e(t) = \frac{\sigma(t)}{E_0} \tag{5-22}$$

and the inelastic or plastic strain and is equal to the total thermally induced strain in the piece of interest. $\sigma(t)$ and E_0 denote total stress at time t and modulus of elasticity, respectively. The total thermal strain at any time t is, of course,

$$\epsilon_T(t) = \alpha\,\Delta T(t) = \alpha[T(t) - T_s] \tag{5-23}$$

so that the inelastic strain is given by

$$\epsilon_p(t) = \alpha\,\Delta T(t) - \frac{\sigma(t)}{E_0} \tag{5-24}$$

In the elongation-time diagrams shown in Fig. 5-16 the inelastic strain is that strain lying above the elastic strains ϵ_1, ϵ_2, ϵ_3, etc., for the particular stresses σ_1, σ_2, σ_3, etc., prevailing in the piece at time t.

The above discussion has assumed straining at constant temperature, which is not the true case in a reactor component part in which strains are induced by differential temperature changes. Neglecting, for the moment, the changing temperature, note that the time rate of change of inelastic strain is the creep rate of the material as determined by standard elongation-time tests. For a one-dimensional geometry this is

$$\frac{d\epsilon_p}{dt} = \alpha\frac{d\,\Delta T}{dt} - \frac{1}{E_0}\frac{d\sigma}{dt} = C(\sigma,\epsilon_{tot}) \tag{5-25}$$

As indicated in Eq. (5-25) the creep rate is generally determinable by the total strain and instantaneous stress, at any time t, for constant-temperature operation. Thus to find the stress-time relation it is necessary to know the form of the function $C(\sigma,\epsilon_{tot})$ for the temperature of interest. For the idealized elongation-time curves shown in Fig. 5-16a, the creep rate (slope of the elongation-time lines above the elastic elongation point) is a function of the stress only, being constant for a particular stress at any total strain and time. Also, from Fig. 5-16b note that the creep rate, at a constant stress, is a function only of the temperature. We might write the creep rate, stress, and temperature relation for this idealized system as

$$C(\sigma,T_0) = MT_0^m + N\sigma^n \tag{5-26}$$

where T_0 is the peak temperature of the system, hence corresponds to the point at which creep is most likely to occur in any thermal-strain situation. This peak temperature is always within the volume of a heat-generating solid: at the centers of rods and spheres and the center planes of plates, for example. For a situation in which the surface temperature is held constant, the rate of strain input is simply $\alpha(dT_0/dt)$, and the stress-temperature-time equation (5-25) can be written as

$$\frac{d\sigma}{dt} + E_0 N \sigma^n = \alpha E_0 \frac{dT_0}{dt} - MT_0^m \tag{5-27}$$

For a constant surface temperature the time variation of T_0 can be found from the desired rate of change of power density, or heat generation rate, with the component of interest, the known density, conductivity, and heat capacity of the material of which the component is constructed, and the equations for maximum internal temperature difference, given previously $[\Delta T = \Psi_1(q/k)]$. Then, knowing the time variation of T_0, Eq. (5-27) can be solved for $\sigma = f(t)$, and an estimate of component reliability (likelihood of survival under thermal stresses) can be made for the operating conditions of interest. Estimation of the thermal stresses under different operating sequences requires repetition of the above process for every condition of interest.

A still simpler and even less realistic, but more tractable, analysis results if the effect of temperature is ignored and the creep rate is expressed only as a function of stress. Here we have

$$\frac{d\sigma}{dt} = E_0 \left(\alpha \frac{d\,\Delta T}{d} - N\sigma^n \right) \tag{5-28}$$

This nonlinear equation can be solved numerically by conversion to a difference equation so that

$$\sigma_{t+\Delta t} = 2\Delta t\, E_0 \left(\alpha \frac{d\,\Delta T}{dt} - N\sigma_t^n + \sigma_{t-\Delta t} \right) \tag{5-29}$$

As an example of the result of such an analysis, Fig. 5-17a shows the form of the peak stress–time behavior of a plate subjected to the repeated internal temperature differences shown in Fig. 5-17b.

For multidimensional systems the foregoing equations must be modified to account for bi- and triaxial stressing. This can be done most simply by use of the parameter Ψ_3, given previously for several geometries of interest in reactor design. This factor modifies Eq. (5-22), for the elastic strain, to

$$\sigma(t) = \Psi_3 E_0 \epsilon_e(t) \tag{5-30}$$

In turn this results in a modification of the complete, constant-temperature stress-strain-time equation (5-25), now including the temperature dependence of creep rate, to

$$\frac{d\sigma}{dt} = \Psi_3 E_0 \left[\alpha \frac{d\,\Delta T}{dt} - C(\sigma, \epsilon_{tot}, T_0) \right] \tag{5-31}$$

where the total strain is the thermal strain (no external loads) and is given by

$$\epsilon_{tot} = \alpha \, \Delta T = \alpha(T_0 - T_s) \qquad (5\text{-}32)$$

As previously discussed, the effects of temperature can generally be accounted for numerically by solution of Eq. (5-31) in piecemeal fashion, varying the creep rate from one piece of the integration to the next to correspond to the successive changes in total strain, stress level, and maximum temperature. In order to do this, elongation-time curves for a wide range of stresses and temperatures must be available for the material of interest. Unfortunately there are, as yet, no handbooks of such data for graphite, molybdenum, tungsten, etc., at high temperatures. Many data are available on graphite, but because of the wide variety of types of graphite, these data are not always applicable for rocket-reactor core design. Figure 5-18 shows the elongation-time behavior of one type of graphite at one temperature and stress condition. Also shown is the peculiar recovery of this graphite on unloading of the previously stretched test sample. Note that this recovery curve resembles an inversion of the initial creep curve. The peculiar shape of this curve is a result of the unique character of graphite.

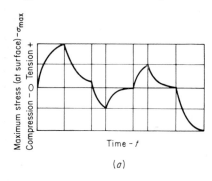

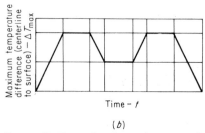

Fig. 5-17. Example of transient stress in volume-heated solids.

Graphite consists of an aggregated crystalline structure with groups of crystalline carbon held together by a "glue" of carbon binder, often resulting from the tarry pitch used in the initial precoking graphite mix. When strained, the bridges of glue between crystalline particles tend to stretch and give way, allowing the particles to shift relative to one another, often "locking" or tending to lock in their shifted positions. On unloading, the stored strain energy due to the shifted, locked particles is exhibited as a force which tries to reshift the particles to their original position. The rapid recovery shown in the first stage of the recovery curve is believed due to this reshifting of particles. Continued relief of stored strain energy proceeds at a slower rate once the major portion of this energy has been released by the initial reshifting of the "elastically" distorted crystalline matrix. In a sense, graphite behaves as a three-dimensional system of stiff but elastic crystals at node points connected by highly damped springs. Initial distortion of this matrix stretches the springs and elastically strains the crystal structure. Further inelastic (creep) distortion causes deformation or destruction of some of the springs themselves by slippage past each other of adjacent nodes of crystals, for example. On unloading, the elastic crystals instantly resume their original form. The deformed springs do not recover, but the remaining viscously damped springs slowly (in a matter of seconds)

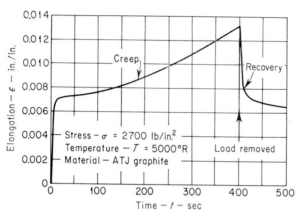

FIG. 5-18. Typical creep and recovery of graphite. (*Private communication from P. J. Wagner, April, 1957.*)

return to their initial, unstretched positions. In graphite, this stretching and recovery of the "spring" corresponds to the "elastic" strains of our previous discussion. Further information on the unique character and behavior of graphite is available in the literature.[12]

In metals the situation is not as complex and elastic strain is truly elastic, being a simple distortion of crystal lattices. However, inelastic creep in metals is greatly complicated by the effects of structure, such as alloying-element concentrations, phase structure and distribution, strain hardening, grain size, and grain growth with temperature, etc. For high stresses at high temperature in aluminum and aluminum alloys, Dorn and Shepard[8] have found that the creep rate is given by an equation of the form

$$C(\sigma,T) = \psi_0 e^{-c_1/T} e^{c_2\sigma} \tag{5-33}$$

where ψ_0 is a metallurgical structure parameter which is largely unknown at the present time, σ is the instantaneous stress, T is the sample temperature, and c_1 and c_2 are constants dependent on the material constitution. For low stresses the second exponential in Eq. (5-33) is replaced by σ^{c_3}, where c_3 is again a constant of the material of interest.

In summary, the rocket-reactor designer can estimate the time variation of stress in volume-heated reactor component parts under any desired operating sequence by relatively straightforward, though trying, numerical methods for the solution of the stress-strain-time equations. In order to do so, curves of elongation or strain vs. time must be available for a wide variety of stresses and temperatures for each material of interest in the investigation. With this done, experimental evidence gives some assurance that failure will not occur during a single thermal-strain cycle if the computed peak stress everywhere within the piece is less than the short-time breaking strength in tension or compression, as the particular case may be, of the material at the design temperature. For repeated thermal-strain cycles the computed peak stress should be less than one-fourth to one-half of the short-time material breaking strength to assure that failure will not occur by fatigue cracking during cycling.

Corrosion and Erosion. As discussed briefly in Chap. 2, one of the chief difficulties encountered in the design and development of heat-exchanger rocket reactors arises from the unfortunate contradiction that low-molecular-weight, and hence high-performance, propellants must contain large fractions of hydrogen, whereas hot hydrogen is a highly reducing and chemically corrosive material.

As is well known, hot hydrogen will react with exposed carbon surfaces to form hydrocarbons, such as acetylene, with a consequent loss of carbon from the surface. Indeed this process, *hydrogenation*, is presently used commercially to produce hydrocarbons from coal, and may one day be our chief source of hydrocarbon fuels, when present reserves of oil are badly depleted by continued profligate use. If the fuel elements or core structure of a rocket reactor is made primarily of graphite, hydrogen corrosion can rapidly destroy the reactor once it has reached operating temperature unless steps are taken to protect the graphite from direct contact with the hydrogen propellant. However, to achieve high core power density it is necessary to transfer as much heat per unit area of fuel element as possible; hence it is undesirable from the heat-transfer standpoint to impose a barrier between the fuel elements and the propellant gas. What is needed here is an impermeable membrane of high thermal conductivity fastened tightly to the surface of the graphite. Unfortunately, the hydrogen atom is small, as atoms go, and can readily diffuse through most materials, even at room temperature. Since most materials will form carbides when in contact with carbon at high temperature, possible candidates for use as protective coatings on graphite are some of the high-melting-point carbides, such as ZrC, NbC, and TaC. While it is known that these materials are themselves stable in hydrogen at $5000°R$, little information is presently available on the chemical and mechanical stability of such coatings on a graphite base at high temperature. Problems of differential thermal expansion between the coating and base material and of adhesion under the surface frictional forces due to the high-velocity flow of propellant must be solved before such coatings can be considered as truly protective.

The mechanism of chemical attack of hydrogen on graphite is similar to that on metals. In both cases the hydrogen reacts preferentially with the material between crystalline grains of base material, forming volatile hydrocarbons by reaction with the bridges between connected graphite crystals and forming brittle metallic hydrides by reaction with material at the grain boundaries of metals. This latter phenomenon is the familiar *hydrogen embrittlement* and often leads to failure of the metal piece by the production of cleavage cracks on the material surface. Such cracks will rapidly propagate if the piece is loaded in tension or is under surface tensile thermal stress by virtue of heat generation within the volume. Similarly, corrosion of the bridges or bonds connecting adjacent graphite crystalline particles can destroy the graphite piece by severe weakening at the point of highest tensile stress: the surface if the piece is surface-cooled. In addition, for graphite, corrosion of the bridges between particles exposes loose or almost loose grains to the action of the coolant flowing over the surface. If the piece under attack is a fuel element or support structure in a high-power-density reactor, the propellant-gas velocity may be several thousand feet per second in the hottest portions of the core and the exposed grains of graphite will be blown away, thus exposing fresh grains and connecting bridges to attack by fresh hot hydrogen. This process can continue until the piece in question is completely eaten away or the reactor core has failed.

One of the drawbacks to the use of tantalum as a fuel element or core structural material is that it forms a brittle hydride between 2000 and 4000°R. This hydride decomposes rapidly above 4000°R, but since all reactors must pass through the hydride temperature range during start-up, tantalum pieces are liable to brittle fractural failure. On the other hand, molybdenum appears to be immune to hydride formation, at least up to 5000°R, as does platinum. It is also probable that tungsten metal does not react with hydrogen up to at least 5000°R. However, another problem exists with tungsten and molybdenum. As discussed in Sec. 5-2, both metals when pure will fail by embrittlement due to continued grain growth at high temperature. To permit use of tungsten or molybdenum above about 3000°R it is necessary to inhibit grain growth by the addition of oxides (ThO_2, UO_2, etc.) to the metal before casting and forming. A small percentage of oxide content will effectively prevent grain growth by sealing off one crystalline grain from another and preventing self-diffusion of the metal atoms from grain to grain. Now consider the effect of hot hydrogen reacting with the oxide at grain boundaries. Here the oxide can be reduced and boundary inhibition destroyed, and grain growth may occur on the exposed surface of the piece. As mentioned, this may lead to failure if the surface is acting in tension by thermal or load distortion. Erosion is not the problem with metal surfaces that it is with graphite, for the lattice structure of metals is much more coherent than the particle-bridge structure of graphite.

Aside from the use of protective coatings, chemical corrosive attack on the surfaces of hot structures can be minimized by the use of propellants which contain in addition to hydrogen other elements which can react in the gas phase with the hot hydrogen present, thus destroying its potential to attack exposed surfaces of graphite, solid hydrocarbons, and some metals. For example, a hydrocarbon propellant which has a molecular carbon-hydrogen ratio sufficiently high to ensure the availability of free carbon in the gas phase for reaction with hydrogen at corrosion temperatures should not chemically react with exposed surfaces of a graphite heating element. That this is actually the case is observed in the heating of propane and many other hydrocarbons in graphite tubes. In fact invariably some of the carbon released by the dissociation of the propane molecule is actually deposited on the walls of the heating element, often plugging the tube. While this is somewhat extreme, the principle is valid. In fact this phenomenon is in commercial use in the "welding" of graphite parts by the decomposition of methane on heated graphite surfaces. For reactor design, exploitation of this action is greatly complicated by the fact that it is dependent on the ratio of surface area to gas volume for the structure under consideration and on the equilibrium constants for the various gas-phase reactions which "eat up" the hot hydrogen. Since these equilibrium constants are all different functions of gas temperature, it is clear that the neutralizing effect will be different at different temperatures; the gas may be completely neutral at T_1, deposit carbon at T_2, and corrode exposed graphite at T_3. The development of "neutral" propellants is a major job in itself, for what is neutral to graphite may not be so to the oxides used in stabilizing tungsten, for example. Furthermore, an almost infinite number of possibilities is evident, since the addition of oxygen, nitrogen, or any other element to the propellant may alter its chemical reactivity in the gas phase. Compounds with the same gross chemical formula but of different molecular structure may react differently, for they will probably decompose, on heating, to yield different short-lived active radicals. Here again, as for stress-strain-temperature-time data, no handbook of information is presently available to guide the designer and there is no substitute for experimentation.

The achievement of minimally corrosive propellants cannot be by the addition of hydrogen, hence inherently involves the use of propellant mixtures of molecular weight greater than 2. In general it is found that molecular weights of 5 to 12 cover most of the potentially useful high-density propellants which are liquids at or near room temperature. Since neutral or semineutral propellants can be formed, in theory, by mixtures within this group, rocket-motor performance using such propellants will be similar to that expected from use of liquids such as propane and ethyl alcohol rather than liquid hydrogen.

Since no rocket reactor will work properly if its internal parts are corroding and eroding away during high-temperature operation, the designer must so restrict his choice of propellants and materials that at least one of the following three conditions prevails:

1. Fuel elements and core structural members are made from inert noncorrodible materials.

2. Protective coatings or claddings are used for corrodible materials in a corrosive-propellant atmosphere.

3. Inert or "neutrally" corrosive propellants are used.

Radiation Effects. Different materials react differently to the effects of irradiation by the fast and slow neutrons, gamma photons, and beta rays present in an operating nuclear reactor. Some structural materials become more brittle with continued exposure to radiation, some change in size because of changes in the lattice structure, and the physical and thermal properties of others vary with radiation dose. This section describes some of the special problems that arise from *radiation damage* of materials which otherwise appear promising for use as nuclear rocket-reactor fuel elements, moderators, control elements, and structural components.

The radiation-induced change in reactor materials which degrades the performance of these materials has been termed "radiation damage."[13] At times it has been referred to as the "Wigner effect" in deference to E. P. Wigner, who first pointed out the possibility of such damage before it was observed experimentally in a reactor.[14] It should be noted that not all radiation-induced changes in materials are harmful; however, in general, the resultant effects of irradiation are viewed as undesirable because modern technology has learned to live with and is based on use of materials in their normal, nonirradiated state.

Radiation damage arises from the interaction of energetic radiation and matter. For example, one effect of this interaction is the displacement of atoms from their equilibrium positions in a crystal lattice. In other aspects of this interaction, transient local high-temperature (kinetic-motion) regions are created, and by neutron capture and radioactive decay or by inclusion of fission fragments, atoms which are impure relative to the base material are introduced. In many cases, chemical bonds are broken and free radicals formed.   Five effects of radiation damage are conventionally recognized from the interaction of radiation and matter. These are called vacancies, interstitials, thermal spikes, impurity atoms, and ionization effects.   All will cause changes in many of the properties of matter, whether it be liquid or solid.   The first four are of most concern in solids, while the last is of most concern in liquids and gases.

In general, neutrons and fission fragments cause the greatest radiation damage in solids.   Nuclear radiations such as beta particles and gamma rays are also capable of causing damage in solids, but their effects are small in comparison with those of neutrons and fission fragments.   This is primarily due to the tremendous amount of energy possessed by these latter particles in relation to the energy required to produce a defect. The neutron, since it is uncharged, must interact by direct collision. However, once a collision has taken place, the knock-on atom rapidly creates subsequent displaced atoms.   Since the incident neutron can travel a considerable distance before it makes another collision, the damage resulting from these fast neutrons is widely spread throughout the reactor.   On the other hand, fission fragments possessing a high initial charge and high mass must dissipate their energy within a few milligrams of material.   Therefore, damage from fission fragments is usually confined to a region close to the fuel volume.   The total energy dissipated in radiation damage is approximately the same for both particles, but the spatial distribution is different.

It is difficult to generalize on the radiation damage that might be expected in an operating reactor, since the type of damage and its extent depend strongly on the material and its environment while being irradiated.   To simplify discussion the results of various radiation-damage investigations have been divided into classes reflecting the particular reactor application of the material.   For the case of nuclear rocket reactors, the classifications of the most interest are those previously used in this chapter: fuel elements, moderators, control materials, and structural materials.

FUEL ELEMENTS.   Fuel elements suffer heavy radiation-damage effects because of the fission processes occurring within them.   Most of the damage results from fission-fragment and fast-neutron interaction with the fuel-element base material and by the production of a large number of impurity atoms (fission products).   If the fuel elements are required to perform any structural functions, the effect of damage on physical properties can be a serious problem.   The radiation damage to fuel-element materials, like many of the other reactor component materials, is related to the size and orientation of the material grains and the techniques used in fabrication.   In uranium-graphite systems, radiation damage occurs because of the anisotropic nature of the graphite.   At low temperature ($<1000°R$), neutron "trapping" by the graphite lattice results in distortion of the lattice, with consequent dimensional changes in graphite fuel elements if operated at low temperature. At high temperature, the carbon atoms in the graphite lattice are moving (oscillating) much more rapidly than at room temperature and trapped neutrons can easily escape the lattice. The dimensional damage to graphite thus "anneals" out at high temperature. Graphite is discussed further in the following section on moderator materials. Another material of potential interest as a fuel-element base or filler is one consisting of uranium-molybdenum alloy. For a high-molybdenum alloy (9 per cent Mo) no appreciable growth results even after an exposure to 2.5×10^{19} n/cm² (neutrons/cm²), but another interesting system, UO_2-BeO, showed some reduction in compressive strength and elastic modulus after exposure to neutron doses of this magnitude.

In summary, radiation damage resulting from mechanical absorption of neutrons in solids is generally trivial for operation of fuel-element materials at temperatures of interest. Gross microscopic local mechanical distortion caused by fission-fragment slowing down is also trivial for rocket reactors where the fractional fuel burnup is very small over the complete reactor life. Changes due to nuclear absorption of neutrons or nuclear and atomic interactions with β and γ rays will generally have little influence on rocket-reactor fuel-element properties.

MODERATORS. Solid materials that are useful as moderators are principally graphite, beryllium, beryllium oxide, and some of the metal hydrides. Since graphite has been most widely used as a solid moderator, changes produced in it by radiation have been extensively investigated. Like the fuel-element materials, radiation-induced changes depend to a large extent on the source of the graphite and the method of manufacture.

Radiation produces a stronger, harder, and more brittle graphite. After a total neutron exposure of 2.5×10^{19} n/cm², the room-temperature compression strength of graphite is approximately tripled. Depending upon the specific application such changes are not always deleterious. Of greater importance to a high-power-density reactor is the change in the thermal conductivity. As shown in Fig. 5-19, the conductivity may decrease markedly with continued exposure to neutrons. Fortunately this effect becomes less important with increasing temperature and effectively disappears above about 2500°R.

Other considerations are the dimensional changes produced in graphite by neutron irradiation, mentioned briefly in the preceding section. Most graphites have been observed to expand anisotropically and at the same time undergo an increase in volume with an increase in exposure. This is shown in Fig. 5-20. All observations to date have shown that the damage to graphite becomes progressively less with increasing temperature. Thus from a radiation-damage standpoint, in a nuclear rocket reactor, every effort should be made to operate graphite components near their maximum temperature, or at least above 2500°R.

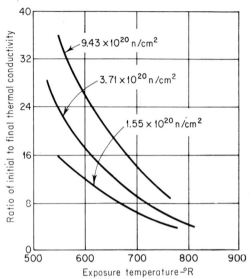

FIG. 5-19. Effect of fast-neutron dose on graphite thermal conductivity.

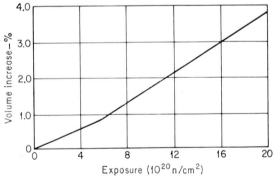

FIG. 5-20. Effect of fast-neutron dose on graphite volume.

Other solid moderators have had a more limited usage; however some radiation-effects investigations have been made on certain materials. Beryllium, for example, has been irradiated with fast neutrons up to 1.5×10^{20} n/cm² with no significant changes in dimension or in most of its physical properties. There have been indications, however, of increased hardness and of some loss in ductility with neutron exposure of this magnitude.[15]

For BeO no serious changes in dimensional or mechanical properties have been noted, but the thermal conductivity was decreased by over 50 per cent by exposure to 1.5×10^{20} n/cm². In regard to the metal hydrides, the information available is rather meager, but what data are available[16] would not eliminate these materials from consideration for use in nuclear rocket reactors.

As previously discussed, the liquid moderators of interest include H_2O, D_2O, some alcohols, and liquid hydrocarbons. The primary effect of ionizing radiation on water is decomposition. The mechanism of this decomposition is[17,18]

$$H_2O \rightarrow H + OH \tag{5-34}$$

$$2H_2O \rightarrow H_2 + H_2O_2 \tag{5-35}$$

The radicals H and OH are available for reaction with one another to form H_2, O_2, and H_2O. If the water is present as an aqueous solution and in a region of low ionization density, most radicals will react with the solutes. In regions of high ionization density radicals recombine to form the products of Eq. (5-35). Since H, OH, H_2O_2, and the intermediate perhydroxy radical HO_2 are either strongly oxidizing or reducing agents, consideration must be given to the corrosion (oxidization or reduction) of the materials in contact with these decomposition products.

In the case of D_2O, decomposition is negligible if the purity is maintained at a high level. If D_2O is allowed to become contaminated (e.g., with H_2O), radiolytic gas will be evolved at a high rate.

For the organic liquids, the reactions induced by radiation are much the same as for organic solids. The effect here is on the two reactions of the polymer, i.e., cross-linking and cleavage. Table 5-7 lists some of

TABLE 5-7. RADIATION-INDUCED CHANGES IN ORGANIC MATERIALS*

Cross-linking	Cleavage
Increases Young's modulus	Decreases Young's modulus
Impedes viscous flow	Reduces yield stress for viscous flow
Increases retardation of strain	
Usually causing:	*Usually causing:*
Increased tensile strength	Decreased tensile strength
Decreased elongation	Increased elongation
Increased hardness	Decreased hardness
Increased softening temperature	Decreased elasticity
Gas formation	*Sometimes causing:*
Embrittlement	Embrittlement
Decreased elasticity	Gas formation

* O. Sisman and J. C. Wilson, Engineering Use of Damage Data, *Nucleonics*, vol. 14, no. 9, pp. 58–62, September, 1956.

the engineering properties associated with cleavage and cross-linking.[19] Though a few liquids show a decrease in viscosity, most organic liquids become more viscous by radiation-induced polymerization. Gassing is prevalent and the tendency to foam may be increased. These effects can be reduced by continuous circulation from an external reservoir, but this method has the disadvantage that radioactive material is being removed from the reactor and may require shielding. It should be noted that liquid hydrocarbons can be used advantageously in this type of system because they do not become very radioactive.

In summary, the chief damage to moderators occurs from radiolytic decomposition of liquids such as H_2O, D_2O, and NH_3 and by polymerization of liquid hydrocarbon moderators. Radiation-induced growth and thermal-conductivity changes in graphite and other solid moderators such as BeO and possibly the metallic hydrides require operation of these materials above some "annealing" temperature at which such effects are effectively washed out by motion of the atoms comprising the solid structure. For graphite this temperature is about 2500°R.

CONTROL MATERIALS. Only a limited amount of information is available on the effects of radiation on control materials such as hafnium, boron, and cadmium.[15] Control materials, like shields, can be expected to suffer larger radiation effects than the average metal or ceramic because of the secondary particles resulting from the neutron capture.

Hafnium has been found to show changes in its mechanical properties after a long period of exposure. Its hardness was increased, while the density decreased; however, no significant dimensional changes were found.

Boron carbide, on the other hand, can be badly damaged by radiation. The B^{10} atom splits to form heavy, energetic Li^7 and He atoms capable of causing considerable displacement damage, as do fission fragments. Two atoms result when each B^{10} atom is split by neutron capture, and the lattice must accommodate the extra atoms. Preliminary data on irradiated extruded stainless steel containing up to 5 per cent boron showed no appreciable changes in dimensions, although the specimens were highly embrittled.

Cadmium, which has been extensively used as control-rod material, appears to be extremely stable under radiation. Clad plates of silver containing up to 25 per cent cadmium have been irradiated for periods up to a year with negligible changes in density and dimensions.

Almost no data are available on the effect of radiation on gadolinium and europium oxides, other candidates for control materials. Since these elements form β and γ emitters by neutron capture, it is not expected that major changes in their structural properties will take place under continued neutron irradiation, as is the case for boron carbide.

STRUCTURAL MATERIALS. In stationary-power-reactor design, the structural materials utilized have been limited primarily to aluminum, steel, and nickel alloys. For a nuclear rocket reactor, where high temperature and low weight are necessities, other structural materials such as molybdenum and titanium, as well as graphite, must be considered.

Experience to date has indicated that radiation damage is slight in aluminum and somewhat greater in steel. The major effect is on the ductility of these metals, as shown in Table 5-8. Note that, for molyb-

TABLE 5-8. DUCTILITIES BEFORE AND AFTER IRRADIATION[*]
Dose $\sim 10^{18}$ to 10^{20} n/cm^2

Material	Elongation at breakage, %	
	Before	After
2SO aluminum	38	21
2SH 14 aluminum	22	20
Normalized carbon steel	22[†]	5[†]
Austenitic stainless steel	49[†]	25[†]
QMV beryllium	1.4	0.2
356 aluminum	2.7	0.6
Molybdenum	44	0

[*] J. H. Kittel, Damaging Effects of Radiation on Solid Reactor Materials, *Nucleonics*, vol. 14, no. 9, pp. 63–65, September, 1956.
[†] Elongation up to maximum load.

denum, postradiation elongation to rupture has decreased to zero. Austenitic stainless steel shows a tendency to transform to ferrite under radiation, but it appears that the changes will not be large enough to affect the stainless (corrosion-resistant) quality of the alloy. At 10^{19} n/cm^2, titanium was reported to have shown no changes in density or dimensional characteristics. It should be pointed out that it is difficult to attempt to predict the effects of radiation on structural materials. Though the changes in many of the physical properties may be only a few per cent, these changes may occur in such a manner that they seriously impair the over-all performance of the material as a reactor structural component. For this reason the structural designer must take account of possible radiation conditions arising from reactor operation, and in-pile irradiation testing of structural materials proposed for rocket-motor, test-stand, and air-frame use may be required.

REFERENCES

1. *a.* "The Reactor Handbook," vol. 2 ("Engineering"), *AECD*-3646, May, 1955.
   b. "The Reactor Handbook," vol. 3 ("Materials"), sec. 1, *AECD*-3647, March, 1955.
2. *a.* Green, L.: High Temperature Compression Tests on Graphite, *NAA-SR*-165,

pp. 6–8 and fig. 7, p. 15, North American Aviation, Inc., Downey, Calif., Jan. 7, 1952.

b. Malmstrom, C., R. Keen, and L. Green: Some Mechanical Properties of Graphite at Elevated Temperatures, *NAA-SR*-79, pp. 19, 33, figs. 3, 77, North American Aviation, Inc., Downey, Calif., Sept. 28, 1950.

3. McCullough, H., and B. Kopelman: Solid Metal Hydrides as Reactor Moderators, *Nucleonics*, vol. 14, no. 11, fig. 3, p. 152, November, 1956.

4. Valovage, W. D.: Effect of Irradiation on Hot-pressed Boron Carbide, *KAPL*-1403, Knolls Atomic Power Laboratory, Schenectady, N.Y., Nov. 15, 1955.

5. Coffin, L. F., Jr.: The Problem of Thermal Stress Fatigue in Austenitic Steels at Elevated Temperatures, in "Symposium on Effect of Cyclic Heating and Stressing on Metals at Elevated Temperatures," pp. 31–50, *ASTM Special Tech. Publ.* 165, June 17, 1954.

6. Shanley, F. R.: Analysis of Stress-Strain-Time Relations from the Engineering Viewpoint, *P*-68, RAND Corporation, Santa Monica, Calif., Mar. 4, 1949. (Rev. September, 1951.)

7. Higgins, T. P., Jr.: Time-dependent Stress-Strain Distributions, *P*-218, RAND Corporation, Santa Monica, Calif., June 18, 1951.

8. Dorn, John E., and Lawrence A. Shepard: What We Need to Know about Creep, pp. 3–30, *ASTM Special Tech. Publ.* 165, June 17, 1954.

9. Freudenthal, A. M.: "The Inelastic Behavior of Engineering Materials and Structures," John Wiley & Sons, Inc., New York, 1950.

10. Carter, J. C.: Temperature and Stress Distribution in Spheres, Rods, Tubes, and Plates in Which the Heat Source Is within the Boundaries of the Solids, *ANL*-4690, Argonne National Laboratory, Chicago, Ill., Sept. 7, 1951.

11. Field, F. A.: Temperature Gradient and Thermal Stresses in Bodies with Uniformly Distributed Volume Heat Sources, *AECD*-3650, Oak Ridge National Laboratory, Oak Ridge, Tenn., February, 1955.

12. Currie, L. M., V. C. Hamister, and H. G. MacPherson: chap. 2, sec. 1, pp. 65–107, in R. Hurst and S. McLain (eds.), "Technology and Engineering," Progress in Nuclear Energy, ser. IV, vol. 1, McGraw-Hill Book Company, Inc., New York, 1956.

13. Billington, D. S.: How Radiation Affects Materials—Basic Mechanisms, *Nucleonics*, vol. 14, no. 9, pp. 54–57, September, 1956.

14. Wigner, E. P.: Theoretical Physics in the Metallurgical Laboratory of Chicago, *J. Appl. Phys.*, vol. 17, no. 11, pp. 862–863, 1946.

15. Kittel, J. H.: Damaging Effects of Radiation on Solid Reactor Materials, *Nucleonics*, vol. 14 no. 9, pp. 63–65, September, 1956.

16. Ref. 3, p. 148.

17. Bresee, J. C., et al.: Damaging Effects of Radiation on Chemical Materials, *Nucleonics*, vol. 14, no. 9, pp. 75–81, September, 1956.

18. Robertson, R. F. S.: chap. 6, sec. 1, pp. 265–280, in R. Hurst and S. McLain (eds.), "Technology and Engineering," Progress in Nuclear Energy, ser. IV. vol. 1, McGraw-Hill Book Company, Inc., New York, 1956.

19. Sisman, O., and J. C. Wilson: Engineering Use of Damage Data, *Nucleonics*, vol. 14, no. 9, pp. 58–62, September 1956.

CHAPTER 6

NUCLEONICS

In introducing this chapter it is perhaps pertinent to discuss what is not presented here as well as what is contained herein. The prime purpose of this chapter is to present and discuss reactor statics, kinetics, geometries, and attendant problems of neutron and gamma heating and shielding from the viewpoint of the reactor design engineer who must use the calculated nucleonic information in the complete structural and heat-transfer design of the rocket reactor. More complete and more elegant treatment of the mathematics is given by Glasstone and Edlund,[1] Murray,[2] and in "The Reactor Handbook,"[3] among others. The reader here is assumed to have some acquaintance with more basic presentations such as those by Stephenson,[4] Thompson and Rodgers,[5] or Soodak and Campbell.[6] This chapter, in fact, is not concerned with the manipulations and mathematical proofs necessary to provide a solid foundation of analysis. The existing treatments are accepted as they stand and are discussed from the viewpoint of engineering usefulness, potentiality, applicability, and capability in order to guide the reactor designer in his choice of analytical techniques desired for application to any particular problem. This chapter is not meant to teach anyone reactor physics from scratch; rather, it is written to aid in the orientation of those with a basic acquaintance with the subject toward an understanding of the possibilities and limitations of the several different available lines of analytical attack on the nucleonics of rocket reactors. In general, the notations and symbols utilized are standard in the reactor field and are defined in the cited references.

6-1. Reactor Statics. Fundamental to the preliminary design of any reactor is a knowledge of the conditions required for nuclear criticality. In addition it is particularly important in all power reactors, not just those for rocket propulsion, to have reasonable estimates of the expected power-generation distributions in steady-state operation. This sort of information is obtained from static calculations of the behavior of neutrons within the reactor. In this section a description is given of the "real" physical processes pertinent to fission (as they are imagined) taking place in a stably operating reactor. This is done in order to make

189

clear the basic phenomena which are partially described by the several mathematical models in common usage for the solution of the reactor-statics problem. Next, the principles of the most "exact" mathematical treatments are presented and reasons are given why these are not extensively used in reactor analysis. The approximate analytical methods in common usage are discussed, and some results of analyses using these methods are also presented.

The Self-sustaining Fission Reaction. When a heavy fissionable nucleus absorbs a neutron, it is raised to an excited state from which it can escape by radiative decay or by fission. In the fission process some unbound neutrons are given off directly and others are emitted from fission-fragment nuclei in excited states. Some of those emitted from fission fragments are given off at a measurable time later than the initial fission. These are called *delayed neutrons* and are of great practical importance in reactor control (Chap. 7). A detailed summary of the delayed-neutron characteristics of fission has been given by Keepin[7] and should be consulted for further information.

Almost all of the neutrons resulting from fission appear at energies between 0.1 and 10 Mev, with a mean energy between 1 and 2 Mev. These "fast" neutrons move unimpeded through space until they interact with other nuclei. In a reactor core containing materials of low atomic number for neutron thermalization, the fission neutron may collide elastically with a low-mass nucleus and lose some of its kinetic energy to the struck nucleus, which exhibits its newly acquired energy by motion within the confines of its structure, banging into its neighboring atoms in a crystal lattice, causing atomic ionization, and producing what is observed as *heat* (kinetic, disoriented, motion). The neutron continues on its way, most probably in a direction different from that in which it was traveling before collision, only to collide with another nucleus, lose more energy, and travel on to undergo more collisions until its escape from the system or absorption by one of the nuclei it strikes. At high energies (e.g., above 0.5 Mev) a scattering collision of a neutron with a nucleus is not at all isotropic in either the center-of-mass or laboratory systems,* the neutron after collision preferentially following a track oriented in the forward direction relative to its incident track.

At low energies the scattering is also not isotropic in the laboratory system, although it is in the center-of-mass system, but differs markedly from isotropy only for the few nuclei of lowest mass number. Here the effect is purely geometric and results from the transformation from center-of-mass coordinates to laboratory coordinates. Hydrogen, with a nuclear

---

* The coordinate systems generally used in neutron-scattering analysis are more fully discussed in S. Glasstone and M. C. Edlund, "The Elements of Nuclear Reactor Theory," D. Van Nostrand Company, Inc., Princeton, N.J., 1952.

mass of 1 is the worst offender here, preferentially scattering neutrons in the forward direction in the laboratory system. Since reactors are built in the laboratory system, hydrogen is a very poor choice for a neutron reflector, although it is a good moderator.

Neutron absorption can take place at any neutron energy, with a variety of results. Such absorption might produce a compound nucleus in an excited state, which will decay to its ground state by β emission, γ emission, or both. This decay to ground state might involve the emission of an α particle, as in the "fission" of B^{10} by neutron capture, for example, or the absorption of a high-energy neutron might produce an excited nucleus which returns to the ground state by emission of a low-energy neutron and possibly attendant β or γ radiation. This latter process is called inelastic scattering; note that it does not remove a neutron from circulation but only exchanges a low-energy neutron for one at high energy. Finally, the absorption of a neutron by a fissionable nucleus can cause a fission, with the production of more neutrons to start the chain of events all over again. In a thermalizing reactor core many fission neutrons lose all of their birth energy by elastic and inelastic collisions and eventually assume or reach the kinetic "temperature" of their surroundings in the reactor. Such neutrons are called *thermal neutrons*. These thermal neutrons can wander through the reactor making elastic collisions, neither gaining nor losing energy, in the net, until they are captured by absorption in some nucleus or lost through the boundaries of the system. Because thermal neutrons move so much more slowly than high-energy neutrons, a much higher neutron density can be attained for a given quantitative loss rate from the system, so that many thermal neutrons are available per unit volume in a predominantly thermal reactor.

These, then, are the mechanisms of the fission chain reaction. Note that the neutrons produced in fissions wander through space and time, travel in straight-line paths of varying length between collisions, and lose energy in stepwise fashion in elastic- or inelastic-collision processes of extremely short duration. The microscopic probabilities (cross sections) of absorption and scattering are a consequence of the structure of the absorbing nuclei and may vary in a different way with incident neutron energy for each target nucleus. Fortunately these nuclear-interaction probabilities are not also functions of position within the reactor, or the situation would be hopelessly complicated. However, the bulk or macroscopic interaction probabilities are linearly dependent on local nuclear densities, thus may vary from point to point within a single material in a reactor if the material density varies with position.

Criticality requires that the number of neutrons stored in the reactor be invariant with time. A reactor in which the neutron population or density is increasing in time is supercritical and will destroy itself if not self-limited or returned to critical. Conversely a reactor in which the neutron density is decreasing is subcritical and will become more so until the neutron density reaches zero (or background) or the reactivity is increased by some means to achieve criticality. The neutron *level* has nothing to do with criticality, but it does determine total reactor power output. Criticality is determined by the *ratio* of neutron level in one generation to that in the next. Determination of the requirements for criticality of any given reactor design thus involves a study of the behavior of the neutrons produced in fission from one fission chain to the next. Such a study requires accounting for all the effects of fission neutrons wandering through space, losing energy, and being captured or escaping the system. If all the neutrons produced in one fission process just succeed in producing *exactly* one more fission, then the reactor will be critical. Solution of this problem reduces to the determination of expressions for the rates of neutron production, leakage, and absorption in the reactor system. Criticality is achieved for a system whose geometry and material densities and distribution are such that the rate of neutron production exactly equals the sum of the rates of leakage and absorption.

For the design of a rocket reactor, or of any other moderate- or high-power-density reactor for that matter, it is not sufficient to know just the specifications for reactor criticality. Coolant flow and power generation must be matched locally throughout the reactor as exactly as possible. Since the temperature-varying physical properties and compressible nature of the core coolant can greatly amplify small differences in heat load per unit flow channel (Chap. 4), any small design deviation from an exact match in a rocket-reactor core can result in a bad local mismatch in practice. The result of such amplification can be large local deviations from the mean in structure temperature, gas temperature, and propellant flow rate per coolant channel. The design of a matched system requires accurate knowledge of the power generation or fission distribution throughout the reactor. The spatial distribution of coolant flow throughout the core can be accomplished by mechanical means and is under the control of the reactor design engineer. However, the spatial distribution of fission density depends on the distributions of neutron-moderating and -reflecting material, neutron poisons, fissionable fuel, coolant, and temperature. The distribution of temperature in turn depends on the coolant and fission density distributions. The fundamental problem of heat-exchanger rocket-reactor design is how to juggle all of these factors to produce a uniform temperature and coolant distribution, and thereby achieve optimum performance. For rocket-reactor use the core geometry of most interest is a cylinder. For optimum heat-transfer performance in this shape of core it may be desirable to vary the fuel loading radially and/or axially to provide proper peak-temperature distributions. Analysis of the spatial distribution of neutrons and nuclear interactions in such a system must thus be done on a two- or three-dimensional basis. The complete problem is incredibly complex and cannot be resolved by a single neutronic calculation, no matter how exact it may be. The solution must be approached in an iterative way, by calculation of the reactor neutronics under an assumed set of reactor material and temperature distributions, thus yielding a first guess at the fission distribution. Engineering analysis will then disclose that some portion of the reactor is too hot or too cold for optimum performance for the assumed coolant distribution. Local fuel loadings (fissionable-material densities) are then modified, coolant-channel dimensions may be changed, with possible consequent change in bulk material densities, and the neutron calculation is repeated. This whole process must be repeated until all the variable factors have been reconciled to the desired level of agreement with the reactor design criteria, whatever they may be.

Mathematical Description of the Process. The previously discussed mechanisms of the chain reaction do not immediately suggest simple methods of analysis which will include all the possible and pertinent effects. In fact, it will develop that no such simple methods exist at the present time. However, the brief definition given for criticality does suggest that it might be possible to determine neutron behavior in the reactor by following one neutron through its life cycle, then another neutron, and another, *ad infinitum.* If this is done for enough neutrons, using the proper probability functions for each possible interaction, a statistical picture of the reactor neutronics, criticality, and neutron-nuclei-interaction distributions will be obtained. Unfortunately, "enough" may mean 10^4, 10^5, or even 10^6 random neutron life cycles, depending on the geometric, structural, and material complexity of the reactor involved in the analysis and on the desired allowable statistical dispersion or error in the final answer. This is called the *Monte Carlo method* and is the only physically exact analytical method presently known for reactor neutronic analysis. The derivation of the name is obvious, for with this method we are following many randomly chosen neutrons through their life cycles in a random way to see how they come out, which is very much like putting your money on a number on the wheel at Monte Carlo in the hope that something useful will happen. The mechanics of a Monte Carlo calculation go somewhat as follows: First, the spatial origin of the first neutron of interest is chosen at random, in the reactor fuel region, but in a weighted manner to account for the assumed fission distribution. The birth energy of this neutron is chosen in a random way and weighted to account for the known spectrum (energy distribution) of fission neutrons;

and the direction of motion is chosen at random, since the emission of neutrons in fission is isotropic in the laboratory system. The neutron path length to first collision is then chosen by a random-weighted process taking account of the postulated material densities in the region around the origin of the neutron and of the various interaction cross sections. The type of first interaction (elastic or inelastic scattering, capture, fission, etc.) is then chosen, again randomly, in accord with the weighted probabilities for each possible type of reaction. If the neutron is scattered, its direction of motion after collision is chosen to conform with the angular-scattering probabilities applicable for the incident neutron energy (preferential forward distributions in high-energy scattering, etc.). Similarly, the energy loss in the collision is determined randomly in accord with the limitations of the energy-scattering probability function. The history of the neutron is thus traced until it passes out of the range of interest either by escaping from the system or by being absorbed to produce an excited nucleus or another fission. If the neutron under observation produces a fission, this fact and the neutron energy and spatial location of the event are recorded for future reference. In any event, following the demise of the first neutron, a second neutron is chosen as before, with a spatial distribution and energy randomly chosen to fit the assumed spatial fission distribution and the fission-neutron energy spectrum, respectively. The course of this second neutron is followed by study of a third neutron, a fourth, etc., until sufficient case histories are available to provide a statistically clear picture of the behavior of neutrons in the reactor. At this point a comparison is made of the spatial distribution of fission-producing captures of neutrons under observation and the fission distribution from which all neutrons were assumed to originate. If these two coincide, the designer is very fortunate and the calculation need not be repeated. If not, the assumed distribution must be modified and the calculation repeated. It is often sufficient to use the observed distribution from one study as the starting point or assumed distribution for the next, and in this way to converge upon the "true" solution. Although not explicitly stated in the above discussion, it is clear that, on the average, one fission must occur for each ν neutrons assumed at fission energy (ν is the number of neutrons released per fission) for the reactor to be critical. As for the fission distribution, it is unlikely that this result will be the case from the first analysis, so that some adjustment in the density of fuel or other material may be necessary in repeated calculations. More detailed expositions of the Monte Carlo method as well as a discussion of one such reactor calculation are available in the literature.[8-10] It is easy to see that this sort of calculation can become extremely complex in any but the simplest geometries (i.e., homogeneous one-dimensional systems) and is certainly beyond the capabilities of hand calculation even for these. In fact this method is so difficult that only in recent years with the advent of large high-speed computers (such as the IBM 704 or Sperry-Rand 1103A computers) has it been possible to analyze simple, real reactors. It is anticipated that continued development of computing machinery will result in an even greater use of the Monte Carlo method for reactor analysis.

Lacking the facilities of high-speed computers, reactor physicists years ago adopted other methods of analysis, inherently less correct than the exact Monte Carlo method described above. The basis of all these approximate methods has been the Boltzmann transport equation used to describe the motion of neutrons through stationary (in the atomic sense) solids. As previously mentioned, reactor analysis is essentially the study of the conditions of neutron absorption, leakage, and production. All three of these phenomena depend upon local neutron and material densities and on neutron energy, hence require the analysis of the mechanisms of neutron energy loss and motion throughout the reactor. The Boltzmann transport equation provides, in principle, an exact description of the motion of monoenergetic neutrons. The neutron-balance equation for monoenergetic neutrons, using the Boltzmann transport equation, is generally written as

$$\nabla \cdot \phi(\mathbf{r},\mathbf{\Omega}) + \Sigma_a \phi(\mathbf{r},\mathbf{\Omega}) + \Sigma_s \phi(\mathbf{r},\mathbf{\Omega})$$
$$= \int_{\Omega'} P(\mathbf{\Omega'} \cdot \mathbf{\Omega}) \phi(\mathbf{r},\mathbf{\Omega'}) \, d\mathbf{\Omega'} + S(\mathbf{r},\mathbf{\Omega}) \quad (6\text{-}1)$$

The terms are defined as follows:

The net leakage loss rate of neutrons from a unit volume $d\tau$ and a unit angle $d\Omega$ around a point r is given by $\nabla \cdot \phi(\mathbf{r},\mathbf{\Omega}) \, d\tau \, d\Omega$, the neutron loss rate by absorption is $\Sigma_a \phi(\mathbf{r},\mathbf{\Omega}) \, d\tau \, d\Omega$, and the loss rate by scattering is similarly $\Sigma_s \phi(\mathbf{r},\mathbf{\Omega}) \, d\tau \, d\Omega$. The integral expression on the right side of Eq. (6-1) is just the number of neutrons scattered from all directions $\mathbf{\Omega'}$ into $\mathbf{\Omega}$ per unit volume $d\tau$ per unit time, and $S(\mathbf{r},\mathbf{\Omega})$ gives the rate of gain of source neutrons by birth in the fission process.

The form of the transport relation given in Eq. (6-1) is relatively intractable, but soluble sets of equations have been obtained by expansion of the flux function in spherical harmonics. Since the equation given describes the transport of neutrons at only one energy, it cannot be used alone to determine the exact neutron balance in a real nuclear reactor in which neutrons of all energies from fission to thermal are interacting with nuclei of the reactor materials. Note that collisions between neutrons are relatively rare because the neutron density is generally greatly less than the nuclear density of the materials within the reactor.

The best approximation used in the analysis of neutron transport in reactors has been the spherical-harmonics method of solution of the transport equation. Here the flux function is expanded in terms of orthonormal functions of the cosine of the angle between the scattered neutron velocity vector and one axis of the laboratory coordinate system. Legendre polynomials are often used for this expansion. In a practical case this method results in substituting the problem of solution of an infinite set of coupled linear ordinary differential equations for a finite set of partial integrodifferential equations [i.e., Eq. (6-1)] previously found from the transport formulation of neutron flux, or density, distribution. If the analysis is set up properly, the flux function (in spherical harmonics) will be convergent and only a finite number of the infinite set of ordinary equations need be solved to achieve any desired degree of accuracy in the expression of flux distribution in space and direction. Even so it is evident that this method of solution is complex and requires the services of a large computer to be of practical utility. A more frequent approximation used in the analysis of neutron transport in reactors has been the assumption that neutrons move through material in accordance with the well-known equations for diffusion of heat through solids, diffusion of gases or liquids through porous media, etc., all of which assume isotropy of fluxes and interaction processes. This is called the "diffusion" approximation to neutron transport.

Basically the diffusion approximation will reduce the transport equation (6-1) to a pair of diffusion equations which can be applied to problems of neutron distribution within a reactor if it is assumed that:

1. Fission neutrons are emitted isotropically.

2. The average scattering cross section in the reactor is much larger than the absorption cross section, i.e., the slowing-down medium is only weakly absorbing.

3. The probability $P(\mu_0)$ that the cosine of the neutron-scattering angle will be μ_0 is given by $2\pi P(\mu_0) = \Sigma_s/2 + 3\bar{\mu}_0\Sigma_s\mu_0/2$, where $\bar{\mu}_0$ is the cosine of the average scattering angle, given by $\bar{\mu}_0 = \frac{2}{3}A$.

4. The angular dependence of the flux may be expressed by an isotropic term and a term in the cosine of the angle between the neutron velocity vector and the net neutron flow vector, that is,

$$\phi(\mathbf{r},\mathbf{\Omega}) = \frac{\phi(\mathbf{r})}{2} + 3\mathbf{J}(\mathbf{r}) \cdot \frac{\mathbf{\Omega}}{2}$$

The two resulting equations are

$$-\frac{\lambda_{tr}}{3}\nabla^2\phi(\mathbf{r}) + \Sigma_a\phi(\mathbf{r}) = S(\mathbf{r}) \tag{6-2a}$$

$$\mathbf{J}(\mathbf{r}) = -\frac{\lambda_{tr}}{3}\nabla\phi(\mathbf{r}) \tag{6-2b}$$

Assumptions 1 and 2 are not particularly restrictive except in the obvious case of analysis of a heavily poisoned reactor, such as might be the case in a moderately fast reactor system which depends strongly on epithermal fissions. Assumption 3 errs in that the scattering function $P(\mu_0)$ for hydrogen is very poorly represented by two terms, and high-energy anisotropic scattering to preferential angles is not shown at all, so that Eqs. (6-2) are not valid for use with hydrogen or at high (> 0.5 Mev) neutron energies. Assumption 4 is poor near localized sources or sinks or near boundaries or interfaces between dissimilar media because in those regions the neutron flux, at any energy, will be very far from isotropic in nature and thus poorly represented by the two-term expression. Since all rocket reactors of the type discussed will have such regions, it appears that the diffusion equations can never be very useful; however it has been found that, in spite of these errors inherent in diffusion theory, the relations given can yield many calculated results within the desired limits of accuracy with a great reduction in computational effort as compared with the transport equation itself or the Monte Carlo method, the only better descriptions of reactor neutron behavior.

The monoenergetic Boltzmann transport equation or its diffusion approximation can be used to describe the spatial motion of neutrons in a single energy group in multi-energy-group reactor analysis, but such an analysis is not strictly physically rigorous since there are no discrete neutron energy "groups" in an operating reactor. In such a multigroup analysis each neutron energy group must be coupled to others above and below it by equations describing the energy-loss processes occurring in neutron-nuclei collisions. These equations describe the slowing down of neutrons and are commonly called slowing-down equations.

Integral expressions which are exact for isotropic center-of-mass system scattering have been obtained giving the neutron density falling below any energy E per unit time. This is called the slowing-down density. One form of the equation for slowing down in an absorbing medium is

$$q^*(E) = P(E)q(E) = \exp\left(-\frac{1}{\xi}\int_E^{E_0}\frac{\Sigma_a}{\Sigma_a + \Sigma_s}\frac{dE'}{E'}\right)$$
$$\int_E^{E/\alpha} F(E')\frac{E - E'}{E'(1 - \alpha)}\,dE' \qquad (6\text{-}3)$$

The scattering-collision density at E' is $F(E')$; α is the ratio of the minimum value of the energy of a neutron after a scattering collision to its initial energy, given by $\alpha = (A - 1)^2/(A + 1)^2$; and ξ is the average logarithmic energy decrement per scattering collision, given by $\xi = 1 + (\alpha \ln \alpha)/(1 - \alpha)$. Here, as for the Boltzmann transport equation, the exact expression is not readily soluble and has been handled principally by use of average values of the energy (or lethargy) loss per collision and group-averaged values of absorption and scattering cross section. As a matter of interest the neutron flux at any energy E in a weakly absorbing medium is directly related to the slowing-down density by the approximate equation

$$\phi(E) = \frac{q^*(E)}{\xi(\Sigma_a + \Sigma_s)E} \tag{6-4}$$

Many approximations have been used in reactor analysis to simplify the picture of neutron slowing down. In order of simplicity these are:

1. One-velocity analysis in which all neutrons have a constant energy and only diffuse about through the reactor.

2. Two-group analysis in which two kinds of neutrons, fast and thermal, are recognized.

3. Multigroup analysis in which the energy range above thermal is divided into an arbitrary number of groups, two or greater, and each group is treated as though monoenergetic in nature. These are discussed more fully in the next section.

Approximate Methods of Analysis. The simplest analytical procedure is the one-velocity-diffusion-theory case with all neutron sources and sinks at the same energy. It is not considered herein, principally because it departs from reality so very badly that it is of little practical interest.

By far the most tractable and aesthetically attractive hand method of analysis is by age-diffusion theory. This method makes use of a continuous slowing-down model (due to Fermi) for the neutron-thermalization process (for all neutron energies above thermal), accounts for above-thermal leakage and absorption by simple probability functions, and treats thermal neutrons by the one-velocity-diffusion-equation method rejected above. The heart of this method is the assumption that the slowing down of neutrons can be represented by a continuous loss of energy by the neutron as it knocks around in the reactor rather than by a series of discrete energy changes on collision as is actually the case. This assumption infers that the behavior of a large number of individual neutrons of any given generation can be described by means of an average neutron, with some average-energy characteristic of the number and type of thermalizing collisions the average neutron has suffered since birth. This picture is most valid for slowing down by moderators of high mass number and fails completely for slowing down by moderators containing hydrogen. This is a consequence of the fact that a neutron can lose all of its energy (to thermal) in a single collision with a hydrogen nucleus (a proton), or alternatively it can lose none if the scattering angle is zero. Here it is obvious that the slowing down of neutrons in hydrogen cannot be characterized by an average neutron, for the energy range over which the average must be taken is that from thermal to fission.

However, the Fermi age model for slowing down has proved reasonably good for use even with heavy-water (D_2O) moderated systems, and modifications to the theory have been made[11] to permit its approximate use with light-water (H_2O) or other hydrogen-moderated systems. The

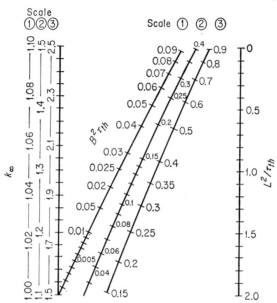

FIG. 6-1. Nomogram for determination of critical size or material constitution of homogeneous reactors by Fermi age theory. (*F. T. Miles and H. Soodak, Nomogram for the Critical Equation, Nucleonics, vol. 11, no. 1, p. 66, January, 1953.*)

The following procedure should be used:

1. Knowing the material constitution and density, determine k_∞ and L^2/τ_{th}.
2. Draw a straight line between the appropriate values on the L^2/τ_{th} and k_∞ scales.
3. Determine critical buckling from the intercept on the appropriate $B^2\tau_{th}$ scale (use scale 1, 2, or 3 to correspond with that used for the k_∞ value).
4. Compute critical size from equations given in Table 6-1.
5. Or, knowing desired critical size, invert the above procedure to determine required values of k_∞ and L^2/τ_{th}, and thus to delineate limits on material constitution.

basic result of the age-diffusion method is expressed in the critical equation

$$k_{eff} = \frac{k_\infty e^{-B^2\tau_{th}}}{1 + L^2B^2} \quad \text{for a homogeneous reactor} \quad (6\text{-}5)$$

where k_∞ = infinite-multiplication factor

B = buckling

τ_{th} = age to thermal

L = the thermal diffusion length

k_{eff} = effective multiplication factor

When $k_{eff} = 1$ the reactor will be critical. Solution of Eq. (6-5) for this condition can be tedious if a wide range of reactor constituents and material densities is to be surveyed. Figure 6-1 is a nomogram[12] for the solution of Eq. (6-5) for criticality. Buckling is a property of the geometry and dimensions of the reactor system. Equations are given in Table 6-1 for the buckling of the bare slabs, rectangular blocks, spheres, and cylinders shown in Fig. 6-2. Also given are equations for the

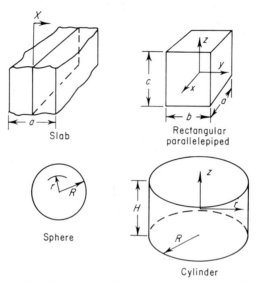

Slab

Rectangular parallelepiped

Sphere

Cylinder

Fig. 6-2. Dimensions and coordinates of bare reactors.

thermal-flux distribution in the reactor at criticality and for the minimum critical volume.

The infinite-multiplication factor is the effective multiplication the reactor would have if the buckling were zero, i.e., if the reactor were infinite. This is determined simply by

$$k_\infty = \nu \frac{\Sigma_f}{\Sigma_a} = \nu \frac{N_{\text{fuel}}\sigma_f}{\sum_1^n N_i \sigma_{ai}} \tag{6-6}$$

for a homogeneous reactor with n material components.

The diffusion length is simply the square root of one-sixth of the mean square distance that a monoenergetic (thermal here) neutron travels from its source (thermalized from high energy) to the point of its absorption and is given by

$$L^2 = \frac{\lambda_{tr}\lambda_a}{3} = \frac{1}{3}\Sigma_{tr}\Sigma_a \tag{6-7}$$

Here the cross sections used are those for thermal neutrons and the subscript tr denotes transport in distinction to scattering. The ratio of

TABLE 6-1. FLUX AND BUCKLING CHARACTERISTICS OF BARE REACTORS

Shape	Buckling	Flux distribution	Minimum critical volume
Slab..........................	$B^2 = \left(\dfrac{\pi}{a}\right)^2$	$\dfrac{\phi_x}{\phi_0} = \cos Bx$	
Rectangular parallelepiped.....	$B^2 = B_x{}^2 + B_y{}^2 + B_z{}^2$	$\dfrac{\phi}{\phi_0} = \phi_x\phi_y\phi_z$	$\dfrac{161}{B^3}$
	$B_x{}^2 = \left(\dfrac{\pi}{a}\right)^2$	$\phi_x = \cos B_x x$	
	$B_y{}^2 = \left(\dfrac{\pi}{b}\right)^2$	$\phi_y = \cos B_y y$	
	$B_z{}^2 = \left(\dfrac{\pi}{c}\right)^2$	$\phi_z = \cos B_z z$	
Sphere..., ...	$B^2 = \left(\dfrac{\pi}{R}\right)^2$	$\dfrac{\phi_r}{\phi_0} = \dfrac{\sin Br}{Br}$	$\dfrac{130}{B^3}$
Cylinder.....................	$B^2 = B_r{}^2 + B_z{}^2$	$\dfrac{\phi}{\phi_0} = \phi_r\phi_z$	$\dfrac{148}{B^3}$
	$B_r{}^2 = \left(\dfrac{2.405}{R}\right)^2$	$\phi_r = J_0(B_r r)$	
	$B_z{}^2 = \left(\dfrac{\pi}{H}\right)^2$	$\phi_z = \cos B_z z$	

NOTE: 1. ϕ_0 is the maximum flux at the center of symmetry of the reactor.
2. The dimensions a, b, c, R, and H all include the extrapolation length $0.71\lambda_{tr}$ beyond the real physical boundaries of the reactor.

TABLE 6-2. NUCLEAR PROPERTIES OF SOME INTERESTING MODERATORS*

Moderator material	Normal density, g/cm³	Thermal-neutron-absorption cross section Σ_a, cm⁻¹	Age-to-thermal τ_{th}, cm²	Slowing-down length $\sqrt{\tau_{th}}$, cm	Diffusion length L, cm	Migration length M, cm
Water, H₂O.......	1.00	2.2×10^{-2}	31.4	5.6	2.9	6.3
Heavy water, D₂O (0.25% H₂O)...	1.10	8.6×10^{-5}	120	10.9	100	101
Beryllium, Be.....	1.85	1.1×10^{-3}	97	9.9	21	25.6
Graphite, C.......	1.65	3.7×10^{-4}	344	18.5	50.5	53.9
Beryllium oxide, BeO..........	2.70	6.0×10^{-4}	130	11.4	30	32

* See also Table 5-6.

scattering mean free path to transport mean free path is $1 - \bar{\mu}_0$, where $\bar{\mu}_0$ is the average cosine of the neutron-scattering angle per collision, in the laboratory coordinate system. The average cosine rapidly approaches zero with increasing mass number of the scattering nucleus. Table 6-2 gives values of L and Σ_a for several moderators of interest.

The age to thermal is similar to the diffusion length squared in that it is one-sixth of the mean square (crow-flight) distance traveled by a neutron from the time of its emission at source energy to thermal energy. As a matter of reference, the sum $L^2 + \tau_{th}$ is called the migration area M^2. M, the migration length, is a measure of the distance traveled by a neutron from birth to capture as a thermal neutron. The square root of the age is sometimes called the slowing-down length. Table 6-2 gives values of τ_{th} and M for five normal-density moderators of interest in reactor design. For elements of mass number higher than helium the age is approximately given by

$$\tau_{th} = \frac{6}{\xi \Sigma_s \Sigma_{tr}} = \frac{3A + 4}{\Sigma_s{}^2} \tag{6-8}$$

where the cross sections are average values of epithermal neutrons. This equation shows that the age is inversely proportional to the square of the material density, so that appropriate corrections may be applied to the data in Table 6-2 when necessary. Although the Fermi age theory does not apply for moderation by hydrogen, a synthetic value of age has been found for water which permits the use of age-diffusion theory in the analysis of simple water-moderated systems. The value of τ_{th} given in Table 6-2 for water is this synthetic value. As mentioned, the age-diffusion method of analysis is valid only for bare reactors. However, by use of the concept of "reflector savings," calculations on bare reactors can often be used to estimate the critical sizes of two-space-region, reflected reactors with homogeneous cores. The reflector savings is defined as the difference in core radius between a bare critical reactor and one contained within a reflector, when the material densities of both cores are identical. Here the bare-core radius R_0 includes the extrapolation distance $0.71\lambda_{tr_{core}}$ and the reflector thickness t_r includes the extrapolation distance $0.71\lambda_{tr_{refl}}$. The reflected-core radius R_r is the actual physical radius of the core. Thus we have the reflector savings δ given by

$$\delta = R_0 - R_r \tag{6-9}$$

Now if the reflector savings is small compared with the core dimension (radius, thickness, etc.), it is given sufficiently accurately for hand calculation by

$$\delta = \frac{\Sigma_{tr_r}}{\Sigma_{tr_c}} L_r \tanh \frac{t_r}{L_r} \tag{6-10}$$

where subscripts c and r denote core and reflector, respectively, and L_r is the diffusion length in the reflector. Having the critical dimension(s) of a bare spherical, cylindrical, or slab (axial dimension of a cylinder) reactor, it is thus possible to estimate the critical core dimensions for a reflected reactor of similar core composition. Data on bare spherical reactors are most often available. The critical dimensions of bare cylinders or rectangular block reactors of similar constituency can be estimated by equating the buckling (Table 6-1) equations for these geometries with that for the sphere of interest. The critical core dimensions for a reflected system can then be estimated as outlined above.[13]

Not all systems are homogeneous. Indeed for use of fuel-element materials with large resonance-absorption cross sections it is desirable to lump the fuel within a matrix of moderator to reduce the exposure of the epithermal neutrons to the resonance absorber and thus to reduce the resonance capture of neutrons in the assembly. In rocket reactors this is the case for use of tungsten or tantalum as fuel-element base material. The age-diffusion critical equation (6-5) is not designed specifically for use in the analysis of matrix or lattice-structured cores, but it may be modified for such use. For use of Eq. (6-5) for a matrix assembly the value of L^2 should be taken as

$$L^2 = L_m{}^2(1 - g) \qquad (6\text{-}11)$$

where L_m is the diffusion length in the moderator only and g is a thermal-utilization factor given by

$$\frac{1}{g} = 1 + \frac{\Sigma_{am}}{\Sigma_{af}} \frac{\phi_m}{\phi_f} \qquad (6\text{-}12)$$

where the subscripts m and f refer to moderator and fuel, respectively, and ϕ_m and ϕ_f are the average values of the thermal flux in each region. Here, as for the other terms of the critical equation, the macroscopic cross sections are based on bulk material densities taken over the entire core volume. k_∞ is determined by Eq. (6-6), as before, but the value of τ_{th} used should be chosen between 1.06 and 1.1 of that for the moderator alone. Modifying the terms in this way permits rough analysis of the size and gross loadings required for criticality of matrix geometries.

Note that, although the thermal flux distribution is given (Table 6-1), the age-diffusion analysis does not provide the sort of fission-density-distribution information that is really helpful to the rocket-reactor designer in the determination of proper local heat-transfer and coolant flow conditions. Exact information can be obtained only from Monte Carlo analyses of the reactor of interest. However, the results of multi-energy-group calculations based on modifications of the neutron-transport equation can yield results sufficiently close to reality, as determined by critical-assembly measurements, to be very useful.

One frequently used technique for simplifying the analysis of the slowing down of neutrons is called the age-diffusion multigroup method. In this treatment the energy of the neutrons, from the source (fission) energy to thermal energy, is divided into a finite set of energy intervals or groups. Within each group the neutrons are assumed to diffuse, without energy loss, until they have undergone the average number of collisions which would be required to decrease their energy to that of the next lower group. It is then assumed that the neutrons are suddenly transferred to the next lower group. This process is continued until the neutrons have "filtered" down through each group to thermal energy, at which point they are handled by monoenergetic-diffusion equations. The neutron-nuclei-interaction probabilities are assumed constant in each group at some average value corresponding to the average energy of neutrons in that group. The key assumption of this method, and the one which permits a straightforward mathematical attack on the neutron slowing down and transport problem, is the assumption of "worlds within worlds" in the form of groups (in energy) of neutrons which can be treated independently of all other energy groups within the reactor.

Many methods, different from the group-diffusion method discussed above, of handling the neutrons in each group have been tried, each with some success in terms of prediction ability. For example, spatial motion of neutrons in each group has often been handled by transport rather than diffusion equations. This is particularly useful in the analysis of small fast reactors or for highly heterogeneous reactors where the angular correlations in flux distribution are important to the neutron distribution within the reactor. Also, in many reactors it is physically possible to scatter neutrons from one group to several energy-group levels below its starting point. In such a reactor, the assumption that all available neutrons from one group pass into the next (which implies the continuous-slowing-down model) is particularly invalid, unless the group-energy widths are so large that they ensure the impossibility of a downward scattering of more than one group. This effect has been handled in some cases by allowing a downscattering of an arbitrary number of groups by the inclusion of neutron-transfer functions as source and sink terms in the diffusion equations for each group.

The first step toward a true multigroup analysis is the two-group diffusion-approximation solution to the problem of a bare homogeneous core. This is somewhat tedious and when carried out leads to a criticality equation which reduces easily to the equation resulting from the Fermi age-diffusion method just discussed. Thus, in the criticality sense, simple age-diffusion analysis is two-group in nature. However, the expressions for the fast and slow flux distributions are more complex than that given by age diffusion for the thermal flux alone. The relative difficulty of two-group analysis of bare reactors has made it worthwhile to apply two-group theory to simple reflected reactors, since little additional complexity is observed compared to the initial increase in complexity from the age-diffusion method. The fundamental equations for a two-energy-group, two-space-region analysis are

$$D_{1x}\nabla^2\phi_{1x} - \Sigma_{1x}\phi_{1x} + k_x\Sigma_{2x}\phi_{2x} = 0 \qquad (6\text{-}13a)$$
$$D_{2x}\nabla^2\phi_{2x} - \Sigma_{2x}\phi_{2x} + k_x\Sigma_{1x}\phi_{1x} = 0 \qquad (6\text{-}13b)$$

where 1 and 2 denote the two energy groups and x denotes the region of interest (c for core and r for reflector). Of course, for a nonmultiplying reflector, $k_r = 0$ and the last term of Eqs. (6-13) drops out. It is thus necessary to solve four simultaneous differential equations. The four boundary conditions are the continuity of fluxes and of neutron currents in each group at the core-reflector interface. In addition, for a symmetrical assembly the gradient of the flux must be zero at the center of the reactor and the flux itself must fall to zero at some synthetic distance outside the containing reflector. The solution of these equations reduces to the evaluation of a 4 by 4 determinant for the critical equation. This can be carried out by hand but is tedious, and the solution and procedure are not given here. However, this method is sufficiently useful in reactor analysis that it has been programmed for automatic computing equipment,[14] which should certainly be used if it is available. Unfortunately, determination of flux distributions even by two-group methods is not sufficiently realistic to be of value to rocket-reactor design.

The required accuracy or agreement with the real physical world can be attained by extension of the method of groups to include more energy intervals. Following Glasstone and Edlund[15] let us suppose there are n groups, with group 1 being that at highest energy and group n that at thermal. Assume further that all neutrons are born at the energy of group 1. The diffusion equation for any group, excluding $i = 1$, is then given by

$$D_i\nabla^2\phi_i - \Sigma_i\phi_i + \Sigma_{i-1}\phi_{i-1} = 0 \qquad (6\text{-}14)$$

where Σ_i is the slowing-down probability (cross section) for all cases except for $i = n$, where it is the true absorption cross section for thermal neutrons. Note that the source term $\Sigma_{i-1}\phi_{i-1}$ for each group here is the slowing-down density from the group just above it. Neutrons scattered down from groups higher in energy than this can be included by the addition of other terms $\Sigma_{i-2}\phi_{i-2}$, $\Sigma_{i-3}\phi_{i-3}$, etc. This adds greatly to the complexity of the analysis, however. For the source fission neutrons in group 1 the diffusion equation is

$$D_1\nabla^2\phi_1 - \Sigma_1\phi_1 + k_\infty\Sigma_n\phi_n = 0 \qquad (6\text{-}15)$$

where Σ_1 and Σ_n are the slowing-down cross section of fission neutrons and the absorption cross section of thermal neutrons. Here the absorption of thermal neutrons is the source of the fission neutrons by the fission process itself. This treatment leads to a set of n differential equations, for a bare reactor, $n - 1$ being of the type in Eq. (6-14) and the additional one being that from Eq. (6-15). Each additional physical region, such as an internal moderating island, an external reflector, an intermediate shell of moderator, etc., adds another set of n equations to the mathematical system. In each case the boundary conditions require neutron flux and current continuity at the interfaces and further require that the flux be zero at the extrapolated boundary of the system. Thus, for an m-region n-group diffusion analysis, mn simultaneous differential equations must be solved. These are generally set in difference form so that the solutions can be carried out on high-speed digital computing machines, although electrical analog networks have been used to solve the set of differential equations directly.[16,17] Experience has shown that about 20 to 30 neutron-energy groups are required to provide adequate flux-distribution data as a function of neutron energy in reactors which have an appreciable fraction of fissions distributed above thermal energy. This is certainly the case with nearly all moderate- or high-power-density reactors. Furthermore a rocket reactor may require 5 to 10 bulk regions of different physical constituency, density, etc., in order to carry out the proper heat transfer, fluid flow, and structural performance. Under these conditions the reactor physicist must solve some 100 to 300 simultaneous second-order differential equations in each reactor calculation. Aside from the practical impossibility of doing this by hand, any desire for repeated calculations of a survey nature absolutely necessitates the use of high-speed digital computers for this work.

In summary, the only exact method of reactor analysis, the Monte Carlo method, requires too much memory and too many operations, hence is too time-consuming for use on present-day computing machines for any but the simplest geometries. The multi-energy-group transport-theory analysis of neutron behavior is the next best analytical method but is sufficiently more complex than multi-energy-group diffusion-theory analysis that its use at present is justified only in highly structured reactors where many boundaries of dissimilar material are found or for small fast reactors where the physical dimensions of the reactor approach the neutron-transport mean-free-path length. Below the multigroup diffusion methods there is a sharp drop in the capability of available useful analytical techniques, for the next real way point is two-group multi-region analysis. This is very useful for survey work of a general nature but of little value for detailed design. It is also complex enough to warrant machine calculations if a range of reactors is to be studied. At the bottom of the list we find the age-diffusion method for determining criticality and thermal flux distribution in bare reactors. This can be solved easily by hand (Fig. 6-1) but unfortunately is not useful in rocket-reactor design for anything but gross estimation of bulk size and critical mass.

We see then, that the analytical neutronic analyses required for proper reactor design must be carried out on large high-speed digital computers and simply cannot be done by hand, no matter how clever the designer may be. Fortunately the reactor business has been growing long enough that a kind of national (and presumably international) library of calculational methods programmed for modern computing machines is presently available. An excellent summary of computer codes available in the United States as of mid-1955 for the solution of reactor problems has been issued by The Division of Reactor Development of the United States AEC.[18] Revised versions of this bibliography will undoubtedly be issued from time to time. In addition, continued classification of available nuclear calculational codes is given in the Newsletters[19] of the Nuclear Codes Group, an organization with membership from many installations concerned with nuclear-reactor design. As the reactor field advances, the rocket-reactor designer may one day be able to choose, from such a listing, the calculational method he desires for the solution of a particular problem, contact the holder of the code, and have the problem rapidly run off on available computing machines.

In closing this section it is pertinent to comment on the relative roles of neutronic calculation and experiment. There is no substitute for good survey calculations to guide preliminary design thinking and even to aid in the evaluation of details of any proposed design. But there is also no substitute for experimental confirmation of a design based largely on calculations. After all, a calculational method is only "good" or "bad" as it agrees or disagrees with the results of critical-assembly experimentation. As we have seen, many of the "useful" calculational methods are very time-consuming, even on computing machines, and it will often be found that variational studies can be made more quickly and more correctly on active critical assemblies than by use of these analytical procedures. Proper reactor design requires both analytical and experimental study of neutron behavior. Neither should predominate, for they are not competitive methods, but can and should usefully supplement each other in any reactor development program.

Results of Calculations. Many reactor neutronic-survey-type calculations have been made by multigroup methods in the past few years. While it is always necessary to perform such calculations for the reactor of specific interest in order to obtain data for detailed design purposes, reference to existing relatively exact calculations can be helpful in preliminary design. In this framework use of such data can supplement or supplant simple age-diffusion or two-group reactor-survey calculations.

This section presents data on the criticality and median fission energy of bare spherical homogeneous cores, computed by multi-energy-group diffusion theory, and on the criticality of reflected cavity reactors, computed by a slightly modified version of transport theory. These calcula-

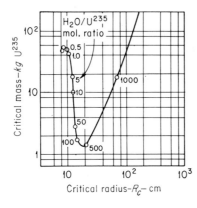
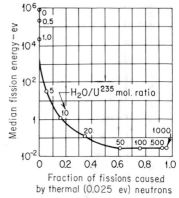

FIG. 6-3. Characteristics of critical mixtures of U^{235} and H_2O. (*G. Safonov, Survey of Reacting Mixtures Employing U^{235}, Pu^{239}, and U^{233} for Fuel and H_2O, D_2O, C, Be, and BeO for Moderator, R-259, RAND Corporation, Santa Monica, Calif., Jan. 8, 1954.*)

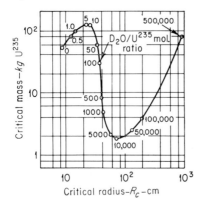
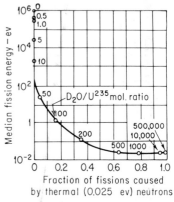

FIG. 6-4. Characteristics of critical mixtures of U^{235} and D_2O. (*G. Safonov, Survey of Reacting Mixtures Employing U^{235}, Pu^{239}, and U^{233} for Fuel and H_2O, D_2O, C, Be, and BeO for Moderator, R-259, RAND Corporation, Santa Monica, Calif., Jan. 8, 1954.*)

tions are the result of much excellent work by G. Safonov[20-23] in the field of reactor analysis.

Figures 6-3 through 6-7 show the critical mass of fuel and the median fission energy as a function of critical size and of moderator-to-fuel mole ratio for homogeneous bare spherical reactors utilizing mixtures of pure

U^{235} with H_2O, D_2O, C, Be, and BeO respectively. The median fission energy is defined by the criterion that one-half of all fissions are caused by neutrons with energy below the median and one-half by neutrons above this energy, and it is thus a measure of the "speed" (fastness or slowness)

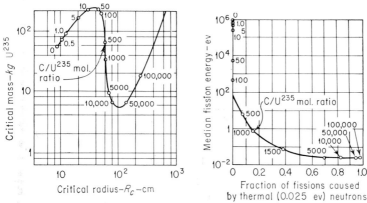

FIG. 6-5. Characteristics of critical mixtures of U^{235} and C. (*G. Safonov, Survey of Reacting Mixtures Employing* U^{235}, Pu^{239}, *and* U^{233} *for Fuel and* H_2O, D_2O, C, Be, *and BeO for Moderator, R-259, RAND Corporation, Santa Monica, Calif., Jan. 8, 1954.*)

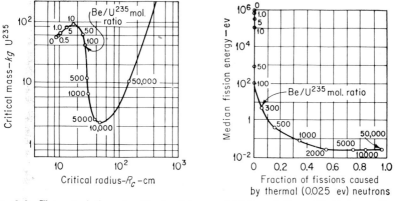

FIG. 6-6. Characteristics of critical mixtures of U^{235} and Be. (*G. Safonov, Survey of Reacting Mixtures Employing* U^{235}, Pu^{239}, *and* U^{233} *for Fuel and* H_2O, D_2O, C, Be, *and BeO for Moderator, R-259, RAND Corporation, Santa Monica, Calif., Jan. 8, 1954.*)

of the various reactors. The total volume of any given mixture is taken as the sum of the moderator and fuel volumes given separately. Fuel and moderator densities used in the calculations are given in Table 6-3. Figure 6-8 shows the critical mass, median fission energy, and fraction of fissions due to thermal neutrons as a function of critical size (radius) and moderator-to-fuel atom ratio for homogeneous bare spherical reactors utilizing three-component mixtures of pure U^{235}, C, and Be.

TABLE 6-3. MATERIAL DENSITIES USED IN MULTIGROUP REACTOR CALCULATIONS

Material	Density, g/cm^3
U^{235}	18.5
H_2O	1.00
D_2O	1.11
C	1.67
Be	1.85
BeO	3.00

All of the information presented in Figs. 6-3 to 6-8 for bare homogeneous reactors can be used for the estimation of criticality of reflected

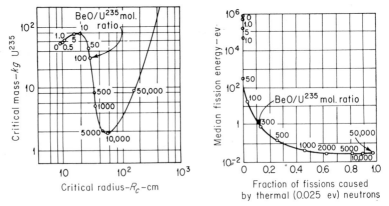

FIG. 6-7. Characteristics of critical mixtures of U^{235} and BeO. (*G. Safonov, Survey of Reacting Mixtures Employing* U^{235}, Pu^{239}, *and* U^{233} *for Fuel and* H_2O, D_2O, C, Be, *and* BeO *for Moderator, R-259, RAND Corporation, Santa Monica, Calif., Jan. 8, 1954.*)

spherical or cylindrical reactors by the methods outlined in the preceding section if the reactors of interest do not make use of reflectors which are thick compared to the over-all core dimensions.

For cavity reactors[23] a highly reflected system is required to achieve criticality. Such reactors are of interest herein chiefly in connection with a concept discussed in Chap. 9. Their basic geometry is that of a cavity filled with dilute fissionable fuel within a relatively thick moderator. This external reflector-moderator returns only thermal neutrons to the fuel-filled cavity; thus the achievement of criticality with a given fuel depends solely on the neutron-thermalizing and -absorbing characteristics of the reflector material. We expect, and observe, that D_2O should be the best reflector material, since it is composed of the two lightest

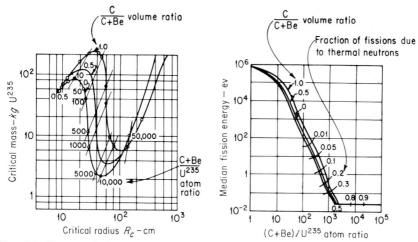

FIG. 6-8. Characteristics of critical mixtures of U^{235}, Be, and C.   (*G. Safonov, Critical Mixtures of* U^{235}*-Be-C Systems, RM-1581, RAND Corporation, Santa Monica, Calif., July* 15, 1955.)

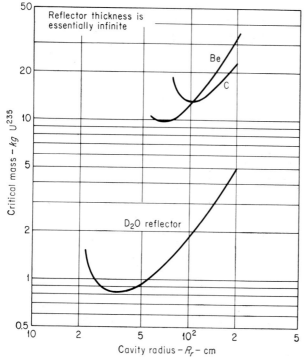

FIG. 6-9. Criticality conditions for cavity reactors.   [*G. Safonov, The Criticality and Some Potentialities of "Cavity" Reactors (Abridged), RM-1835, RAND Corporation, Santa Monica, Calif., July* 17, 1955.]

"magic" elements, both of which have extremely stable and therefore non-neutron-absorbing nuclei. Figure 6-9 shows the critical mass of fuel as a function of cavity radius for external reflectors of Be, C, and D_2O of infinite thickness. Reflectors which are six to ten times as thick as the slowing-down length for fission neutrons (Table 6-2) are essentially infinitely thick for this application. Note that these curves are for "pure" reflector–U^{235} fuel systems. Because of the highly thermal nature of the fission process within the core, it is probable that the introduction of small amounts of neutron poisons, such as structural metals, into the core cavity or reflector or particularly at the core-reflector interface will have profound effects on the criticality of the system. Therefore these curves should only be used as lower-limit estimates of the critical mass of real, structured, cavity-type reactors.

6-2. Reactor Kinetics. While it is possible to determine the nuclear design of a rocket reactor entirely by use of neutron-statics calculations, it is not per se evident that such a design would be capable of operation. All reactors must undergo time-varying changes in neutron density and distribution during the course of start-up, steady-state operation, and shutdown. Even steady-state operation is not truly "steady" for rocket reactors because the total operating time of such reactors is comparable to or less than the saturation time for production of delayed-neutron precursors, delayed gamma emitters, etc. For these reasons it is important to ensure that the reactor of interest will be stable under time-variant changes in reactor neutronic conditions. This section deals briefly with this subject of reactor kinetics, first considering the time-dependent character of the neutron behavior and then moving on to a discussion of the approximate methods of analysis in current use. Some nonmathematical justifications are given for neglecting the pursuit of exact methods of analysis, and some simplified methods of estimating parameters pertinent to the use of the approximate time-dependent neutron equations are given.

The Time-dependent Fission Process. In the early days of nuclear-reactor development, problems of fissionable-fuel loading and neutron flux distributions were of prime importance, principally because they had never been solved before and it had not been fundamentally determined whether or not criticality could be achieved with a given assembly. Such problems belong in the realm of reactor statics, discussed in the preceding sections of this chapter. Interest in the analysis of the time behavior of reactors was not very strong because most reactors were of low power, had high heat capacities, and were physically incapable of failing in ways which would produce large excess reactivity. As time went on more became known about reactor statics and more fissionable fuel highly enriched in U^{235} also became available. This latter occurrence stimulated the design and development of smaller reactors of higher power density for central power stations and particularly for mobile propulsion use. Now we are considering reactors for use in the propulsion of rockets. In this case the picture has completely changed. For, as we have seen, a rocket re ctor of necessity must operate at a core power density which is enormous by earlier standards, must be physically small, and must be made critical with enriched fuel. This results in a situation where large excess reactivities can arise in the event of an "accident." For nuclear rocket reactors, then, accurate knowledge of the reactor neutron kinetics is as essential as criticality information, since small deviations from design conditions of the neutron balance can completely destroy such a reactor in fractions of a second.

Unfortunately, as for reactor-statics calculations, the only exact method of analysis here is the Monte Carlo method, which becomes hopelessly complex from the practical standpoint of carrying out the mathematical operations when the dimension of time is added to those of space and neutron-energy variation. At present it appears unlikely that time-dependent Monte Carlo calculations will ever be generally used for reactor-kinetics analysis. The next step down in accuracy, or rather in agreement with reality, is the neutron-transport equation, now with time dependence, as well as its diffusion-theory approximations. Here, as for statics problems, the treatment of neutrons slowing down requires use of multiple energy groups, each with its own set of time-dependent neutron-diffusion equations. But like the Monte Carlo method, the addition of time dependence has proved in practice to be extremely difficult, and further simplifications in the method have been necessary in order to carry out reactor-kinetics analyses. By much experience, it has been found that the most complex mathematical treatment which can be handled satisfactorily is based on the time-dependent diffusion of a few (two or three) energy groups of neutrons. This use of a simplified model is justified when the nature of the kinetics problem is considered.

Changes in reactor geometry, size, shape, material densities, and mean thermal base all influence reactivity. Many of these changes are the result of material distortions under load or temperature differences, of material corrosion, erosion, or chemical change, or of phase change in coolants, for example. In rocket reactors, uniquely troublesome problems can arise from corrosion of fuel elements during operation, with subsequent loss of fuel, and by the loss of delayed-neutron precursors by diffusion through the fuel elements into the propellant-gas stream. Quantitative estimation of the magnitudes of such effects must be made by using the engineering data available for the materials and structures of interest. As is well known, such data on expansion coefficients, corrosion rates, stress-strain-temperature relations, heat-transfer coefficients, thermal conductivities, etc., is normally reliable only to the order of ± 10 to ± 20 per cent at best. Faced with this sort of error in input data, the reactor analyst has little incentive to devise methods which permit calculations to ± 1 per cent, or even to ± 10 per cent. Partly because of this and partly because of the necessity of performing such a large number of numerically relatively inexact studies of time-dependent behavior in connection with the design and analysis of the over-all reactor control system, the simplified reactor kinetic equations are often solved on analog simulators. This particular problem is discussed in more detail in Chap. 7.

For time-dependent behavior, the diffusion equation becomes

$$D\nabla^2\phi(t) - \Sigma_a\phi(t) + S = \frac{1}{v}\frac{\partial\phi}{\partial t} = \frac{\partial n}{\partial t} \tag{6-16}$$

where v is the neutron velocity and t is the time variable. Using Fermi age-diffusion theory this can be solved to yield

$$\frac{k_\infty e^{-B^2\tau_{th}}}{1 + L^2B^2} - 1 = \frac{l_0}{1 + L^2B^2}\frac{1}{\phi(t)}\frac{d\phi(t)}{dt} \tag{6-17}$$

which reduces to

$$\phi(t) = \phi_0 e^{t\delta k/l^*} \tag{6-18}$$

Here $\delta k = k_{eff} - 1$, which is the left side of Eq. (6-17), and l^* is the mean lifetime of the thermal neutrons in the finite medium of the reactor, given here by the coefficient of the $\phi(t)$ terms in Eq. (6-17). The reactor e-folding period is obviously $l^*/\delta k$ in Eq. (6-18). This case is strictly correct only for zero-time step changes in the reactivity $\delta k/k_{eff}$ of a reactor operating close to criticality and completely neglects the effects of delayed neutrons, thus really only describes the behavior of a thermal reactor operating at prompt critical, subjected to sudden step changes in control-rod position, coolant density, etc.

The effect of delayed neutrons is found by inclusion of the delayed-neutron-source term in Eq. (6-16). The rate of formation of the delayed-neutron precursors of the ith delay group is

$$\frac{\partial C_i}{\partial t} = \beta_i\frac{k_\infty\phi(t)}{Pl_0v} - \lambda_iC_i \tag{6-19}$$

where λ_i and C_i are the decay time and instantaneous concentration, respectively, of the delayed-neutron precursors. The total rate of production of delayed neutrons is simply the sum of the rate of decay of the precursors for each group. The delayed-neutron-source term, including fast leakage, by Fermi age theory, and resonance-absorption effects, is then

$$S_d = pe^{-B^2\tau_{th}}\sum_{i=1}^{m}\lambda_iC_i \tag{6-20}$$

where p is the resonance-escape probability for neutrons slowing down to thermal. The prompt-neutron-source term due to fission is

$$S_p = (1 - \beta)k_\infty \Sigma_a \phi(t)e^{-B^2\tau_{th}} \tag{6-21}$$

where β is the total fraction of fission neutrons which are delayed. Combining these two sources with the fundamental diffusion equation (6-16),

$$D\nabla^2\phi(t) - \Sigma_a\phi(t) + (1 - \beta)k_\infty\Sigma_a\phi(t)e^{-B^2\tau_{th}}$$

$$+ pe^{-B^2\tau_{th}} \sum_{i=1}^{m} \lambda_i C_i(t) = \frac{1}{v}\frac{\partial\phi(t)}{\partial t} = \frac{\partial n}{\partial t} \tag{6-22}$$

Now, for step changes in reactivity of a near-critical reactor, Eq. (6-22) can be modified by Fermi age theory to yield

$$\frac{\delta k - \beta k_{eff}}{l^*}\frac{\phi}{v} + pe^{-B^2\tau_{th}} \sum_{i=1}^{m} \lambda_i C_i = \frac{1}{v}\frac{d\phi}{dt} = \frac{dn}{dt} \tag{6-23}$$

For a critical reactor in which the probabilities of fast leakage and resonance absorption are zero, Eq. (6-23) reduces to the familiar kinetic equation

$$\frac{dn}{dt} = \frac{\delta k - \beta}{l^*} n + \sum_{i=1}^{m} \lambda_i C_i \tag{6-24}$$

For these conditions Eq. (6-19), describing the time behavior of the delayed-neutron precursors, becomes

$$\frac{dC_i}{dt} = \frac{\beta_i n}{l^*} - \lambda_i C_i \tag{6-25}$$

Exact solution of Eq. (6-23) is tedious and leads to an expression for neutron flux as

$$\phi(t) = A_0 e^{\omega_0 t} + A_1 e^{\omega_1 t} + \cdots + A_m e^{\omega_m t} \tag{6-26}$$

where the A_i are constants determined by the initial conditions of the reactor in the steady state and the ω_i are the m roots of the equation

$$\frac{\delta k}{k_{eff}} = \frac{1}{l^*\omega + 1}\left(l^*\omega + \sum_{i=1}^{m} \frac{\omega\beta_i}{\omega + \lambda_i}\right) \tag{6-27}$$

The $(m + 1)$-term flux equation (6-26) is sometimes set up and solved on analog-simulation equipment, but more often the number of delayed-neutron groups is assumed to be 1, with a decay constant weighted to reflect the relative abundances of the actual m groups. It is generally presently accepted[7] that there are no more than six delayed-neutron groups of importance in reactor-kinetics analysis. For a single delayed-neutron group, Eq. (6-27) can be modified and reduced to

$$\frac{\delta k}{k_{eff}} = l^*\omega + \frac{\omega\beta}{\omega + \lambda} \tag{6-28}$$

where λ is the weighted average decay constant of the delayed-neutron precursors. This is solved for ω, and the variation of thermal flux with time is found to be

$$\frac{\phi(t)}{\phi_0} = \frac{\beta k_{eff}}{\beta k_{eff} - \delta k}\left[\exp\frac{\lambda\delta kt}{\beta k_{eff} - \delta k} - \frac{\delta k}{\beta k_{eff}}\exp\left(\frac{\delta k - \beta k_{eff}}{l^*k_{eff}}t\right)\right] \tag{6-29}$$

This holds only for positive excursions from criticality of roughly $\delta k < \beta/2$, and is valid only for step changes in reactivity. This restriction on maximum positive δk is also a restriction on the shortest reactor period for which the analysis is valid. For reactors fueled with U^{235} this restriction leads to a minimum analytically tractable [by Eq. (6-29)] stable reactor period of about 20 sec. Since a rocket motor used to fly a missile must reach full power from almost zero power in a matter of 30 sec or less, it is obvious that the foregoing analysis is not very useful for our purposes. In fact for a factor of 10^5 change in reactor power in 30 sec the reactor must be brought to full power with a stable period of some 2.6 sec. Here, because of the multiple-structured nature of a heat-exchanger rocket reactor, the rapidity of change in reactor neutronic conditions, the large number of epithermal fissions in a typical reactor, and the changing rate of build-up of delayed-neutron precursors, the analysis must be carried out by a multi-delay-group, multi-neutron-energy-group, multi-space-region method. Fortunately the use of even two or three groups for each multicomponent segment of the analysis yields a vast improvement over the simple analysis described in Eqs. (6-16) to (6-29) above.

In addition, it is obvious that not all reactivity changes will be stepwise in zero time. The mathematical analysis of time-dependent reactivity changes is more complex than that outlined above and has been carried out for some cases with the aid of digital computing machines.[24] Most often, however, electronic analog equipment capable of the approximate solution of a large number of simultaneous differential equations is used in reactor-kinetics and -control analysis. Some of this equipment is discussed and shown in Chap. 7.

Reactivity Coefficients. The discussion of reactor kinetics would not be complete without consideration of the various reactivity coefficients which can arise in an operating reactor. Changes in constitution, density, temperature, etc., all will occur in a high-temperature reactor during operation and all lead to time-varying changes in reactivity, thus influence the time-dependent neutron distribution as described in the preceding section.

One example of the origin of reactivity variations is the fluctuation of temperature of a rocket-reactor core, from 500 to perhaps 5000°R or so in the course of reactor operation. This large temperature variation will cause a change in the thermal-neutron energy level of neutrons thermalized in the core from 0.025 to the order of 0.25 ev, and will cause variations in the density as well as changes in the over-all dimensions of the core. Similarly, changes in reflector temperature, if a reflector is used, will influence the thermal-neutron energy level in the reflector and will in turn cause changes in reflector shape and density, all of which affect the reactor kinetics.

For a constant-temperature, core-moderated reactor, the reactivity coefficients due to temperature can be crudely estimated from age-diffusion theory for a reactor operating at or close to critical. Simple differentiation of the age-diffusion equation for criticality [Eq. (6-5)] can be used to find expressions for the reactivity coefficients due to various causes, such as change in fuel density, change in cross sections from changes in neutron temperature, and change in core size. Three such expressions of some interest are

$$\frac{1}{k_{eff}}\left(\frac{\partial \delta k}{\partial T}\right)_{\rho, B^2} \approx -\frac{B^2 L^2}{2T k_\infty} \tag{6-30a}$$

$$\frac{1}{k_{eff}}\left(\frac{\partial \delta k}{\partial T}\right)_{B^2, \sigma} \approx -\frac{6\alpha(k_\infty - 1)}{k_\infty} \tag{6-30b}$$

$$\frac{1}{k_{eff}}\left(\frac{\partial \delta k}{\partial T}\right)_{\sigma, \rho} \approx +\frac{2\alpha(k_\infty - 1)}{k_\infty} \tag{6-30c}$$

Equation (6-30a) expresses the change in reactivity due only to a change in neutron thermal base, assuming all absorbers have cross sections which follow the $1/v$ law. The coefficient is always negative for this condition. However, for rocket reactors the required operating temperature is so high that an appreciable fraction of the Maxwell-Boltzmann distribution of hot thermal neutrons are exposed to various U^{235} absorption resonances in the 0.25- to 5-ev region. For these resonances the $1/v$ law does not hold, and detailed neutronic calculations using closely spaced energy groups in this low-energy-resonance region are necessary for correct estimation of the reactivity due to thermal-base shift. Equation (6-30b) gives the change in reactivity due only to changes in material density within the reactor, where α is the average coefficient of linear expansion of the reactor materials. Here, as for Eq. (6-30a), the geometry and dimensions of the reactor are assumed invariant with temperature. This equation is reasonably valid and useful for an isothermal core-moderated reactor. Equation (6-30c) describes the reactivity change due only to a change in reactor size, given by the buckling, hence is useful in the preliminary-design stage for determining the effect of small changes in over-all core dimensions from some known critical assembly. Here the material densities and cross sections are assumed constant. Note that this is a positive reactivity coefficient in distinction to the two preceding coefficients, both of which are negative. These simple relations do not apply to a reflected rocket reactor in which the reflector plays an important role in neutron thermalization or is thermally weakly coupled to the core. However, they may be used as long as the application of their results is made with reasonable care and judgment.

For a reflected reactor with weak thermal coupling between the core and reflector, the effect of core thermal-base shift [Eq. (6-30a)] depends on the relative number of neutrons causing fissions at core thermal energy compared to those causing fissions at reflector thermal energy. The situation is complicated by the fact that there is a spatial dependence in this phenomenon, for "cold" thermal neutrons returning to the hot core from the "cold" reflector will be scattered up in energy rather than down, as is usually the case, and will become hotter and hotter with greater penetration into the core. This condition can be properly analyzed only by multi-energy-group and multi-space-region methods.

Another difficult problem for rocket reactors is the determination of the effect of propellant addition and distribution in the core. The hydrogen in hydrogenous propellants is a good moderator; it is also a fairly strong absorber of thermal neutrons. If appreciable hydrogen is introduced into a region of the reactor where a large fraction of the fissions is caused by epithermal neutrons, it will generally increase the reactivity of the system by an increase in the local thermalization of neutrons. However, if it is added to a region where the fissions are predominantly due to thermal neutrons, it can decrease the over-all reactivity by absorption of thermal neutrons. In general, the effect of the local introduction of absorbers is proportional to the square of the local flux normalized to the average flux across the reactor. To complicate the picture still further, the designer must consider the various cases of transient start-up operation when cold propellant is first supplied to the reactor and the local propellant density may vary rapidly in time. In all, the only satisfactory way to determine the various possible reactivity coefficients with sufficient accuracy to permit their use in defining limits on reactor operating conditions is by a series of exact reactor-statics calculations covering the projected variations in dimensions, material densities and distributions, and system operating temperatures. Here then, as in many other fields, there is no substitute for the best.

6-3. Reactor Geometries. While many different geometries can be used for heat-exchanger rocket reactors, they can generally all be categorized by the type of core structure utilized. The two major subdivisions commonly employed are *homogeneous* and *heterogeneous* core structures.

HOMOGENEOUS CORES. Though no heat-exchanger reactor core is truly homogeneous, it is permissible to consider cores as homogeneous if the dimensions of detailed core structure are all small compared to the scattering mean free path of neutrons within the core. In the design of structured heat exchangers for rocket-reactor use it will be found that this is generally the case (see Chap. 4 for typical fuel-element dimensions). For purposes of discussion in this section we consider only reactor cores which are spherical shells, finite cylindrical shells, or finite solid cylinders.

Optimum minimum-volume performance of temperature-limited heat exchangers requires that the heat-generating solids operate at a constant (maximum) temperature throughout the reactor core. To achieve this it is necessary to vary the fission power density along the coolant flow path to match the varying capability for heat extraction by the coolant as it is heated from room temperature to a temperature approaching the limiting structure temperature of the heat-exchanger materials. This variation generally requires a peak heat-generation rate at some point near the front (inlet end) of the coolant flow path and a monotonically decreasing heat-generation rate along the flow path from this point. For a reactor loaded uniformly with fuel, the fission distribution due to neutrons of a given energy will exactly follow the neutron density distribution throughout the reactor, hence is given by the equations for monoenergetic neutron flux as a function of position. A complete determination of the fission distribution requires knowledge of the flux shape for all neutron energies and can most practically be obtained by multigroup analysis or by actual measurement. The matching of the actual fission distribution with that for optimum performance can be accomplished by varying the local fuel density, which produces a second-order change in flux shape, or by varying the flux distribution by proper choice or modification of reactor geometry. From the practical standpoint of fuel-element fabrication it is most desirable to minimize the required variation in fuel distribution and to achieve optimum fission density distribution by adjustment of the flux shape. Furthermore, neutron-statics calculations are somewhat more difficult for reactors in which the fuel density varies widely with position in the core; thus from the calculational standpoint it is desirable to utilize flux- rather than fuel-distribution variations to achieve the desired goal. Since the flux falls off toward the edge of the core in all bare or lightly reflected homogeneous cores, such cores are best suited for use with radial outward flow of coolant. Unfortunately this direction of coolant flow is not always the most desirable for other reasons; thus the designer must consider ways to achieve peak performance with radial inflow or axial flow (in cylinders), for example. In opposition to the falling off of flux and fission density at the boundaries of a core-moderated bare reactor, the fission density is peaked at the edges of the core in a heavily reflected reactor with a poorly moderating core. Somewhere between these two extremes in flux shape, shown in Fig. 6-10, it is possible to achieve near-flatness, radially, for a homogeneous core by use of an external reflector of proper shape, material, and thickness. Generally it will be found that the required reflector weight is excessive for good nuclear-powered-missile performance; thus some compromise must be made between variations in fuel loading and use of reflectors.

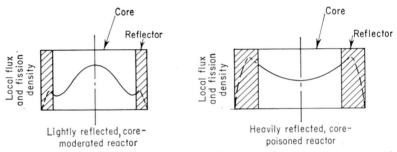

FIG. 6-10. Extremes of fission density distribution in homogeneous-core reactors.

HETEROGENEOUS CORES. In a heterogeneous core the general problem is similar but the details are different. Here two flux distributions are of interest: that across the width dimension of any single lumped fuel bundle and that across the reactor core as a whole. This latter, the gross flux shape, follows the arguments given above for homogeneous cores, wherein it is possible to achieve over-all fission density flatness solely by use of an appropriate external reflector, or by gross variations in fuel loading from one fuel bundle to the next, or by some combination of both methods. The detailed fission density variation across a single fuel bundle in a matrix-moderated core also follows these same arguments on a smaller physical scale, for each fuel bundle is in a sense a self-sustaining fissioning assembly in an infinite moderating reflector immersed in a uniform flux of neutrons. Since neutron thermalization here is achieved almost entirely by moderation by the core matrix material, the flux and fission density will always peak at the outer boundaries of the fuel bundle; hence such a reactor is most suited to the flow of coolant radially into each bundle. For axial (along the bundle) coolant flow the fuel density must be varied radially across the bundle to achieve proper heat-exchanger performance. Two extremes in the variation of fission density across a matrix-geometry core are shown in Fig. 6-11.

The calculation of static neutron distributions is considerably more difficult for heterogeneous- than for homogeneous-core reactors just because the fission distribution in a heterogeneous reactor depends upon the two basic flux shapes mentioned above, that across the core and that across a bundle, as compared to the dependence on only one, that across the core, for homogeneous reactors. Nevertheless, heterogeneous cores are of great practical interest, for they yield the lowest critical mass of either type and can be made to operate (fission) almost entirely on thermal neutrons in small sizes for which nonhydrogenous homogeneous cores are nearly fast reactors.

6-4. Gamma and Neutron Absorption and Leakage. In the design and testing of nuclear rocket reactors, knowledge of the radiation energy deposited within and leaking out of the reactor core is of extreme importance. In order to estimate the magnitude of the possible effects, it is first necessary to know the total radiation energy available from the fission process.

The fission process releases large amounts of energy distributed among several different types of particles and radiation. Within a few milliseconds after the fission of a U^{235} nucleus, the total energy released is distributed about as follows:

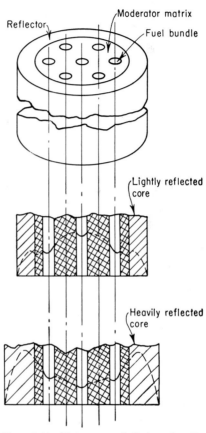

Fig. 6-11. Extremes of fission density distribution in a heterogeneous-cylindrical-core reactor.

166 Mev in kinetic energy of fission fragments
6 Mev in prompt-fission γ radiation with an energy spectrum $N_p(E_\gamma)$
4 Mev in prompt-capture γ radiation from (n,γ) reactions within the reactor
5 Mev in kinetic energy of fission-produced fast neutrons
11 to 14 Mev in energy carried off by neutrinos

Some of the fission fragments decay by β and γ emission, and thus the total energy released by one fission process integrated over all time, including the delayed decay energy of active nuclei produced by neutron capture, must include roughly:

6 Mev in decay γ radiation with an energy spectrum $N_d(E_\gamma)$
2 Mev in decay energy of neutron-capture products
6 Mev in decay β radiation

In a rocket reactor the time of operation is comparable to or shorter than the half-life of several of the fission-product decay chains; thus the total energy released per fission during reactor operation will include more than 8 to 10 Mev but less than 14 to 18 Mev of γ radiation and less than 6 Mev of β radiation.

The fission fragments and β rays are not very penetrating; hence they will deposit most of their energy in the fuel elements close to the point of fission.   At the other extreme the neutrinos are extremely penetrating and carry essentially all of their energy far out of the reactor.   This leaves only the fast neutrons and gamma rays, which are both capable of penetrating many centimeters into reactor materials.   Thermalization of neutrons involves, by definition, the exchange of energy from the neutron to the moderator, thus results in heating of the moderator. This heat energy must be removed, or continued exposure to fast neutrons will eventually melt or vaporize the moderator material.   Similarly, gamma radiation interacting with the atoms of any material results in the transfer of energy from the gamma photon to the surrounding material, principally by local ionization reactions.   Here again cooling of the heated material is required.   The radiation-damage effects resulting from the interaction of radiation with matter have little or no effect on over-all reactor neutronics.   Such effects are of most importance in the engineering structural analysis and design of reactor components and, as such, are discussed in Chap. 5.

Some of the fast neutrons, free thermalized neutrons, and gamma photons will inevitably leave the reactor system completely and spread out through the space surrounding the reactor.   This leakage radiation presents severe biological hazards, and shielding must be provided if it is anticipated that people will be required in the area around the reactor while it is in operation or radioactive after shutdown.   The design of cooling systems for nonfissioning components of a reactor and the estimation of radiation doses around a reactor for the purpose of determining biological-shield requirements are thus extremely important facets of the over-all reactor design.   Improper analysis of neutron and gamma heating can lead to reactor failure during operation, and improper shielding estimation can result in serious injury or death if other normally employed safety precautions are also neglected.   Approximate methods and techniques useful in such analyses are given in this section along with a general discussion of more exact methods of analysis which it may be worthwhile to employ for any particular reactor design. Further discussion of the radiation hazards attendant on reactor operation and methods for the determination and control of the hazards are given in Chap. 8.

Heating Effects. Of first importance to the development of a successfully operating reactor is the correct design estimation of the heating load due to radiation-energy absorption by reactor component structures. Because of the engineering approximations involved in the use of heating-load calculations for cooling-system design, it is generally sufficient to use relatively simple, though not exact, methods for the estimation of neutron and gamma heating. This section presents the major features of some simplified, approximate methods which have been found useful in reactor design.

GAMMAS. Gamma radiation from the fission process appears over a wide range of energies, from ∼100 ev to 10 Mev. The importance of the various possible methods of interaction (energy exchange) of gamma rays with matter depends upon the gamma-ray energy. At low energies, gamma absorption by the photoelectric effect is the most important phenomenon. This is superseded, with increasing gamma energy, by Compton scattering, which is most important from about $\frac{1}{2}$ to 3 Mev in heavy materials. Electron-positron pair production next assumes a dominating role for energies above about 5 Mev in dense materials (e.g., lead) and 20 Mev in light materials (e.g., aluminum). The gamma ray is physically absorbed in pair production and by the photoelectric effect, but simply loses energy by scattering collisions with atomic electrons in the Compton scattering process. Compton scattering is thus roughly analogous to the slowing down of neutrons in reactor neutron-statics analysis, while pair production and the photoelectric effect correspond to neutron-absorption phenomena, but with the release of energy. From this analogy, remembering that gammas are born in the fission process over a wide range of energies $N_d(E_\gamma) + N_p(E_\gamma)$, it is evident that the exact analysis of gamma-ray penetration and absorption suffers from almost the same complexity as does exact neutron-statics analysis. Analyses of gamma-ray absorptions and distributions are somewhat simpler than neutron-statics analysis, for the distribution of gamma sources does not depend on the distribution of gamma sinks, as is the case for neutrons. Monte Carlo methods have been used with some success in the design of simple gamma shields, but the use of such methods has been hampered, as for neutron analysis, by the nonexistence of high-speed computers of sufficient capacity for the solution of complex (real) geometrical situations. However, the development of computing machines in recent years has resulted in the use of the Monte Carlo method for the solution of gamma-absorption problems in two-dimensional cylindrical reactors, thus permitting relatively accurate estimation of local gamma heating in such reactors. Another analytical approach involves the use of gamma-energy groups, treating each group individually and using gamma-attenuation and -absorption coefficients characteristic of the average energy of the group of interest. This is similar to multigroup neutron analysis and must be carried out on large computing machines. Although these relatively exact methods should be used for detailed design and analysis of rocket reactors, it is possible to obtain reasonably correct estimations of the heating due to gamma absorption by use of some quite simple equations.

The linear attenuation of gammas emitted from an infinite-plane source is given by[25]

$$\frac{I_p(\rho)}{I_0} = \int_{\mu\rho}^{\infty} \frac{B(\mu r)e^{-\mu r}}{r}\,dr \qquad (6\text{-}31)$$

where μ = energy-dependent gamma-attenuation coefficient

ρ = linear distance from source

I_0 = surface-source flux intensity per unit area (one-half of isotropic surface source)

$I_p(\rho)$ = energy flux at ρ

$B(\mu r)$ is a "build-up" factor used to account for local production of low-energy gammas, resulting from Compton scattering interactions with photons in the primary beam. In a sense this has an effect equivalent to that which would result from a general "hardening" and consequent greater penetrating ability of the primary source beam. Accurate values of the build-up factor in several materials are shown in Fig. 6-12; however, for purposes of rough calculations the build-up factor can be taken as

$$B(\mu r) = 1 + \mu r \qquad (6\text{-}32)$$

For this build-up factor Eq. (6-31) can be reduced to the two-term expression

$$\frac{I_p(\rho)}{I_0} = E_i(\mu\rho) + e^{-\mu\rho} \qquad (6\text{-}33)$$

where $E_i(\mu\rho)$ is an exponential integral defined by

$$E_i(\mu\rho) = \int_{\mu\rho}^{\infty} \frac{e^{-q}}{q}\,dq \qquad (6\text{-}34)$$

values of which are tabulated in standard handbooks. For large values of $\mu\rho$ the first term of Eq. (6-34) reduces to $E_i(\mu\rho) = e^{-\mu\rho}/\mu\rho$, so that the dose rate almost follows a simple exponential attenuation law at large $\mu\rho$.

The foregoing remarks apply strictly only to an infinite-plane source; however, it has been shown[26] that this treatment is correct within a few

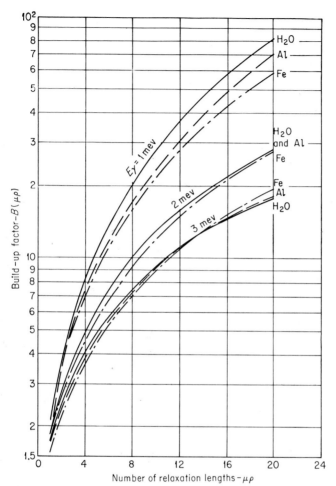

FIG. 6-12. Build-up factor for gamma-photon absorption. (*John Moteff, Miscellaneous Data for Shielding Calculations, APEX-176, ANPD, p. 72, General Electric Company, Cincinnati, Ohio, Dec. 1, 1954.*)

per cent for finite planar sources of a few feet in diameter. These equations for the radiation flux arising from a planar-surface source can also be used to estimate the fluxes external to cylindrical- and spherical-surface sources. The appropriate correction factors to be used for this are

$$\frac{I_c(\rho)}{I_p(\rho)} = \sqrt{\frac{r_0}{\rho + r_0}} \qquad \text{for an infinite cylinder} \qquad (6\text{-}35a)$$

and

$$\frac{I_s(\rho)}{I_p(\rho)} = \frac{r_0}{\rho + r_0} \qquad \text{for a sphere} \qquad (6\text{-}35b)$$

where r_0 is the radius of the sphere or cylinder in question and ρ is the distance from the receiver to the surface of the source. For a finite cylinder the corrections are more complex. It is often useful in this case to compute the fluxes by both the infinite-cylinder and sphere equations and to use an average value of the results of these two computations.

The equivalent *isotropic*-surface-source strength of a planar, volume-distributed source of constant strength P_0 is

$$S_0 = \lambda_0 P_0 \tag{6-36}$$

where λ_0 is the attenuation length of the source material and is equal to $1/\mu_0$. The surface-source *flux* intensity is given by

$$I_0 = \frac{S_0}{2} \tag{6-37}$$

for all geometries. Equations (6-36) and (6-37) may be used for the estimation of surface flux intensity from cylindrical- and spherical-volume sources if r_0 is greater than about $4\lambda_0$. Self-absorption corrections are available in the literature for other geometries.[27]

The volume-source strength P_0 to be used in calculation is determined by the volumetric fission rate (bulk core power density). While the foregoing equations hold only for a source of constant strength, if the core-power-density variation with distance is small over one absorption mean free path (λ_0), the local core power densities may be used for the determination of gamma fluxes within $2\lambda_0$ of the point in the core having the power density in question. The volume-gamma-source strength is related to the fraction of the maximum possible decay gammas released during the time of reactor operation and is given roughly by

$$P_0 = 0.06(1 + 0.8f_\gamma)P_f \tag{6-38}$$

where P_f is the local or average bulk fission density (including void volume) and f_γ is the fraction of decay gamma energy released.

The rate of energy absorption within a material surrounding a source is simply the rate of change of beam strength with distance away from the source. This is given by

$$P(\rho) = \tau_a I(\rho) \tag{6-39}$$

where τ_a is the energy-absorption coefficient of the absorbing material of interest. This is distinguished from the interaction coefficient μ_a by the fact that τ_a does not include the pure scattering-interaction aspects of the Compton scattering process but only covers the energy degradation and includes the losses due to the photoelectric effect and pair production. These energy-absorption and -interaction coefficients are commonly given in a form which is normalized to the density of the material of interest. The units of τ and μ are inverse centimeters, while τ' and μ', the *mass* absorption coefficients, are in square centimeters per gram. In

all calculations the material densities used should be bulk densities including the effect of voids in the reactor material. As previously mentioned,
the gamma-ray-interaction coefficients are functions of energy, and thus
accurate calculations necessitate treating the gammas on an energy-group
basis. However, by comparison with experiments and accurate calculations in a variety of reactor designs it has been found satisfactory to use

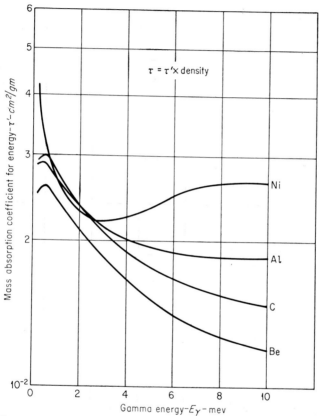

FIG. 6-13. Energy-absorption coefficient for various materials. (*John Moteff, Miscellaneous Data for Shielding Calculations, APEX-176, ANPD, p. 72, General Electric
Company, Cincinnati, Ohio, Dec. 1, 1954.*)

interaction coefficients chosen for an average gamma-photon energy
between 1 and 2 Mev. Absorption coefficients for several materials of
interest in rocket-reactor design are shown in Figs. 6-13 and 6-14. These
data have been taken largely from the compilation made by J. Moteff[25]
of information for gamma-ray-penetration analysis.

A set of easier and simpler, though inherently incorrect, formulas for
estimation of gamma fluxes and local energy absorptions can be obtained

from the equation for linear attenuation from a collimated plane source with "straight-ahead" scattering only. This is

$$\frac{I_p(\rho)}{I_0} = B(\mu\rho)e^{-\mu\rho} \qquad (6\text{-}40)$$

Use of this for cylindrical- and spherical-volume sources whose radii are large compared to their attenuation length requires correction by geomet-

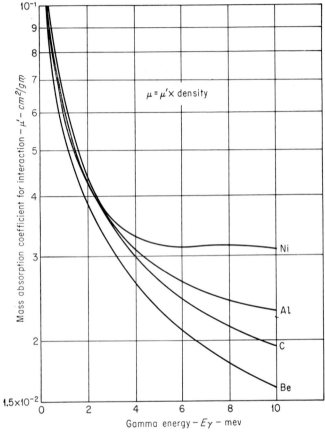

FIG. 6-14. Total interaction coefficient for various materials. (*John Moteff, Miscellaneous Data for Shielding Calculations, APEX-176, ANPD, p. 72, General Electric Company, Cincinnati, Ohio, Dec. 1, 1954.*)

rical "spreading" factors of $r_0/(\rho + r_0)$ and $[r_0/(\rho + r_0)]^2$ respectively. For this simplified method the equivalent-surface flux source given by Eqs. (6-36), (6-37), and (6-38) must be used, and the local power densities follow Eq. (6-39) as before. Figure 6-15 shows the geometries used in these considerations and summarizes the correct and approximate equations for local monoenergetic gamma flux.

Source geometry	Gamma flux		Gamma-energy-absorption density
	Exact	Approximate	
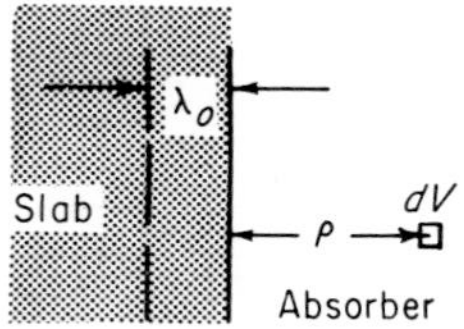 Slab	$\dfrac{I_p(\rho)}{I_0} = \displaystyle\int_{\mu_a\rho}^{\infty} \frac{B(\mu_a r)e^{-\mu_a r}}{r}\, dr$	$\dfrac{I'_p(\rho)}{I_0} = B(\mu_a\rho)e^{-\mu_a\rho}$	$P_p(\rho) = \tau_a I_p(\rho)$ $= \tau_a I'_p(\rho)$
Sphere or cylinder	$\dfrac{I_c(\rho)}{I_p(\rho)} = \sqrt{\dfrac{r_0}{\rho + r_0}}$	$\dfrac{I'_c(\rho)}{I'_p(\rho)} = \dfrac{r_0}{\rho + r_0}$	$P_c(\rho) = \tau_a I_c(\rho)$ $= \tau_a I'_c(\rho)$
	$\dfrac{I_s(\rho)}{I_p(\rho)} = \dfrac{r_0}{\rho + r_0}$	$\dfrac{I'_s(\rho)}{I'_p(\rho)} = \left(\dfrac{r_0}{\rho + r_0}\right)^2$	$P_s(\rho) = \tau_a I_s(\rho)$ $= \tau_a I'_s(\rho)$
All geometries............	$I_0 \approx 0.03(1 + 0.8f_\gamma)P_r\lambda_0$		$B(\mu_a\rho) \approx 1 + \mu_a\rho$

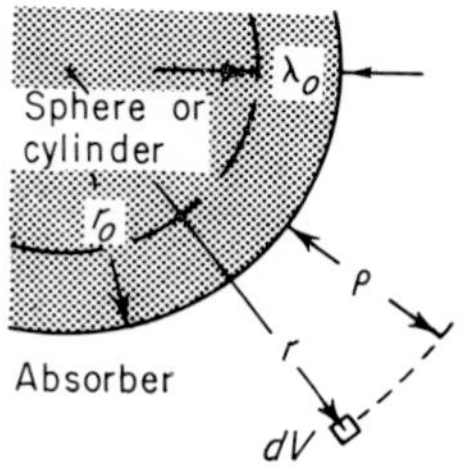

Fig. 6-15. Flux and power density for gamma absorption in various geometries.

Estimation of the gamma-energy-absorption density within the core is more difficult, requiring integration of the point-absorption kernels (Green's functions) within the boundaries of the gamma source. However, it is easy to estimate the gamma-heating density at the boundary, and an upper limit can be placed on the value at the center of the core. Heating density at the core outer boundary is obtained from Eqs. (6-36) through (6-39) as

$$P_{\text{surface}} = \frac{0.03(1 + 0.8f_\gamma)P_f\tau_0}{\mu_0} \tag{6-41}$$

where subscript 0 refers to the core characteristics. The peak possible value within the core, even in an infinite core, is given by Eq. (6-38). This value will be approached at the center of a core whose radius is large compared to the mean free path for absorption of gammas, but will never be exceeded. This maximum value is only $2\mu_0/\tau_0$ times greater than that given by Eq. (6-41) for the core surface.

NEUTRONS. Heating by neutrons is principally by neutron slowing down, as already discussed. Secondary effects such as heating resulting from the production of protons, beta rays, and alpha particles from (n,p), (n,β), or (n,α) reactions are relatively unimportant in most reactors and will not be considered here. Heating from absorption of gammas produced by neutron capture is somewhat more important, but is again a second-order effect and can be handled within the inherent error of the equations just given for gamma heating. These generalities obviously do not hold true for heating in special reactor materials such as B^{10}, used in control rods, where heating is predominantly the result of an (n,α) reaction.

The space-local neutron-energy loss rate per unit volume in the slowing-down process can be obtained from the approximate relation

$$P_n(\rho) = \sum_n \phi_i(\rho)\Sigma_{si}(\rho)\,\delta E_i \tag{6-42}$$

where $\phi_i(\rho)$ = neutron flux in the ith energy group at point ρ

$\Sigma_{si}(\rho)$ = macroscopic scattering cross section at point ρ for neutrons of the ith group

δE_i = energy loss per scattering collision within the ith group

n = number of energy groups used in the calculation

The scattering-collision density is given by $\phi\Sigma_s$. To compute neutron-heating power density by this method it is necessary to know the flux distribution for each neutron-energy group. This information can be obtained only from the results of multigroup neutron-statics calculations on the reactor of interest. Scattering cross sections are

$$\Sigma_{si}(\rho) = N_m(\rho)\sigma_{si} \tag{6-43}$$

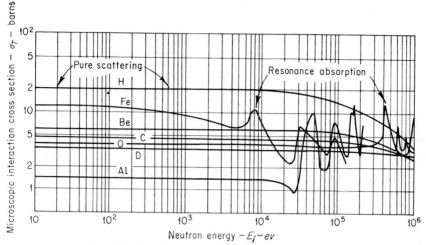

FIG. 6-16. Total cross sections for several materials.

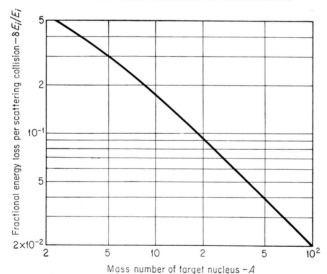

FIG. 6-17. Approximate energy loss in neutron slowing down.

where $N_m(\rho)$ is the nuclear density of the neutron-heated nuclei. The total interaction cross section is principally the result of scattering processes except in the region of resonance absorption. Values of this cross section are given in Fig. 6-16 for several materials of interest in rocket-reactor design.

The energy loss per collision is closely given, for all materials but H, by

$$\delta E_i = E_i \left[1 - \exp\left(- \frac{6}{3A + 2} \right) \right] \tag{6-44}$$

where A is the mass number of the struck nucleus and E_i is the mean energy of the ith neutron group. This is plotted in Fig. 6-17 for convenience in calculation. For H the *average* energy loss per collision is

$$\delta E_{i_{\mathrm{H}}} = E_i \left(1 - \frac{1}{e}\right) = 0.63 E_i \qquad (6\text{-}45)$$

Having the neutron flux distribution in various groups from a multi-group reactor calculation, the neutron heating can be estimated by use of the data in Figs. 6-16 and 6-17 in conjunction with Eqs. (6-42), (6-43), and (6-44).

It is generally found that the neutron-heating density in most good moderators is of the same order of magnitude as the gamma-heating density. However, in structural materials of high atomic weight (e.g., aluminum and heavier) the neutron-heating density is generally trivial, while gamma absorption is higher than that in moderators and provides the prime heat source.

Radiation Dose Levels. In order to understand the magnitude of the problems involved in shielding a nuclear rocket reactor, this section presents some simple formulas which permit the calculation of radiation dose rates around an operating reactor as a function of distance from the reactor. The units of dose and dose rate and the allowable biological tolerances for different radiations are discussed in Chap. 8 and are not repeated here. Further, it is not the purpose of this section to outline the procedures for shield design, as these can be found in many of the standard texts in the field.[3,4,26,29] Rather, the methods given here can be used to define the amount and kind of shielding needed to satisfy any particular set of dose-rate requirements for a given reactor test. It should be borne in mind that complete shielding of a nuclear rocket reactor, even in a ground test, is virtually impossible because of the necessity for leaving a large void exposing one face of the core and a large hole through the reactor pressure shell to permit the exhaust of hot propellant gas from the reactor. The difficulties attendant on shielding a flight-type reactor are obvious and fundamental, since a nuclear rocket-reactor propulsion system must be light in weight to be worthwhile and radiation shields are notoriously heavy.

The operating power level of a typical rocket reactor is so high (thousands of megawatts) that it is intuitively clear that the dose rates at the surface of the reactor pressure shell will be far, far in excess of the biologically limiting values. It is therefore of little interest to estimate the dose rates on or just outside the reactor outer surface. The dose rate at great distances is of interest, however, for the inverse-square effect of distance is a powerful "shielding" mechanism, and dose levels can be reduced to tolerable values by distance alone. For distances from the reactor outer surface which are large compared to the neutron- or gamma-interaction mean free path within the shell, the reactor can be treated as a point source of radiation. This approximation is used through this section.

GAMMAS. The leakage flux of gammas from a point fission source operating at P_r Mw is given by

$$\phi_\gamma(r) = \frac{3.4 \times 10^{16}}{4\pi} \frac{P_r}{r^2 A_s} \frac{E_\gamma^\circ}{E_\gamma} \qquad (6\text{-}46)$$

where ϕ_γ = gamma leakage flux, gamma photons/(sec)(cm²)
   r = source-receiver separation distance, cm
   E_γ° = total gamma energy released per fission, Mev
   E_γ = average gamma energy per photon, Mev
A_s is an attenuation factor, discussed below. From the preceding section it is observed that the total gamma energy available depends on the fraction of decay gammas produced during the operating time of the reactor and is roughly given by

$$E_\gamma^\circ = 10(1 + 0.8 f_\gamma) \qquad (6\text{-}47)$$

Now, the conversion from gamma flux to dose rate is

$$D_\gamma = \frac{\phi_\gamma E_\gamma}{5.6 \times 10^5} \qquad \text{rep/hr or rads/hr} \qquad (6\text{-}48)$$

Combining these three equations, the gamma dose rate is expressed by

$$D_\gamma(r) = 4.8 \times 10^{10}(1 + 0.8 f_\gamma) \frac{P_r}{r^2 A_s} \qquad \text{rep/hr or rads/hr} \quad (6\text{-}49)$$

The parameter A_s is an effective gamma-attenuation factor due to air scattering and/or shielding (i.e., absorption), as the case may be, and is given by

$$A_s = \prod_1^n A_{s_i} = A_{s_1} A_{s_2} \cdots A_{s_i} \cdots A_{s_n} \qquad (6\text{-}50)$$

where A_{s_i} is the attenuation factor due to the ith method of attenuation in a series of n attenuating mechanisms. For example, following the photons produced in core fissions, some of the photons are absorbed by core structure (A_{s_1}); some of those leaking out of the core are absorbed in the reflector (A_{s_2}) and reactor pressure shell (A_{s_3}); those leaking out of the shell are attenuated by absorption in air (A_{s_4}) and by any structure (A_{s_5}) housing the reactor or test personnel. The A_{s_i} concerned with these material absorptions are given approximately by

$$A_{s_m} = \frac{e^{\mu_m s}}{1 + \mu_m s} \qquad (6\text{-}51)$$

where μ_m and s are the gamma-interaction coefficient and thickness or line-of-sight path length through the material of interest.

In analyzing air-scattering effects to be accounted for when using shadow shielding, the geometry shown in Fig. 6-18 is assumed. Here the shadow shield subtends a half angle θ_s about the source center, measured from the source-receiver axis, and a half angle θ_r from this axis

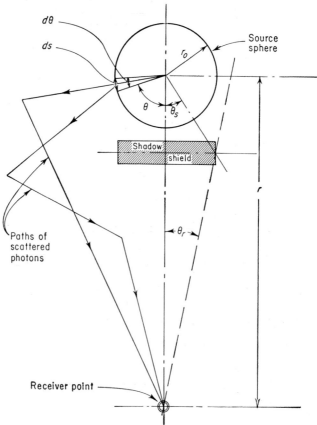

FIG. 6-18. Geometry for gamma-ray air-scattering effects with shadow shielding.

about the receiver center point. The shadow shield is assumed to be less than one photon-scattering mean free path in the ambient medium (generally air) from the source, and the receiver is assumed distant from the shield any arbitrary amount greater than this, so that θ_r is always less than θ_s. By definition a shadow shield always subtends an angle θ_r large enough that the receiver point can not "see" the source directly, i.e., no line-of-sight source-receiver radiation flow is possible. It is evident that shadow shielding can provide complete protection in a vacuum, since only line-of-sight radiation can reach the receiver from the source. In the atmosphere, however, photons leaking out from behind the shadow shield (at angles $\theta > \theta_s$) interact with atoms of the air and are scattered toward the receiver. The dose rate due to these air-scattered photons is much reduced from that without shadow shielding, for two reasons:

1. The total source strength is effectively reduced by the ratio of the solid angle remaining outside the shield (as viewed from the source) to all space (4π).

2. The first few photon–air scattering collisions greatly reduce the photon energy; thus those originating from the "back" of the reactor, relative to the receiver position, are much less effective than those leaking from the sides.

Exact analysis of the air-scattering process is complex and tedious. For most purposes it is sufficient to estimate gross attenuation factors A_a by use of attenuation functions incorporating the angular dependence in an approximate way. Two such representations, equally useful and plausible, of the attenuation function are

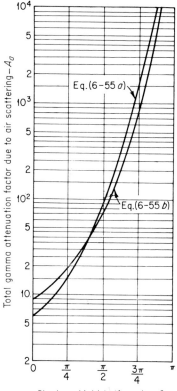

FIG. 6-19. Air-scattering attenuation factor for a shadow-shielded gamma source.

$$F_1(\theta) = \frac{20^{\cos\theta}}{20} \qquad (6\text{-}52a)$$

or

$$F_2(\theta) = 20^{-2\theta/\pi} \qquad (6\text{-}52b)$$

where θ is the angle about the source center from the source-receiver axis to the radiating-source-surface-area element dS. Note that the effective source is assumed to be a sphere of radius r_0, greater than the outer radius of the reactor by no more than several gamma-interaction mean free paths within the reactor. The fractional source area per unit angle is then

$$\frac{dS}{S_{tot}} = \frac{2\pi r_0^2 \sin\theta\, d\theta}{4\pi r_0^2} = \frac{\sin\theta\, d\theta}{2} \qquad (6\text{-}53)$$

The total attenuation due to air scattering is also linearly dependent upon the local air density, so that the complete attenuation factor for shadow shielding over a source-cone half angle θ_s is given by

$$A_a = \frac{\dfrac{\rho_0}{\rho_a}}{\displaystyle\int_{\theta_s}^{\pi} F(\theta)\, \frac{dS}{S_{tot}}} \qquad (6\text{-}54)$$

where ρ_0/ρ_a is the ratio of sea-level air density to local air density. For the attenuation functions given in Eqs. (6-52) the total attenuation factor becomes

$$A_{a_1} = \frac{40 \ln 20}{20^{\cos \theta_s} - 20^{-1}} \frac{\rho_0}{\rho_a} \qquad (6\text{-}55a)$$

or $\quad A_{a_2} = \dfrac{\rho_0}{\rho_a} \dfrac{2[(4/\pi^2)(\ln 20)^2 + 1]}{20^{-2} + 20^{-2\theta_s/\pi}[(2/\pi)(\ln 20) \sin \theta_s + \cos \theta_s]} \qquad (6\text{-}55b)$

For ready reference these are both plotted in Fig. 6-19, which clearly shows the great gains in reduction of radiation dose level possible by use of "infinitely" absorbing shadow shielding. Note that the two different attenuation functions yield results in reasonable agreement with each other, and certainly in agreement within the uncertainties of absorption-coefficient data and the inaccuracies inherent in the method of analysis. The implication here, that a factor-of-2 uncertainty in estimating radiation dose level is good or acceptable, is completely correct.

The air-scattering attenuation factor should be included in A_s whenever complete line-of-sight shielding is used between the reactor and the receiver point. Note also that a reduction in dose approaching a maximum of a factor of 2 must be included for a reactor operated close to the ground to account for the gammas emitted or scattered downward and subsequently absorbed in the downward half space. Here then we have

$$A_{s_6} = 2 \qquad (6\text{-}56)$$

Combining Eqs. (6-51) and (6-56) with (6-49) and (6-50), the gamma dose rate for a spherically symmetric and/or symmetrically shielded source (not including shadow shielding) is given by

$$\frac{A_m D_\gamma(r)}{P_r} = 2.4 \times 10^{10}(1 + \mu_a r)(1 + 0.8 f_\gamma) \frac{e^{-\mu_a r}}{r^2} \qquad \text{rep/Mwhr} \quad (6\text{-}57)$$

Here A_m is the total attenuation factor due to absorption by material placed symmetrically around the reactor core, viewed here as a point source, and/or the receiver point (e.g., interior of reactor control blockhouse). The attenuation coefficient for 1- to 2-Mev gammas in air is roughly

$$\mu_a = 5.5 \times 10^{-5} \frac{\rho_a}{\rho_0} \qquad \text{cm}^{-1} \qquad (6\text{-}58)$$

Using this and assuming 50 per cent saturated gamma activity so that

$f_\gamma = 0.5$, the gamma dose rate at sea-level air conditions, per unit reactor power, is shown in Fig. 6-20 for an interesting range of separation distances.

FAST NEUTRONS. The leakage flux of fast neutrons from a point fission source is given approximately by

$$\phi_{nf}(r) = \frac{3.4 \times 10^{16}}{4\pi} \frac{P_r f_n}{r^2 B_s} \tag{6-59}$$

where f_n is the effective fast-neutron leakage from the reactor, expressed as fast leakage neutrons per fission, and B_s is the effective source-receiver

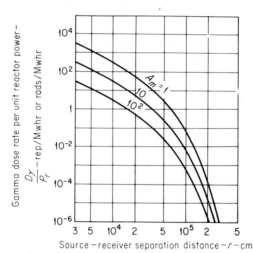

FIG. 6-20. Gamma dose rate at sea level for a symmetric source.

fast-neutron attenuation factor due to air scattering and neutron absorption. As for the analysis of gamma dose rate, the total attenuation factor is taken as the product of all the series attenuations from the reactor outer surface to the receiver point and is thus

$$B_s = \prod_1^n B_{s_i} \tag{6-60}$$

As for gammas, many of the fast neutrons emitted or scattered downward will be absorbed in ground-level operation of a reactor; consequently a factor approaching

$$B_{s_1} = 2 \tag{6-61}$$

must be included in the final dose-rate equation.

The conversion from fast-neutron flux to dose rate is given by

$$D_{nf} = 1.62 \times 10^{-3} \phi_{nf} \quad \text{rep/hr or rads/hr} \tag{6-62}$$

so that the fast-neutron dose becomes

$$D_{nf}(r) = 4.4 \times 10^{12} \frac{P_r f_n}{r^2 B_s} \qquad \text{rep/hr or rads/hr} \qquad (6\text{-}63)$$

The fast-neutron attenuation within the reactor pressure shell is absorbed in the factor f_n, the fast-neutron leakage per fission. This factor depends principally on the thermalization and absorption characteristics of the material comprising the reactor core and reflector (if any) and is given from age-diffusion theory as

$$f_n = 1 - e^{-B^2 \tau_{th}} \qquad (6\text{-}64)$$

For ready reference, values of τ_{th} are given in Table 6-2 for several materials useful in rocket reactors.

Estimates made from standard cross-section data[30] indicate that a scattering mean free path in air is of the order of 500 ft for fast neutrons

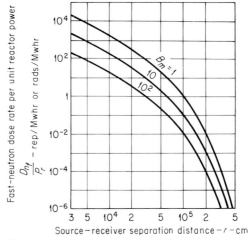

FIG. 6-21. Fast-neutron dose rate at sea level for a symmetric source.

$(0.01 < E_n < 5.0 \text{ Mev})$. Thus, for predominantly isotropic scattering a slight reduction in neutron dose can be achieved by pointing the major neutron leakage path away from the receiver. For a nonsymmetrically shielded source, shadow-shielded for line-of-sight attenuation only, this reduction in dose due to air scattering is approximately given by $2\rho_0/\rho_a$, and this factor should be included in B_s when such nonsymmetric shielding is used.

In addition to air-scattering effects and the reduction in fast-neutron flux by thermalization in the reactor, the fast-neutron dose is attenuated by thermalization and absorption in the air and in any other material placed symmetrically around the source or the receiver point. The appropriate attenuation factor is given by

$$B_{s_m} = e^{\Sigma_{r_m}r} \tag{6-65}$$

where Σ_{r_m} is the effective fast-neutron-removal cross section for the material of interest.

Combining Eqs. (6-61), (6-63), and (6-65), the fast-neutron dose rate for a spherically symmetric or symmetrically shielded reactor operating within the atmosphere is then

$$\frac{B_m D_{nf}(r)}{P_r} = 2.2 \times 10^{12} f_n \frac{e^{-\Sigma_{r_a}r}}{r^2} \qquad \text{rep/Mwhr} \tag{6-66}$$

where B_m is the total attenuation factor due to fast-neutron removal by material placed symmetrically around the source (reactor) or receiver. Use of standard fast-neutron-scattering and thermal-neutron-absorption cross-section data[30] indicates that about 1,000 ft of travel in sea-level-density air is required to thermalize and absorb fast neutrons, so that the effective removal cross section is roughly

$$\Sigma_{r_a} = 3 \times 10^{-5} \frac{\rho_a}{\rho_0} \qquad \text{cm}^{-1} \tag{6-67}$$

Using this value and assuming a leakage factor of $f_n = 0.1$ fast neutron per fission, the dose rate at sea-level air conditions, per unit reactor power, is shown in Fig. 6-21 as a function of source-receiver separation distance.

THERMAL NEUTRONS. At points close to the source the leakage flux of thermal neutrons is given, as before, by

$$\phi_{nth} = \frac{3.4 \times 10^{16}}{4\pi} \frac{P_r f_{th}(1 - f_n)}{r^2 C_s} \tag{6-68}$$

where C_s is the total thermal-neutron attenuation factor between source and receiver and is

$$C_s = \prod_1^n C_{s_i} \tag{6-69}$$

for n series attenuation mechanisms. The factor $1 - f_n$ in Eq. (6-68) is simply the maximum fractional number of thermal neutrons which can be produced from the one available excess fast neutron per fission produced in the core. This must be multiplied by the thermal-leakage probability f_{th} to determine the fractional thermal-neutron leakage per fission. The thermal-leakage probability from age-diffusion theory is

$$f_{th} = \frac{L^2 B^2}{1 + L^2 B^2} \tag{6-70}$$

so that the total thermal-neutron leakage per fission is given by

$$f_{th}(1 - f_n) = \frac{L^2 B^2}{1 + M^2 B^2} \qquad (6\text{-}71)$$

The interaction of thermal neutrons with tissue in the human body is very complex, proceeding by a variety of nuclear reactions resulting from thermal-neutron capture by body constituents (see Chap. 8). It is thus impossible to prescribe a "correct" factor for the conversion of thermal-

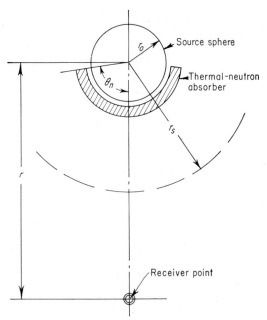

FIG. 6-22. Geometry for thermal-neutron close-in shadow absorption.

neutron flux to dose in the units of radiation absorption doses per hour (or roentgens equivalent physical per hour) previously used for gammas and fast neutrons. For our purposes the approximate conversion relation

$$D_{nth} \approx 10^{-4} \phi_{nth} \qquad \text{rep/hr or rads/hr} \qquad (6\text{-}72)$$

will be adequate.

Attenuation by absorption in the ground half space for a ground-operated reactor reduces the effective dose by a factor of nearly 2 so that

$$C_{s_1} = 2 \qquad (6\text{-}73)$$

The attenuation factor for absorption of thermal neutrons by absorbers placed symmetrically around the source or the receiver roughly follows the exponential law

$$C_{s_m} = e^{\Sigma_{r_m} t} \qquad (6\text{-}74)$$

where Σ_{r_m} is the effective removal cross section of thermal neutrons in material m of thickness t. This equation holds true for absorption in the atmosphere as well as for absorbers per se; however for atmospheric absorption, the absorber thickness is simply $r - r_s$, where r_s is the effective radius of the thermal-neutron source, taken as the radius to the point of first collision after leaving the reactor.

Since the scattering cross section of air is about four times larger for thermal than for fast neutrons, the thermal-neutron transport between the reactor and receiver is predominantly by diffusion processes beyond

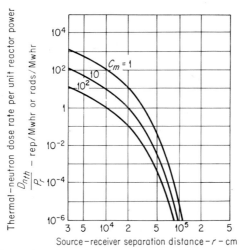

FIG. 6-23. Thermal-neutron dose rate at sea level for a symmetric source.

the point of first collision, rather than by line-of-sight geometrical spreading as is roughly the case for gamma rays and fast neutrons. The geometrical attenuation for thermal neutrons thus goes more nearly as $1/r$ rather than $1/r^2$. Taking account of this fact and combining Eqs. (6-68), (6-72), (6-73), and (6-74), the thermal-neutron dose is given by

$$\frac{C_m D_{nth}(r)}{P_r} = 1.35 \times 10^{11} f_{th}(1 - f_n) \frac{e^{-\Sigma_{r_a}(r - r_s)}}{rr_s} \quad \text{rep/Mwhr} \quad (6\text{-}75)$$

For absorbers placed symmetrically about the source-receiver axis but located close to the reactor, as in Fig. 6-22, the effective thermal-neutron dose will be reduced by a factor of

$$C_{s_2} = \frac{2}{1 + \cos \theta_n} \quad (6\text{-}76)$$

This is due simply to a reduction in the available radiating area about the source. Unlike gamma rays, no appreciable attenuation results from air scattering through large scattering angles, so the gain by use of axisymmetric shadow shielding is not as great for thermal neutrons as for gamma rays. However this attenuation factor should be included whenever such shielding is used.

The absorption cross section of air is about six to ten times as great for thermal as for fast neutrons and the e-folding attenuation length (relaxation or diffusion length) is estimated from standard cross-section data[30] to be about 200 ft, or 6,000 cm, in sea-level air, so that the effective thermal-removal cross section is approximately

$$\Sigma_{r_a} = 1.6 \times 10^{-4} \frac{\rho_a}{\rho_0} \quad \mathrm{cm}^{-1} \tag{6-77}$$

The distance to point of first collision is similarly found to be about $r_s = 3,000$ cm.

Using these values and assuming equal thermal and fast-leakage factors, $f_{th} = f_n = 0.1$, the thermal-neutron dose rate per unit reactor power is estimated as shown in Fig. 6-23, for sea-level air conditions.

REFERENCES

1. Glasstone, S., and M. C. Edlund: "The Elements of Nuclear Reactor Theory," D. Van Nostrand Company, Inc., Princeton, N.J., 1952.
2. Murray, R. L.: "Nuclear Reactor Physics," Prentice-Hall, Inc., Englewood Cliffs, N.J., 1957.
3. "The Reactor Handbook," vol. I ("Physics"), sec. 1, *AECD*-3645, March, 1955.
4. Stephenson, R.: "Introduction to Nuclear Engineering," chaps. 3, 4, and 7, McGraw-Hill Series in Chemical Engineering, McGraw-Hill Book Company, Inc., New York, 1954.
5. Thompson, A. S., and O. E. Rodgers: "Thermal Power from Nuclear Reactors," chaps. 1–3, John Wiley & Sons, Inc., New York, 1956.
6. Soodak, H., and E. C. Campbell: "Elementary Pile Theory," John Wiley & Sons, Inc., New York, 1950.
7. Charpie, R. A., et al. (eds.): "Physics and Mathematics," chap. 7, Progress in Nuclear Energy, ser. I, vol. 1, McGraw-Hill Book Company, Inc., New York, 1956.
8. Mayne, A. J.: Monte Carlo Methods for Solving Neutron Problems, *AWRE Rept.* 0-18/55, United Kingdom Atomic Energy Authority, July 18, 1955.
9. Podgor, S., and L. A. Beach: Monte Carlo Reactor Calculation, *NRL Rept.* 4673, Naval Research Laboratory, Dec. 9, 1955.
10. Kalos, Malvin H., and Herbert S. Wilf: Monte Carlo Solves Reactor Problems, *Nucleonics*, vol. 15, no. 5, pp. 64–68, May, 1957.
11. Ref. 2, par. 10.4, pp. 275–280.
12. Miles, F. T., and H. Soodak: Nomogram for the Critical Equation, *Nucleonics*, vol. 11, no. 1, p. 66, January, 1953.
13. Prohammer, F. G.: A Comparison of One-dimensional Critical Mass Computations with Experiments for Completely Reflected Reactors, *ORNL*-2007, Oak Ridge National Laboratory, Mar. 16, 1956.
14. Lamarsh, John, and Stuart S. Rideout: A Two-group Reactor Card Program for a Small Digital Computer, *BNL Rept.* 378 (*T*-69), Brookhaven National Laboratory, Upton, N.Y., May, 1956.

15. Ref. 1, secs. 8.59–8.64, pp. 247–249.
16. Spooner, R. B.: Using a Reactor Simulator for Design Analysis, *Nucleonics*, vol. 12, no. 4, pp. 36–39, April, 1954.
17. Bayly, J. G., and R. M. Pearce: Method of Studying Multi-region Reactors with an Analog Computer, *CRRP*-606, Atomic Energy of Canada, Ltd., April 6, 1956.
18. Radowsky, A., and R. Brodsky: A Bibliography of Available Digital Computer Codes for Nuclear Reactor Problems, *AECU*-3078, Naval Reactors Branch, Division of Reactor Development, U.S. AEC, Oct. 14, 1955.
19. *Nuclear Codes Group Newsletter*, nos. 1 and 2, AEC Computing Facility, New York University, New York, 1956.
20. Safonov, G.: Notes on Multi-group Techniques for the Investigation of Neutron Diffusion, *R*-233, RAND Corporation, Santa Monica, Calif., Jan. 1, 1952.
21. Safonov, G.: Survey of Reacting Mixtures Employing U^{235}, Pu^{239}, and U^{233} for Fuel and H_2O, D_2O, C, Be, and BeO for Moderator, *R*-259, RAND Corporation, Santa Monica, Calif., Jan. 8, 1954.
22. Safonov, G.: Critical Mixtures of U^{235}-Be-C Systems, *RM*-1581, RAND Corporation, Santa Monica, Calif., July 15, 1955.
23. Safonov, G.: The Criticality and Some Potentialities of "Cavity" Reactors (Abridged), *RM*-1835, RAND Corporation, Santa Monica, Calif., July 17, 1955.
24. Ash, Milton: Solutions of the Reactor Kinetics Equations for Time-dependent Reactivities, *UCRL*-4622, University of California Radiation Laboratory, Livermore, Calif., Dec. 14, 1955.
25. Moteff, John: Miscellaneous Data for Shielding Calculations, *APEX*-176, *ANPD*, p. 72, General Electric Company, Cincinnati, Ohio, Dec. 1, 1954.
26. Glasstone, S.: "Principles of Nuclear Reactor Engineering," sec. 10.78–10.79, p. 600, D. Van Nostrand Company, Inc., Princeton, N.J., 1956.
27. Ref. 25, p. 74.
28. Ref. 26, chaps. IX and X.
29. Rockwell,T heodore, III (ed.): "Reactor Shielding Design Manual," *TID*-7004, Naval Reactors Branch, Division of Reactor Development, U.S. AEC, March, 1956.
30. Hughes, D. J., and J. A. Harvey: "Neutron Cross-sections," *BNL*-325, Brookhaven National Laboratory, Upton, N.Y., July 1, 1955, and subsequent supplements.

CHAPTER 7

SYSTEM CONTROL

In principle, the control of a nuclear reactor is comparatively simple, for by controlling the fission process any level of power can be achieved. In practice, however, the factors which influence the fission process, such as the neutron-energy distribution, fission and absorption cross-section variations with temperature, geometrical changes in the core structure, and control-rod effectiveness, all tend to increase the complexity of the problem. For the particular case of nuclear rocket reactors, the additional requirements of reaching operating conditions in as short a period as possible in order to conserve propellant and of in-flight thrust programming for proper guidance introduce further complications. As a consequence, a complete and comprehensive treatment of the control problem cannot be covered in a single chapter. Instead the general approach and the methods utilized in analyzing and designing a control system are presented, with further details available in some of the excellent texts[1,2] on the subject. Included is a discussion on a typical nuclear rocket propulsion system, a review of certain mathematical methods of control-system analysis, the use of analog simulation, operating requirements of the system, and a description of reactor-control instrumentation.

7-1. Typical System. In the design of any missile control system, it is necessary to consider the influence of each component on every other and on the system as a whole. The mutual influence of structural deflection on stability and guidance, propellant consumption on center-of-gravity position, launching attitude and accelerations on thrust requirements and drag effects are just a few of the interactions that might exist. In cases where thrust programming is necessary, the engine control system (pumps, turbines, bleed gas, and attitude control) must also be coupled to the guidance system. However, in practice it is necessary to understand fully the behavior of each subsystem before attempting to analyze the over-all system. Since guidance-system characteristics as well as missile air-frame aerodynamic and structural characteristics will differ for each particular design, payload, and mission, it is not feasible to include a generalized discussion of such subsystems in this text. Instead, the discussion herein is limited to an examination of what might comprise a typical control system for a nuclear rocket-engine installation, keeping in mind that this is only a portion of the over-all control problem.

Major Components. The major components of a nuclear rocket-motor installation consist of a propellant supply system, including valves; a propellant turbopump, with its turbine-gas supply; a nuclear heat source and heat exchanger; and a nozzle. Since the operation of the system will depend upon the time-varying characteristics of the components, a programmer and some controllers must also be included. Figure 7-1 is a sketch showing these components arranged schematically. The propel-

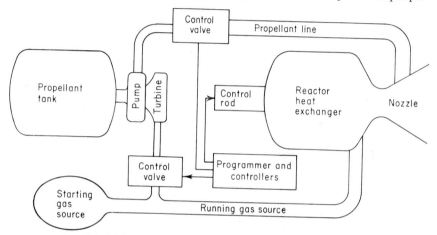

FIG. 7-1. Major components of a typical nuclear rocket system.

lant is contained in pressurized tanks and is fed into the suction side of the propellant pump by tank pressurization. The turbopump system consists of a turbine-gas source, control valve, gas turbine, and propellant pump. In order to start the system, a separate source of turbine gas is needed, but once the system is operating, a portion of the reactor-heated propellant may be bled off and used to supply the turbine. This procedure is called "bootstrapping." From the pump the low-temperature propellant is first used to cool regeneratively the nozzle and the pressure shell before being passed through the heat-exchanger core and exhausted from the nozzle. The characteristics of the turbine, pump, lines, valves, reactor, heat exchanger, and nozzle are, to a large extent, fixed because of the design constraints imposed by the thermodynamic, nucleonic, and material problems associated with the steady-state performance requirements. Any flexibility in the system must then come from the type of controller selected and the location of the control point. The controller must be designed to compensate for the tolerances inherent in the fixed components and to meet the transient performance requirements.

Performance. In establishing the performance criteria of any system, its behavior must be specified for both the static and dynamic state. The static performance requirements are related to the absolute stability of the system. That is, the design must yield a balance between power developed and power required at specified operating levels. It is obvious that a system must possess static stability before consideration can be given to dynamic performance.

Dynamic stability requirements are based on the manner in which a system responds to changes in some reference input signal and the ability of the system to compensate for disturbances. In general, the dynamic criteria are specified in terms of maximum response time, maximum over-

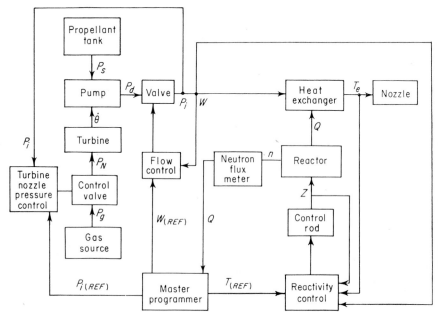

Fig. 7-2. Block diagram of a typical nuclear rocket control system.

shoot, and maximum steady-state error. As these requirements at times can be extremely severe, careful investigation and analysis of the system are required. In order to undertake this investigation, a knowledge of the dynamic characteristics of the components must first be determined.

System Dynamics. For a dynamic analysis of the system shown in Fig. 7-1, it is convenient to represent the system in block-diagram form. In some cases, it is even necessary to represent a single component by a series of blocks, each of which describes a particular physical characteristic of that component. Figure 7-2 shows a block-diagram representation of the previously considered system, and Table 7-1 contains the dynamic equations which describe the behavior of the various components.

Over-all control is obtained by regulating the power of the reactor through the propellant flow rate and pressure and the control-rod position. This is accomplished by means of a master programmer which receives an indication of the reactor power level from a neutron counter, and in turn supplies a reference flow rate to the flow controller, a reference propellant inlet pressure to the turbine nozzle-pressure controller, and a reference propellant exit temperature to the reactivity controller.

The flow controller compares the reference flow rate with the actual flow rate, while the turbine nozzle-pressure controller compares the reference pressure with the measured propellant core-inlet pressure. The error or difference existing between the measured and reference values is then used as a command signal to the flow-control valve and the turbine nozzle-pressure control valve, respectively. The reactivity controller receives measured values of propellant exit temperature, propellant flow rate, and control-rod position, as well as the propellant exit reference temperature from the master controller. From these data, the reactivity controller establishes whether or not reactivity is to be added or removed from the reactor and converts this requirement into a demand on the control-rod position.

To analyze such a control system completely is a considerable undertaking. In brief, what is required, besides a knowledge of the equations which represent the behavior of each of the components, is the study of the stability characteristics of the system and its components by analytical methods and in most cases by simulation techniques. Unfortunately, a comprehensive treatment of either of these phases of control-system design is well beyond the scope of this text, particularly since excellent texts exist in this field.[1-4] As a consequence, the material presented in the following two sections is intended to serve primarily as an introduction to the principles and methods used in control-system design and analysis, with emphasis on application to the problems of nuclear rocket-motor propulsion systems.

7-2. Mathematical Methods. In representing a physical system in a block-diagram form, similar to those in the preceding section, it is implied that each block of the system depicts a particular physical process that in most instances can be described by a mathematical equation. This equation can be an integral or an integrodifferential equation, but very often it is a differential equation; and in the cases where there is only one independent variable, like time, it is also an ordinary differential equation. In this section the discussion will be limited to ordinary differential equations.

A differential equation is called *linear*, and the system described by the differential equation, a *linear system*, if each term of the equation contains at most only first powers of the dependent variable or its derivatives. The terms should not contain higher powers of the dependent

TABLE 7-1. GENERAL SYSTEM DYNAMIC EQUATIONS*

Elements and equations	Symbols

Turbine

Torque balance

$$I\ddot{\theta} = \mu_t - \mu_p$$

Turbine efficiency

$$\eta_t = K_1 \frac{U}{V_t}\left(1 - K_2\frac{U}{V_t}\right)$$

Torque developed

$$\mu_t = \frac{W_t V_t \eta_t r}{2g_c U}$$

$$\mu_t = \frac{W_t}{g_c}(K_3 r V_t - K_4 r^2\theta)$$

Weight flow of gas into turbine

$$W_t = \frac{A_n P_n g_c}{C_t{}^*}$$

Turbine gas-spouting velocity

$$V_t = K_5 C_t{}^*\left(K_6 - K_7\frac{P_t}{P_n}\right)$$

Propellant pump

Flow equation

$$H = \frac{P_d - P_s}{\rho} = K_8\theta^2 - K_9 Vol$$

Power equation

$$\frac{\mu_p}{\rho\theta^2} = K_{10} + K_{11}\frac{Vol}{\theta}$$

Control valve

Weight flow of turbine gas

$$W_t = K_{12}P_g A_v\psi$$

Weight flow of propellant

$$W_p = K_{13}p_d A_v\varphi$$

Heat exchanger

Heat removal from fuel element

$$\rho_f c_{p_f}\frac{\partial T_f}{\partial t} = Q + k_f\frac{\partial^2 T_f}{\partial y^2}$$

$$Qb = \left(k_f\frac{\partial T_f}{\partial y}\right)_w = h(T_w - T_{aw})$$

Symbols:

I = turbine-pump-assembly inertia
θ = turbopump speed
μ_t = turbine torque developed
μ_p = pump torque required
η_t = turbine efficiency
U = Turbine-wheel peripheral speed
  $= r\theta$
r = turbine-wheel radius
V_t = turbine-gas spouting velocity
K = proportionality constant
W_t = weight flow of gas into turbine
g_c = mass conversion factor
A_n = turbine nozzle area
P_n = turbine nozzle pressure
$C_t{}^*$ = turbine-gas characteristic velocity
P_t = turbine exhaust pressure

H = head rise
P_d = pump discharge pressure
P_s = pump suction pressure
ρ = propellant mass density

Vol = propellant volumetric flow

P_g = source-gas pressure
A_v = valve area
ψ = compressible-flow coefficient
$$\psi = \psi_0\left(\frac{P_n}{P_g}\right)$$
W_p = weight flow of propellant
φ = flow coefficient
$$\varphi = \varphi_0\left(\frac{P_d}{P_i}\right)$$
P_i = propellant core-inlet pressure

Q = heat generation per unit volume
ρ_f = fuel-element material density
c_{p_f} = fuel-element specific heat
T_f = fuel-element temperature
t = time
k_f = fuel-element thermal conductivity
y = fuel-element thickness coordinate
b = fuel-element half thickness
h = heat-transfer coefficient

TABLE 7-1. GENERAL SYSTEM DYNAMIC EQUATIONS* (*Continued*)

Elements and equations	*Symbols*

T_w = fuel-element wall temperature

T_{aw} = adiabatic wall temperature

Flow of propellant

Continuity

$$\frac{\partial \rho}{\partial t} + \frac{\partial (\rho V)}{\partial x} = 0$$

V = propellant flow velocity

x = core length coordinate

Momentum

f = friction factor

p = core propellant pressure

$$\frac{\rho}{g_c} \frac{\partial V}{\partial t} + \frac{\rho}{g_c} \frac{V \partial V}{\partial x} = -\frac{\partial p}{\partial x} - \frac{4f}{D} \frac{1}{2} \frac{\rho V^2}{g_c}$$

D = hydraulic diameter

Energy

$$\rho \frac{\partial c_p T}{\partial t} + V \frac{\partial c_p T}{\partial x} = \frac{\partial p}{\partial t} + \frac{V \partial p}{\partial x} + \frac{4Qb}{D}$$

T = propellant temperature

c_p = propellant specific heat

Reactor

Fission heat generation

$Q = nvE\Sigma_f$

n = neutron density

v = neutron velocity

E = energy released per fission

Σ_f = fission cross section

δk = excess multiplication factor

Neutronics

$$\frac{dn}{dt} = \frac{\delta k - \beta}{l^*} n + \sum_{i=1}^{6} \lambda_i C_i$$

l^* = mean effective neutron lifetime

β = total fraction of delayed neutron

$$\frac{dC_i}{dt} = \frac{\beta_i n}{l^*} - \lambda_i C_i$$

$$\beta = \sum_{i=1}^{6} \beta_i$$

$$\delta k = K_{14} Z - K_{15} T_c + K_{16} W_p$$

λ_i = decay constant for ith group

C_i = concentration of delayed-neutron precursors for ith group

Z = control-rod position

T_c = temperature of core

* Assumptions are as follows:

Turbine and pump

1. Constant pump-suction pressure
2. Constant characteristic velocity for the turbine gases C_t*
3. Turbine-gas spouting velocity V_t not a critical function of shock or under-expansion
4. Constant turbine-wheel blocking coefficient
5. Constant specific-heat ratio for gases

Heat exchanger

1. One-dimensional conduction
2. One-dimensional propellant flow
3. Constant thermal conductivity
4. Heating by frictional stresses negligible

variable or cross products of the dependent variable and its derivatives. Otherwise, the differential equation is called *nonlinear*, and the system described by the differential equation, a *nonlinear* system. Linear systems can be further subdivided into systems with constant coefficients and systems with variable coefficients. Constant-coefficient systems have constants as the coefficients of the terms in the differential equation describing the system. Variable-coefficient systems have coefficients that are functions of the independent variable.

If one analyzes any physical system in great detail, it is almost a certainty that it will be found nonlinear, but by reasonable engineering approximation a sufficiently accurate linear system which will adequately describe the process generally can be devised. Sufficiently accurate approximations mean that the deviations from the nonlinear-system behavior are so small as to be unimportant, for the specific problem being considered. Therefore there is no general absolute criterion; whether or not a system is linear can only be determined under clearly defined circumstances. Similar approximations can be made under particular circumstances to describe linear systems with variable coefficients by systems with constant coefficients.

It goes without saying that linear systems with constant coefficients are easiest to study, and when the engineering approximations are made, a large number of the physical systems fall into this classification. It is for this reason that theories of stability and control are most developed for these particular systems. They will be the ones treated in this section.

Method of Laplace Transform. After the physical system has been described by a system of linear differential equations with time t as the independent variable, there are a number of mathematical methods that can be used in obtaining solutions to the problem. The one that is usually employed, however, is that of the Laplace transform. This method has a particular appeal to the engineering designer in that it reduces all problems to a standardized and uniform basis. The theory and practical use of the Laplace transform are discussed in many texts[3-6] and will not be repeated here. Instead, a brief description of the nature of the method and the manner in which it is normally utilized is presented.

If $y(t)$ is a function of the time variable t defined for $t > 0$, the Laplace transform $Y(s)$ of $y(t)$ is defined as

$$Y(s) = \int_0^\infty e^{-st} y(t) \, dt \tag{7-1}$$

where s is a complex variable having a positive real part, $Rs > 0$. For other values of s, the function $Y(s)$ is defined by the analytic continuation. The dimension of $Y(s)$ is the dimension of y multiplied by t.

When $Y(s)$ is known, the original function for which $Y(s)$ is the Laplace transform can be obtained in all cases by the inversion formula

$$y(t) = \frac{1}{2\pi i} \int_{\gamma - i\infty}^{\gamma + i\infty} e^{st} Y(s) \, ds \tag{7-2}$$

where γ is a constant greater than the real part of all the singularities of $Y(s)$. In actually evaluating $y(t)$, the path of integration can be deformed in accordance with the character of $Y(s)$.

Due to the fact that the Laplace transform is defined as an operation on a function which in turn is defined for a time $t > 0$, the method is particularly adapted to initial-value problems, that is, for cases where the initial state of the system and the forcing function for a time $t > 0$ are given and the problem is to find the behavior of the system for time $t > 0$. For example consider an nth-order system, with coefficients a_n, a_{n-1}, $\ldots$, a_0 for the derivatives, and a nonhomogeneous term, or forcing function, $x(t)$. The differential equation describing the system is then

$$a_n \frac{d^n y}{dt^n} + a_{n-1} \frac{d^{n-1} y}{dt^{n-1}} + \cdots + a_0 y(t) = x(t) \tag{7-3}$$

with the initial conditions usually specified as

$$\left(\frac{d^{n-1} y}{dt^{n-1}} \right)_{t=0} = y_0{}^{(n-1)} \tag{7-4}$$

$$\cdots \cdots \cdots \cdots \cdots$$

$$(y)_{t=0} = y_0$$

Now the differential equation (7-3) and the initial-conditions equation (7-4) determine uniquely the behavior of the system for time $t > 0$.

In solving the problem by means of the Laplace transformation, first multiply both sides of Eq. (7-3) by e^{-st} and integrate from $t = 0$ to $t = \infty$:

$$\int_0^\infty e^{-st} \left[a_n \frac{d^n y}{dt^n} + a_{n-1} \frac{d^{n-1}}{dt^{n-1}} + \cdots + a_0 y(t) \right] dt = \int_0^\infty e^{-st} x(t) \, dt \tag{7-5}$$

and remembering that, from Eq. (7-1),

$$\int_0^\infty e^{-st} y(t) \, dt = Y(s)$$

we obtain from integration by parts and imposing the initial conditions of Eq. (7-4)

$$\int_0^\infty e^{-st} \frac{dy}{dt} \, dt = -y_0 + s \int_0^\infty e^{-st} y(t) \, dt = -y_0 + s Y(s)$$

$$\int_0^\infty e^{-st} \frac{d^2 y}{dt^2} \, dt = -y_0{}^{(1)} - s y_0 + s^2 Y(s) \tag{7-6}$$

$$\cdots \cdots \cdots \cdots \cdots \cdots \cdots$$

and

$$\int_0^\infty e^{-st} \frac{d^n y}{dt^n}\, dt = -y_0^{(n-1)} - s y_0^{(n-2)} - \cdots - s^{n-1} y_0 + s^n Y(s)$$

Now if the Laplace transform of the forcing function $x(t)$ is written as $X(s)$ and defined as

$$X(s) = \int_0^\infty e^{-st} x(t)\, dt \qquad\qquad (7\text{-}7)$$

then Eq. (7-3) together with the initial-conditions equation (7-4) is transformed to

$$(a_n s^n + a_{n-1} s^{n-1} + \cdots + a_1 s + a_0) Y(s) = a_n y_0 s^{n-1}$$
$$+ (a_n y_0^{(1)} + a_{n-1} y_0) s^{n-2} + (a_n y_0^{(2)} + a_{n-1} y_0^{(1)} + a_{n-2} y_0) s^{n-3}$$
$$+ \cdots + (a_n y_0^{(n-1)} + a_{n-1} y_0^{(n-2)} + \cdots + a_1 y_0) + X(s) \qquad (7\text{-}8)$$

By defining the polynomials $D(s)$ and $N_0(s)$ as

$$D(s) = a_n s^n + a_{n-1} s^{n-1} + \cdots + a_1 s + a_0 \qquad\qquad (7\text{-}9)$$

and

$$N_0(s) = a_n y_0 s^{n-1} + (a_n y_0^{(1)} + a_{n-1} y_0) s^{n-2} + \cdots$$
$$+ (a_n y^{(n-1)} + a_{n-1} y_0^{(n-2)} + \cdots + a_1 y_0) \qquad (7\text{-}10)$$

the solution of Eq. (7-8) becomes

$$Y(s) = \frac{N_0(s)}{D(s)} + \frac{X(s)}{D(s)} \qquad\qquad (7\text{-}11)$$

It should be noted that the first term of the right side of Eq. (7-11) depends, through Eq. (7-10), upon the initial conditions. At the most, $N_0(s)$ is of order $n - 1$ and thus is of lower order than $D(s)$. In addition, if the initial values specified by Eq. (7-4) vanish, $N_0(s)$ will also vanish. In that case $Y(s)$ is given by the second term alone, which in turn is dependent upon the forcing function. Therefore in the language of the solution to differential equations, the first term $N_0(s)/D(s)$ can be called the complementary function and the second term $X(s)/D(s)$ the particular integral. To obtain the actual solution $y(t)$ the inversion formula of Eq. (7-2) must be applied to $Y(s)$. Normally, however, the right side of Eq. (7-11) can usually be expressed as a number of simple fractions, and by using readily available tables of Laplace-transform pairs, the original function $y(t)$ can be obtained without resorting to the inversion formula. Table 7-2 is an abridged version of such transform pairs. For a more extensive listing, reference should be made to the cited texts.

$Y(s)$	$y(t)$
$\dfrac{1}{s}$	A constant value of unity; or the unit-step function $x(t)$
$\dfrac{1}{s^n}$	$\dfrac{1}{(n-1)!}\,t^{n-1}$
$\dfrac{1}{s+a}$	e^{-at}
$\dfrac{1}{(s+a)^n}$	$\dfrac{1}{(n-1)!}\,t^{n-1}e^{-at}$
$\dfrac{a}{s^2+a^2}$	$\sin at$
$\dfrac{s}{s^2+a^2}$	$\cos at$
$\dfrac{a}{s^2-a^2}$	$\sinh at$
$\dfrac{s}{s^2-a^2}$	$\cosh at$

From Eq. (7-11), it is evident that the behavior of a linear system with constant coefficients depends essentially upon the polynomial $D(s)$. Even in the generalized case, if the initial values of $y(t)$ and the initial derivatives necessary to specify the problem are all zero, the behavior of the system is completely determined by a ratio $N(s)/D(s)$ of two polynomials, which can be denoted as $F(s)$.

By rewriting Eq. (7-11) in the form

$$Y(s) = Y_c(s) + Y_i(s) \qquad (7\text{-}12)$$

where $Y_c(s)$ is the Laplace transform of the complementary function and $Y_i(s)$ is that of the particular integral, it can be shown that, if the Laplace transform of the forcing function is $X(s)$, as previously, the Laplace transform of the particular integral $Y_i(s)$ is

$$Y_i(s) = \frac{N(s)}{D(s)}\,X(s) = F(s)X(s) \qquad (7\text{-}13)$$

Equation (7-13) can be considered as an operator equation; that is, when $X(s)$ is operated on by $F(s)$ the result is $Y_i(s)$, so that $F(s)$ transfers $X(s)$ into $Y_i(s)$. For this reason $F(s)$ is called the *transfer function*. $X(s)$ is referred to as the Laplace transform of the input $x(t)$, and $Y_i(s)$ as the Laplace transform of the output $y_i(t)$. In order to specify the fact that $y_i(t)$ implies the particular integral only, without the complementary function introduced by the initial conditions, $y_i(t)$ is called the *output due to input*. The complementary function $y_c(t)$ is called the *output due to initial conditions*.

From the foregoing, it can be seen that the advantage of the Laplace-transform method is to reduce a problem in differential equations to an algebraic one. In practice, the step of going from $Y(s)$ to $y(t)$ is seldom necessary, as the behavior of $y(t)$ is fully determined by $Y(s)$. Thus, it is possible to translate the engineering requirements on $y(t)$ to a set of requirements on $Y(s)$ or, with the input characteristics specified, to a set of requirements on the transfer function $F(s)$. Accordingly, the fundamental technique in the study and analysis of control and servomechanism design is by means of the transfer function.

Feedback and System Stability. The control system of a nuclear rocket, like that of any other high-performance system, must possess a high degree of stability, while from a performance viewpoint, a capability of extreme accuracy is also desired. These requirements of stability and accuracy are mutually incompatible. The higher the desired accuracy the smaller is the actuating error that can be tolerated for proper corrective action and the sooner must full corrective action be initiated. Thus, to be accurate, a system requires high amplification. In turn, however, systems with high amplification and significant delays in their time response can become unstable. It is through the concept of feedback that a basis is provided for the design of accurate and rapidly responding control systems; it demands, however, advanced techniques in analyzing the stability and performance characteristics of the system. Since most nuclear rocket control systems and subsystems are of the feedback type, a brief review of the concept and the methods employed in investigating their stability is presented.

FEEDBACK. The concept of feedback is best demonstrated by means of a specific application. Let us consider the problem of controlling the rotational speed of a rocket-motor turbopump at some arbitrary value. One means of accomplishing this is by means of an open-loop control, where the torque output of the turbine is balanced by the torque absorbed by the pump. In many instances, these torques will not be exactly balanced and will differ by some error torque $x(t)$, which will tend to accelerate or decelerate the machine. If $y(t)$ denotes the speed deviation from the desired value and I is the moment of inertia of the rotating components of the device, with c a damping coefficient that is proportional to the speed change, the differential equation of the system is

$$I \frac{dy}{dt} + cy = x(t) \tag{7-14}$$

By taking the Laplace transform of Eq. (7-14), we obtain for the output due to input [omitting the subscript on $Y_i(s)$]:

$$Y(s) = \frac{1}{Is + c} X(s) = F_1(s) X(s) \tag{7-15}$$

with the block diagram representing this open-loop system shown in Fig. 7-3. The characteristic time of the system is I/c, and the ratio of the steady-state value of the speed deviation to the error torque is $1/c$. Now if I is large because of the mass of the rotating components but c is small, the characteristic time will be long, resulting in a condition where any speed deviation will be difficult to correct. In addition, small speed deviations require an extremely small error torque because of the large magnification factor $1/c$. Under these circumstances proper control of the system at a constant speed would be difficult to achieve.

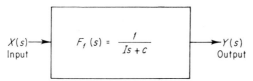

FIG. 7-3. Block diagram of an open-loop system.

It is evident, then, that some other method must be employed if an effective speed control is required. Let us examine the consequences of changing the system to a closed-loop control. In this type of system, the control torque will be dependent upon the control variable. In other words, the demand for increased torque depends not only on the

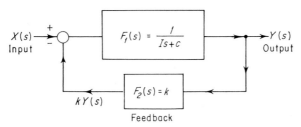

FIG. 7-4. Block diagram of a closed-loop system.

load but on the speed deviation y. If this second parameter has a proportionality factor of $-k$, a speed that is too high will reduce the accelerating torque by an amount ky. Conversely, if the speed is too low, the accelerating torque is increased by an amount ky. The differential equation for this system is now

$$I \frac{dy}{dt} + (c + k)y = x(t) \tag{7-16}$$

The only difference between Eqs. (7-14) and (7-16) is the replacement of c by the sum $c + k$. Hence the characteristic time is now $I/(c + k)$ and the steady-state speed deviation–error torque ratio is $1/(c + k)$. We can now greatly reduce both the characteristic time and the speed errors by making k much larger than c, thereby having a closed-loop design which has both rapid response and accurate control. The block diagram of this closed-loop system is shown in Fig. 7-4. The speed deviation y is measured at the output side, fed through a feedback loop to the input side, and used to generate a control torque. Thus it is appropriately called a feedback control system.

While for simple systems the analysis can be made by comparing the differential equations, more complicated designs are more readily analyzed by means of the transfer functions. Since certain characteristics of the transfer function also determine the stability of the system, further consideration of some of the features of the transfer function will later prove useful.

Let us reconsider a feedback system similar to that shown in Fig. 7-4 with arbitrary transfer functions $F_1(s)$ for the *forward loop* and $F_2(s)$ for the *feedback loop*. The relationship between the input $X(s)$ and the output $Y(s)$ is expressed by

$$Y(s) = F_1(s)[X(s) - F_2(s)Y(s)] \qquad (7\text{-}17)$$

Solving for $Y(s)$ gives

$$\frac{Y(s)}{X(s)} = \frac{F_1(s)}{1 + F_1(s)F_2(s)} = F_s(s) \qquad (7\text{-}18)$$

where $F_s(s)$ is the *system* transfer function, or the output-input ratio of the complete system.

In practice, it is convenient to express the transfer function in terms of its gain K and a nondimensional function $G(s)$. That is,

$$F_1 = K_1 G_1(s) \qquad (7\text{-}19)$$
$$F_2 = K_2 G_2(s)$$

The dimensions of the transfer function are contained in the gain K, while the mathematical characteristics of the transfer function are contained in the term $G(s)$. This separation of effects is useful in the design of systems, since the influence of each can in most cases be considered independently of the other.

Using the relations of Eq. (7-19), Eq. (7-18), which describes a *general feedback system*, can be rewritten as

$$\frac{Y(s)}{X(s)} = F_s(s) = \frac{K_1 G_1(s)}{1 + K_1 G_1(s) K_2 G_2(s)} = \frac{1}{1/K_1 G_1(s) + K_2 G_2(s)} \qquad (7\text{-}20)$$

If the error $e(t)$ of the system is defined as the difference between the input $x(t)$ and the output $y(t)$ and the Laplace transform of the error is $E(s)$, then

$$\frac{E(s)}{Y(s)} = \frac{X(s) - Y(s)}{Y(s)} = \frac{1}{F_s(s)} - 1 = \frac{1}{K_1 G_1(s)} - [1 - K_2 G_2(s)] \qquad (7\text{-}21)$$

For a simple feedback system as shown in Fig. 7-5, the output is only measured but not modified by the feedback loop, resulting in a feedback-loop transfer function of unity. With this simplification Eqs. (7-20) and (7-21) become

$$\frac{Y(s)}{X(s)} = F_s(s) = \frac{KG(s)}{1 + KG(s)} = \frac{1}{1/KG(s) + 1} \qquad (7\text{-}22)$$

$$\frac{E(s)}{Y(s)} = \frac{1}{KG(s)} \qquad (7\text{-}23)$$

STABILITY. As previously mentioned, a necessary requirement for a control system is that it be stable. This means that the output $y(t)$ should be damped, except possibly for steady sinusoidal motions. To

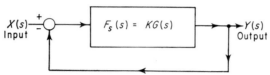

FIG. 7-5. Block diagram of a simple feedback system.

establish a criterion for stability, let us further examine the transfer function. Since the transfer function $F(s)$ is generally a ratio of two polynomials in s, a complex variable, the function $F(s)$ is determined except for a constant by the zeros and poles of $F(s)$. The constant in turn can be fixed by knowing the value of $F(s)$ at any particular s. In fact, if the origin is taken as the particular s, it has a physical meaning. It is the ratio of output to input with a constant non-time-varying input, or the *gain*. That is,

$$F(0) = K \qquad (7\text{-}24)$$

For example, the transfer function given by Eq. (7-15) has a gain of unity, has a simple pole at $-c/I$, and has no zeros. In passing, another representation of $F(s)$ can be shown to be the complex function $F(i\omega)$, where ω is real, which for all values of ω is called the *frequency response* of the system.

Our requirement of stability can then be mathematically equivalent to the statement that $F_s(s)$ should have no poles in the right-hand half of the s plane, where the real part of s is positive. For the general feedback system, given by Eq. (7-20), the poles of $F_s(s)$ are zeros of

$$\frac{1}{F_s(s)} = \frac{1}{K_1 G_1(s)} + K_2 G_2(s) \qquad (7\text{-}25)$$

For the simple feedback system, given by Eq. (7-22), the poles of $F_s(s)$ are the zeros of

$$\frac{1}{F_s(s)} = \frac{1}{KG(s)} + 1 \qquad (7\text{-}26)$$

Accordingly the criterion for stability of feedback systems is that

The function $1/F_s(s)$ *of the system should not have any zeros in the right-hand half of the s plane.*

The above analysis also establishes a design criterion for the rapid response that is desirable in feedback systems. If s_r is a pole of $F_s(s)$, it can be shown that the output has a component $e^{s_r t}$. Therefore, the quickness of response is determined by the magnitude of s_r. Large values of s_r give short time scales, and thus rapid response. For this requirement the design criterion becomes

The zeros of $1/F_s(s)$ *should all be of large magnitude and be far to the left of the imaginary axis of the s plane.*

If a feedback control system is designed for controlling the output to follow the input signal, the steady-state output, after the transients are removed, should be made to be as close as possible to the input. Therefore, one requirement for such "positional" controls is that the ratio $E(0)/Y(0)$ between the steady-state error and the steady-state output should be as small as possible. By using Eqs. (7-21) and (7-23) this requirement can be fulfilled by imposing additional conditions on the gains of the transfer functions. For positioning control of a general feedback system described by Eq. (7-21), accuracy of control requires that

$$\frac{1}{K_1} - (1 - K_2) \approx 0 \qquad (7\text{-}27)$$

and for simple feedback systems described by Eq. (7-23)

$$K \gg 1 \qquad (7\text{-}28)$$

These three conditions are the design criteria of feedback control systems. In practice, the latter two conditions are difficult to satisfy as fully as might be desired, and compromises must be made. The stability requirement is a necessity, however, and various methods for analyzing the problem have been developed. Only a brief description of some of these methods is given, and the reader is thus referred to the cited literature for the theory and details of the analytical procedures.

For transfer functions that are usually ratios of two polynomials, the stability criterion given above resolves itself into a determination of the nonexistence of roots of a polynomial which has positive real parts. This problem has received considerable attention; the classic method consists of determining the nature of the roots of the *characteristic* equation of the system by applying Routh's criterion. This method, named for E. H. Routh, uses certain inequalities involving the coefficients of the characteristic equation. It has the advantage that the roots of the characteristic equation need not be evaluated in order to determine whether or not the system is stable. Although it is rapid and exact, it does not provide a direct measure of stability as would be the case if the values of the real portions of the roots were known. Another disadvantage of the Routh method arises from the obscure manner in which the inequalities vary with changes in the coefficients of the characteristic equation. A preferable method is one which uses the transfer functions of the system directly, since these functions are readily available and are understood by the designer.

A method that has such an advantage is one devised by H. Nyquist in 1932, while he was working on feedback-amplifier design. Since 1940, it has been used extensively in the field of servomechanisms. The Nyquist method is based upon the following theorem of Cauchy for an analytical function $f(s)$ of a complex variable s:

If $f(s)$ has n zeros and m poles within a closed contour C, then as s travels along C once in a clockwise direction, the vector $f(s)$ carries out $n - m$ clockwise revolutions about the origin.

In carrying out the procedures outlined in the theorem, the transfer function is used and the vector representation is shown on a graphical plot called a Nyquist diagram of the system. Besides these advantages, the Nyquist method possesses additional desirable features necessary to control-system stability analysis. First, of course, it provides definitive information on the existence of any roots of the function $1/F_s(s)$ in the right-hand half of the s plane. Secondly, the same plot that indicates the stability of the system may also be employed to give quantitative data regarding performance of the system under varying steady-state sinusoidal inputs. In addition, the method permits an independent consideration of the effects on stability of the various elements of the system, and also the direct use of experimental data. Its major disadvantage is that it does not present as complete a picture of the frequency response and degree of stability as may be required.

To overcome these disadvantages the root-locus method devised by W. R. Evans is often used. This method determines the roots of the desired equation in terms of the gain K, which for the simple feedback system of Eq. (7-26) would be

$$0 = \frac{1}{F_s(s)} = 1 + \frac{1}{KG(s)} \tag{7-29}$$

with $G(s)$ given. When this has been accomplished, the proper choice of the magnitude of the gain K can be made for any set of specifications for the roots. The main virtue of the Evans root-locus method is that it goes much further than just providing a means of satisfying the stability criterion; it actually solves the design problems for all three of the previously stated criteria.

It is hoped that the foregoing "capsule" treatment of the methods and procedures employed in analyzing a control-system design provides sufficient material to enable the uninitiated to understand better the problems involved and the techniques that are used to solve them.

7-3. Simulation. In the preceding section we have seen how certain mathematical methods may be employed in analyzing control systems that are represented by a system of ordinary linear differential equations, particularly those with constant coefficients. Unfortunately, during many phases of a nuclear rocket design, the complexity, nonlinearity, and the varying coefficients of the systems involved make the direct-analysis approach impracticable. In these instances the usual practice is to study the problem by means of system simulators. The heart of such simulators is the electronic analog computer. Not only can *design* analyses be made, but upon completion of the system design, actual control components may be included in the simulation circuits and their performance checked. In fact, with sufficient computer capacity, the characteristics of the complete control system including its instrumentation may be studied.

In this section a brief review of elementary analog-computer techniques and components is presented, with examples of how they might be applied to a few of the nuclear rocket control problems. As for the section on mathematical methods, only an introduction to the subject is given, and it is recommended that the reader avail himself of the extensive material in the field of analog simulation for the theory and further details.[4,7]

Electronic Analog Computers. As mentioned briefly in Chap. 4 when discussing heat-conduction problems, many different physical systems follow the same mathematical pattern. Thereby, by observing the behavior of one system, one may be able to predict the performance of another. An analog computer represents the variables of a given problem by *machine variables*, such as shaft rotations or voltages, which are made to obey mathematical relations analogous to those of the system being studied. These relations are established by a set of *computing elements* capable of enforcing suitable physical relationships. Observations of the values and behavior of conveniently measurable machine variables will then represent solutions to a desired problem. In an electronic analog computer, the machine variables are represented by time-varying voltages. The principal computing elements are amplifiers with resistive and capacitive feedback networks. Parameter values and coefficients are usually varied by means of adjustable potentiometers or rheostats.

While it is possible to obtain solutions by connecting linear passive electrical networks, that is, ones that usually use only resistors and capacitors, such networks unfortunately load each other in the interconnection process, which in turn requires modification of the basic equations.

Therefore, the basis of design for most simulators is the operational amplifier, which is designed to prevent these loading effects. An operational amplifier is a direct-coupled amplifier whose transfer function is mainly determined by its feedback networks. The forward gain of the amplifier is usually made as high as possible in order to make the transfer function stable. Another design requirement is that the amplifier have no zero offset or drift; that is, the output for zero input must be zero volts. In addition, the maximum absolute values of the voltages of operational amplifiers must not exceed the range of linear amplifier operation, which is usually about 100 volts; and for purposes of unloading interconnecting elements and accurate computation, the input impedance should be high and the output impedance low. In comparison to other computing devices, such as digital computing machines and fire controllers, the electronic analog computer is a simple device. This is because of the ease with which the fundamental computing operations of multiplication (by constants), addition, differentiation, and integration can be performed by using basic laws of current flow.

Figure 7-6 gives a summary of how these fundamental computing operations are accomplished by means of operational-amplifier circuits. The inputs and outputs are voltages that are measured with respect to a ground reference.

Another necessary computer component is the *function* generator. It is so designed that, by means of tapered and tapped potentiometers, the output voltage can be made equal to a nonlinear function of the shaft setting and thus of the second input voltage. Such servo-driven function generators permit the multiplication of a constant or variable voltage by a function of another voltage. With these servo-driven devices, however, the speed of computation is limited by the speed with which the motor can follow the variations of the second input voltage.

In order to make up a complete analog-computer assembly, components in addition to those mentioned above are required. The following breakdown will provide a feeling as to what constitutes a complete analog computer.

1. *Linear electronic computing elements* consisting of operational amplifiers and associated networks. These units will perform the necessary operations of amplification, phase inversion, differentiation, and integration.

2. *Potentiometers or attenuators* needed to set constant coefficients.

3. *Nonlinear electronic or electromechanical computing elements* for performing multiplication, division, function generation, and limiting.

4. *Problem-board patch cords and jacks* by which the various computing elements are interconnected.

5. *Control circuits* for starting and stopping the machine.

6. *Recording or measuring instrumentation*, usually consisting of recording milliammeters or servo plotting boards which furnish a permanent record.

7. A regulated *power supply* which furnishes the voltage to the electronic components.

An example of how these components are arranged in a computer installation is shown in Fig. 7-7.

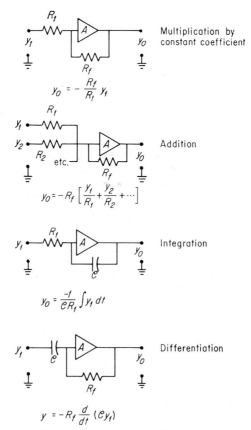

$$y_0 = -\frac{R_f}{R_1} y_1$$

Multiplication by constant coefficient

$$y_0 = -R_f \left[\frac{y_1}{R_1} + \frac{y_2}{R_2} + \cdots \right]$$

Addition

$$y_0 = \frac{-1}{CR_1} \int y_1 \, dt$$

Integration

$$y = -R_f \frac{d}{dt} (Cy_1)$$

Differentiation

FIG. 7-6. Summary of simple computing circuits using operational amplifiers.

Applications. To illustrate how the analog simulation is carried out, let us first examine a second-order ordinary differential equation with constant coefficients which represents a system with a single degree of freedom:

$$A \frac{d^2y}{dt^2} + B \frac{dy}{dt} + Dy = F(t) \qquad (7\text{-}30)$$

rearranging to the form

$$A \frac{d^2y}{dt^2} = F(t) - B \frac{dy}{dt} - Dy \tag{7-31}$$

with

$$\frac{dy}{dt} = \int \frac{d^2y}{dt^2} \, dt \tag{7-32}$$

$$y = \int \frac{dy}{dt} \, dt \tag{7-33}$$

Now by the use of the operational amplifiers given in Fig. 7-6, and without specifying the function generator, the analog network for the

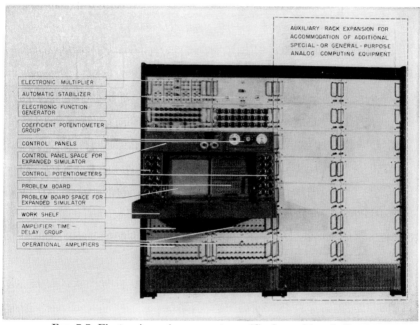

FIG. 7-7. Electronic analog computer. *(Goodyear Aircraft Corp.)*

solution to Eq. (7-31) is shown in Fig. 7-8. Amplifier 1 multiplies $A\ddot{y}$ by the constant $1/A$; integrating amplifiers 2 and 3 satisfy Eqs. (7-32) and (7-33), respectively; amplifier 4 multiplies $\dot{y}$ by the constant B, and amplifier 5 multiplies y by the constant D, with amplifier 6 being used as a sign changer. Amplifier 7 sums the three terms $-F(t)$, By, and Dy and satisfies Eq. (7-31). The resistances R_1 through R_{14} and the capacitances $\mathcal{C}_1$, $\mathcal{C}_2$ are so chosen that $R_2/R_1 = 1/A$, $\mathcal{C}_1 R_3 = 1$, $\mathcal{C}_2 R_4 = 1$, $R_6/R_5 = B$, $R_8/R_7 = D$, $R_{10}/R_9 = 1$, $R_{14}/R_{11} = 1$, $R_{14}/R_{12} = 1$, and $R_{14}/R_{13} = 1$. In practice, this network can be reduced by a summing integrator and by combining some of the operations. Separation of the processes in this example was made deliberately in order to focus attention on the particular operations.

While the above example demonstrates how an electronic analog network simulates a simple system, a more practical problem in which the

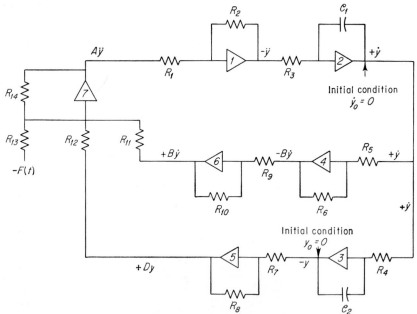

FIG. 7-8. Analog network of a single-degree-of-freedom system.

technique is useful is in the simulation of nuclear-reactor kinetics.* From Chap. 6, the kinetic equations are

$$\frac{dn}{dt} = \frac{\delta k - \beta}{l^*} n + \sum_{i=1}^{6} \lambda_i C_i + S \tag{7-34}$$

$$\frac{dC_i}{dt} = \frac{\beta_i n}{l^*} - \lambda_i C_i \tag{7-35}$$

where n = neutron density
δk = excess multiplication factor
l^* = mean effective neutron lifetime
β_i = fraction of total neutrons in ith delay group with $\beta = \Sigma \beta_i$
C_i is the concentration of delayed-neutron precursors for group i, with λ_i being the decay constant and S the externally supplied source term.

* The material given in this section follows closely the description of an elementary reactor kinetic simulator given in M. A. Schultz, "Control of Nuclear Reactors and Power Plants," McGraw-Hill Series in Nuclear Engineering, McGraw-Hill Book Company, Inc., New York, 1955.

Combining Eqs. (7-34) and (7-35) and multiplying by l^*, we obtain

$$l^* \frac{dn}{dt} = \delta k n - l^* \sum_{i=1}^{6} \frac{dC_i}{dt} + l^*S \qquad (7\text{-}36)$$

It is Eq. (7-36) that will be solved by an analog network. Examining the form of Eq. (7-36) in order to determine what type of circuits will make up the network, we see that, if the output voltage of the network is proportional to the neutron density, the term on the left side of the

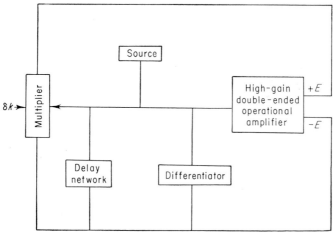

Fig. 7-9. Block-diagram of an elementary reactor kinetic simulator.

equation requires a differentiation circuit, while the first term on the right side requires a multiplication circuit. The second term on the right side of the equation represents the delayed neutrons and will require delay networks; the last or source term will require an addition-source network. In block form, Fig. 7-9 shows how this system might be simulated. The voltage output of the operational amplifier is double-ended, having two output voltages equal in magnitude but opposite in sign. An adding bus is connected to the input of the amplifier, and when the gain of the amplifier is very high, any voltage on this bus causes the output voltage to vary so as to reduce the input voltage to zero.

The networks that perform the operations given in the block diagram are shown in Fig. 7-10. The multiplication is done by a multiplying potentiometer, the differentiation by a capacitor circuit, the delay networks by a series of resistance-capacitance circuits, and the addition source is from a separate voltage supply through a potentiometer.

Now by use of the second law of Kirchhoff, the current flow in the network of Fig. 7-10 has the relationship

$$I_7 = I_8 - \sum_{i=1}^{6} I_i + I_9 \qquad (7\text{-}37)$$

resulting in an equation that has the same form as Eq. (7-36). By assigning the proper values to the electrical components, each term in Eq. (7-37) can be made to represent a similar term in Eq. (7-36). This

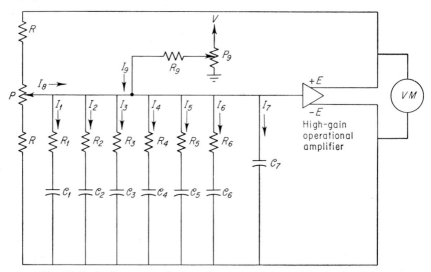

Fig. 7-10. Analog network of an elementary reactor kinetic simulator.

can be done in the following manner: Assume the output voltage is proportional to the neutron density, so that

$$E = \epsilon n \qquad (7\text{-}38)$$

where ϵ is the proportionality constant. Then from the behavior of a capacitor circuit

$$I_7 = \mathcal{C}_7 \frac{dE}{dt} = \frac{\epsilon \mathcal{C}_7}{l^*} l^* \frac{dn}{dt} \qquad (7\text{-}39)$$

By direct network analysis the current leading from the multiplying potentiometer can be shown to be

$$I_8 = \frac{\epsilon}{R(1 + R/P)\,\delta k_{\max}}\,\delta k n \qquad (7\text{-}40)$$

For the delay networks, if Q_i is the capacitor charge in coulombs,

$$E = \frac{Q_i}{\mathcal{C}_i} + R_i \frac{dQ_i}{dt} \qquad (7\text{-}41)$$

where $\mathcal{C}$ denotes capacitance. The delayed-neutron equation, which corresponds to Eq. (7-35), can be written as

$$n = \frac{l^*}{\beta_i} \lambda_i C_i + \frac{l^*}{\beta_i} \frac{dC_i}{dt} \tag{7-42}$$

where, by matching Eqs. (7-41) and (7-42) term by term and making use of the proportionality of Eq. (7-38), we find that

$$Q_i = \frac{\epsilon l^*}{\beta_i R_i} C_i \quad \text{and} \quad R_i C_i = \frac{1}{\lambda_i} \tag{7-43}$$

and the current contributed by each simulated group of delayed neutrons becomes

$$I_i = \frac{dQ_i}{dt} = \frac{\epsilon}{\beta_i R_i} l^* \frac{dC_i}{dt}$$

$$I_i = \frac{\epsilon}{\beta_i R_i} \beta n - \frac{\epsilon}{\beta_i R_i} l^* \lambda_i C_i \tag{7-44}$$

where $\epsilon/\beta_i R_i$ is a scaling factor which can be the same for all i groups. The source current, for a constant voltage V, is found to be

$$I_9 = \frac{D_9 V}{R_9} \tag{7-45}$$

where D_9 is the fraction of P_9 tapped off. If D_9 is used to represent $S/S_{\max}$, then

$$I_9 = \frac{V}{R_9 S_{\max} l^*} l^* S \tag{7-46}$$

Substituting all the individual currents into Eq. (7-37) we obtain

$$\frac{\epsilon C_7}{l^*} l^* \frac{dn}{dt} = \frac{\epsilon}{R(1 + R/P) \delta k_{\max}} \delta k n$$

$$- \frac{\epsilon}{\beta_i R_i} l^* \sum_{i=1}^{6} \frac{dC_i}{dt} + \frac{V}{R_9 S_{\max} l^*} l^* S \tag{7-47}$$

Now, by making all the scaling factors equal to each other, Eq. (7-47) reduces to the original form of Eq. (7-36) and the analog is complete.

This example indicates how the reactor kinetics can be simulated. Many such devices have been built, and their descriptions can be found in the current literature. When operated in the open-loop condition, the kinetic response characteristics of the reactor can be studied. When they are connected to other components of the control system in a closed-loop configuration, the transient responses of the complete system can be obtained.

7-4. Operational Considerations. Operation of any power-producing device requires that it pass through various phases. In general, these can be considered as start-up, power operation, and shutdown. Nuclear reactors must meet these requirements, and because of their nature careful consideration must be given to the control system in order safely to arrive at and depart from the desired power level. In particular, the start-up phase is a most critical one. Actually three different types of start-up are recognized. The first is when the reactor is started from a "cold" condition and is called the *initial start-up;* the second is when the reactor is started within a short period after accidental or deliberate shutdown, and is referred to as *start-up after scram;* the third is when the power has been reduced to a very low value of its full rating and it is desired to bring it back up to full power; this is called *power-range start-up.* Except during development testing, the initial start-up is the only type that is important to nuclear rocket-reactor operation, and is the one which will be considered further.

Initial Start-up. All start-up operations face a similar problem: the reactor must be made critical and the neutron flux must be measured until the desired power level is reached. For initial start-up this procedure can be difficult, for the range from zero to full power covers fission processes involving just a few neutrons per second to those involving billions of neutrons per second. It is during the low range that care must be taken, since it is here that the control instrumentation is the most unreliable. As a consequence, the problem reduces to one of getting the initial neutron level up high enough that it may be measured before any control-rod action takes place. While spontaneous fissions within the core material can result in the creation of a few neutrons, they are usually too few in number to be satisfactorily detected. Instead, a physical source of neutrons, normally from radioactive material, is inserted within the reactor, and it is these neutrons that are observed by the start-up-range detecting instruments. This range of start-up power level is normally referred to as the source or counter range.

With the reactor now operating within the source range, the next step is to bring the reactor up to critical. This can be done in a number of ways depending on the detailed construction of the device, such as by moving reflector material, addition of moderator, or removing poisoned control rods. In any event, the result is the same. The multiplication factor of the reactor is raised from some fractional value to unity. The time required to arrive at the critical condition can vary considerably, depending to a certain extent upon the type of instrumentation employed. Scalar neutron-level detecting instruments with large time constants require a longer time than counting-rate meters which indicate the rate of rise of neutron level. When criticality has been reached, the start-up operation begins what is called the *period range*. In passing through this range the neutron level moves from the low, *source* range up to an appreciable power level (generally ~ 1 per cent of rated full power), thus may cover a neutron flux variation of 10^7 or more. Operation through this range prepares the reactor for full-power operation. At the end of the period range, sufficient fission power is being generated to heat the reactor core at a rate of 10 to $100°F/sec$ if no coolant is flowing through the reactor core proper.

MULTIPLICATION FACTOR. As previously defined, the multiplication factor k is the ratio of the number of neutrons in any one generation to the number of corresponding neutrons of the preceding generation, and for a chain reaction to take place k must be equal to or slightly greater than unity. For the chain reaction to persist, the production of neutrons must equal those absorbed plus the leakage, which means

$$k = \frac{\text{production}}{\text{absorption and leakage}}$$

In specific reactors, the neutron multiplication factor that is used is normally referred to as the *effective multiplication factor* k_{eff}. The amount this multiplication factor differs from unity is called the excess multiplication factor δk, which in turn is used to define the reactivity ρ. That is,

$$\rho = \frac{\delta k}{k_{eff}} = \frac{k_{eff} - 1}{k_{eff}} \qquad (7\text{-}48)$$

For a just-critical reactor, $k_{eff} = 1$, and the reactivity and excess multiplication factor are both zero. Obviously the reactivity characteristics of the reactor determine the basic features of the control system.

NEUTRON LEVEL. Since the power output of a reactor is proportional to the fission rate (3×10^{10} fissions per second per watt of power) and the fission rate is proportional to the local neutron density and hence to the total number of neutrons present at any given time, a knowledge of the neutron level permits determination of the power level of the reactor.

From the definition of reactivity [Eq. (7-48)] the excess of neutrons in a reactor from one generation over the preceding generation is δk. The rate of increase in each generation for an initial n neutrons per unit volume is then $n(\delta k)$, and the time rate of change of the number of neutrons becomes

$$\frac{dn}{dt} = \frac{\delta k}{l^*} n \qquad (7\text{-}49)$$

where l^* is the mean effective lifetime of a neutron, defined as the *mean* elapsed time from the fission production of the neutron to the absorption or loss of the neutron from the reaction. For large reactors or for one-group calculations, l^* can be considered as

$$l^* = \frac{l_0}{k} \tag{7-50}$$

where l_0 is the neutron lifetime of an infinite reactor.

Integrating Eq. (7-49) gives the relationship

$$n = n_0 \exp\left(\frac{\delta k}{l^*} t\right) \tag{7-51}$$

where n_0 is the initial number of neutrons per unit volume and n is the number after a time t. From Eq. (7-51) it is evident that, if the reactivity is positive, the number of neutrons and the power rise exponentially with time.

REACTOR PERIOD. If the period of a reactor is defined as

$$\text{Period} = \frac{1}{\dfrac{d(\ln n)}{dt}} = \frac{1}{\dfrac{1}{n}\dfrac{dn}{dt}} \tag{7-52}$$

by use of Eq. (7-49) the period becomes

$$\text{Period} = \frac{l^*}{\delta k} = T \qquad \text{sec} \tag{7-53}$$

and substituting back into Eq. (7-51) we obtain

$$n = n_0 e^{t/T} \tag{7-54}$$

From Eq. (7-54) we see that the period of a reactor is the time it would take to change the neutron or power level by a factor of $e = 2.718$. It should be noted that the period is finite only when the power level is being changed.

As a consequence of the exponential character of the rise in power, it is evident that the control system must contain adequate safeguards. There is, however, a built-in safety feature inherent in the fission process. In Eqs. (7-51) and (7-53) it was assumed that all the neutrons were given off at the instant of fission and had a mean effective lifetime of l^*. In reality, a small fraction of neutrons are given off at different discrete times after the fission process has occurred. These neutrons are called *delayed neutrons* and provide a practical basis for reactor control. In many problems it is convenient to consider all the delayed neutrons as a single group having a total fraction of $\beta = 0.0075$ with an average decay constant $\lambda = 0.1$ sec^{-1}. While these delayed neutrons provide a time delay in the build-up of the neutron level, it is possible for the effective multiplication factor to become large enough that a chain reaction can be sustained without the need of the delayed neutrons. This condition is when $k_{eff} = 1.0075$ and is called *prompt critical*. The amount of reactivity which will cause prompt criticality is commonly referred to as "one dollar" of reactivity. If the neutron mean effective life is taken as 10^{-3} sec, at prompt critical the reactor period will be 0.68 sec. In other words the power level will increase by a factor of 10 in 1.57 sec. This is a potentially dangerous situation, and the control system should be designed to prevent a prompt-critical condition.

In certain types of reactors, the time it takes for the reactor to reach rated power is relatively unimportant. Therefore, during the period range, the reactivity can be small and the period long. For a nuclear rocket reactor, the time it takes the reactor to reach full power is extremely important. Since the amount of propellant used during start-up must be minimized, if the missile size is also to be minimized, a rapid build-up to full reactor power is a necessity. Thus, a short reactor period is an added requirement for the nuclear rocket control-system designer.

Power Range. Upon reaching a power level of two decades from the rated value, the reactor is said to be operating in the *power range*. Having reached this stage, the neutronic operation of a stable reactor is a reasonably simple process. The power level is controlled through an automatic-control programmer by use of a reactivity-limited regulator rod and perhaps a single shim rod or a group of shim rods. The allowable rate of change of reactivity due to movement of the shim rods is usually 10 to 100 times slower than that permitted for the regulating rod. In general, the items that might cause a reactor system to require a change in reactivity in the power range will include thrust or power programming; changes in core temperature, propellant flow rate, or system pressure; depletion (burnup) of fuel or poisons; and build-up of fission-product poisons.

For a nuclear rocket reactor, the latter two do not present a serious problem, since the running time of typical nuclear rocket reactors is normally much too short for poisoning and depletion to have any appreciable effect. The importance of the rest of the items depends a great deal on the particular reactor design, and as a consequence not much of a general nature can be prescribed. However, there is a basic design principle that always applies: If the system is such that rapid fluctuations or changes in the design parameters are kept to a minimum, the chances of an accident are greatly reduced.

Shutdown. It is impossible to shut a reactor down to the source level once it has been operated at power, because the decay of fission products remaining within the core will continue to produce gamma photons and neutrons [by (γ,n) reactions] for extremely long periods. However, from a thermal-power standpoint, it is possible to shut down the reactor to nearly zero in a few days. There are two types of shutdown that must be considered. The first is a normal shutdown, where the control rods are slowly inserted and the neutron level decreases rather rapidly initially and then settles down to falling off with the delayed-neutron period of 80 sec. A normal shutdown is rather a routine and unexciting affair. The second type is the rapid or emergency shutdown and is referred to as a *scram* operation. In a scram, the control rods are inserted so as to reduce the neutron level as quickly as possible.

For a nuclear rocket, the shutdown problem exists primarily during the development testing, where repeated operation or post-mortem examination of the reactor is desired. In an operational flight-type motor, it appears advantageous to separate the reactor from the missile and let it vaporize by decay heat, thus reducing the hazard of having solid active material contaminate an inhabited area.

Since the problems, control circuits, and accident-protection devices associated with scramming systems are covered elsewhere in the literature,[1,2,8] they are not discussed further.

In summary, the major concerns of the designer in providing an operational control system are the initial start-up, where the reactor must be made critical, and the rise to power through the period range and the power range, where the period of the reactor must be controlled to a safe value while at the same time reaching rated power in as short a time as is practicable.

7-5. Control Instrumentation. For nuclear rocket-motor control, certain measurements are needed as inputs to the control system. These normally include gas and core temperature, propellant flow rate, and power level. In this section instrumentation for power-level indication is discussed, while temperature and flow-rate instrumentation is covered in a section of Chap. 8 on test instrumentation.

In considering the operational requirements of the reactor control system it was shown that the power level, in terms of neutrons, covered so many decades that it was necessary to separate the phases of operation into a source or counter range, period range, and power range. For safety the neutrons must be monitored at all times, requiring the detecting instrumentation to be sensitive and at the same time cover an extreme range. At the present stage of development, no one instrument can be utilized satisfactorily over more than three or four decades. Consequently, to cover the complete range, multiple overlapping instrumentation must be used or a movable sensitive instrument that changes position relative to the reactor with increase in power level must be employed. This latter method has certain disadvantages, the principal one being that the neutron level as a function of distance from the reactor is usually nonlinear and may even contain extreme changes in slope at boundaries of different materials, which makes calibration extremely difficult.

In addition to requirements of accuracy and rapid response, an ideal instrument for reactor control should be capable of detecting neutrons in the presence of strong gamma-radiation fields. These requirements conflict in many instances of reactor operation when the gamma radiation is high while the neutron count is low, but for the normal operation of a nuclear rocket motor, gamma radiation is proportional to the neutron flux. The exception would be during development testing when the reactor is being shut down or restarted after a power run. When the gamma radiation is high and the neutron flux low, an ionization chamber

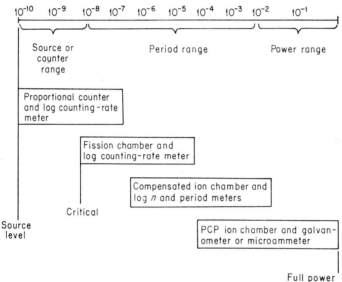

FIG. 7-11. Range of coverage for multiple-fixed-instrumentation system.

or a proportional counter in conjunction with a pulse-rate counting system is desirable because it can discriminate between the small pulses due to gamma rays and the large pulses produced by neutrons. However, for accuracy, long integrating times are needed; this in turn will cause the response to be slow. If the response rate is increased, the accuracy will of course suffer. At the higher neutron flux levels, such a counting-rate meter will have a more rapid response, but the resolving time of the system will then set an upper limit on its value. Fortunately, for high pulse rates an integrating or current-measuring type of instrument is both accurate and rapid in response. While the source or counter, period, and power ranges have been considered as more or less distinct, this is not actually the case. As a consequence the various measuring devices will overlap and provide a continuous record of neutron flux or power level. Figures 7-11 and 7-12 show the types of instruments and how they might be employed to cover the complete operating range. The following brief description of a few of these instruments indicates some of their basic design features.

Proportional Counter. In the source or counting range a proportional or pulse-counting type of instrument is required. The most sensitive

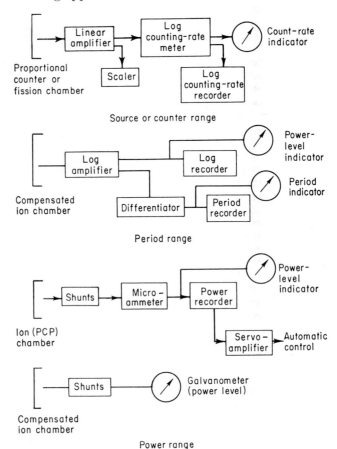

FIG. 7-12. Block diagram of reactor control instrumentation for start-up and operation. (*S. Glasstone, "Principles of Nuclear Reactor Engineering," D. Van Nostrand Company, Inc., Princeton, N.J., 1955.*)

of the proportional counters are usually boron-lined or filled with boron trifluoride. These counters, like most other neutron detectors, rely on the detection of ionized particles which are produced by a neutron-induced reaction. In the case of the BF_3 counter, the gas is ionized by a boron alpha particle emitted in the reaction, and the electrons formed in this primary ionization are accelerated toward the collecting electrode by the electric field in the counter tube. Secondary ionization is caused by the primary electrons as they gain energy, causing additional electrons to form. All of the electrons are collected at a central electrode, resulting in a voltage pulse across the load resistor. The voltage pulse is thus a linear function of the neutron flux level to which the counter is exposed. Owing to this short recovery time very high counting rates can be measured accurately with well-designed proportional counters.

Fission Chambers. Unlike proportional counters, where the pulse chamber is either lined with boron or filled with boron trifluoride, in fission chambers the interior of the chamber or the electrode surface is coated with a uranium compound enriched with uranium 235. A neutron

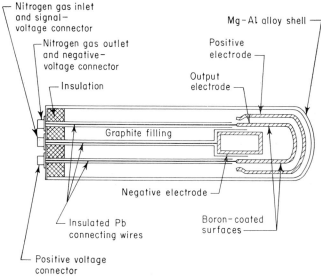

FIG. 7-13. Gamma-compensated ionization chamber.

entering the chamber causes fission of the uranium, with the fragments from the fission in turn producing ionization in the gas. The electrons resulting from this ionization are collected in a manner similar to that used in a proportional counter, and a voltage pulse results. An advantage of this type of counter is that the pulse due to the fission fragments is so large that discrimination, even in the presence of pulses from gamma rays, is no difficulty. Because of the high fission cross section for thermal neutrons, fission chambers are primarily useful for measuring thermal-neutron flux levels.

Compensated Ion Chambers. In the period range, where the detecting instrument must operate over a wide range, a compensated ionization chamber is used. The range of this instrument is increased by balancing out or compensating for the component of signal caused by gamma rays.

This is done by making use of two chambers, one sensitive to neutrons and gamma rays, the other sensitive only to gamma radiation. Measuring the difference in the ion current results in an indication of the level of neutron flux alone. Figure 7-13 is a sketch of a gamma-compensated ionization chamber developed for reactor control at the Oak Ridge National Laboratory. Since the gamma flux intensity to the instrument is position-dependent with respect to the reactor, the design of the instrument is such that the compensating volume is adjustable.

The pulse counters and various ionization chambers just discussed are the instruments principally used in reactor neutronic-control measurements. Other detecting devices such as neutron thermopiles and scintillation counters have found some use. While the neutron thermopiles are rugged and do not require high-voltage insulation, a compromise must be made between their sensitivity and time response, with the response time usually suffering. As a consequence they have not been used for direct reactor-control measurements. In regard to scintillators, their sensitivity to both neutrons and gammas is about the same, and the susceptibilities of some of their components to thermal effects are definite disadvantages. However, some use has been made of scintillation counters as low-power gamma detectors.

While the foregoing discussion presented some features of a few of the neutron detectors used in reactor control, nothing has been said of the problems associated with the installation of such instruments. For information regarding instrument calibration, effects of temperature, and control-rod shadowing, reference should be made to the literature cited.[1,8]

REFERENCES

1. Schultz, M. A.: "Control of Nuclear Reactors and Power Plants," McGraw-Hill Series in Nuclear Engineering, McGraw-Hill Book Company, Inc., New York, 1955.
2. Gore, M. P., and J. J. Carroll: Dynamics of a Variable Thrust Pump Fed Bipropellant, Liquid Rocket Engine System, *Jet Propulsion—J. Am. Rocket Soc.*, vol. 27, no. 1, p. 35, January, 1957.
3. Tsien, H. S.: "Engineering Cybernetics," McGraw-Hill Book Company, Inc., New York, 1954.
4. Korn, G. A., and T. M. Korn: "Electronic Analog Computers," 2d ed., McGraw-Hill Book Company, Inc., New York, 1956.
5. Pipes, L. A.: "Applied Mathematics for Engineers and Physicists," 2d ed., McGraw-Hill Book Company, Inc., New York, 1958.
6. Gardner, M. F., and J. L. Barnes: "Transients in Linear Systems," John Wiley & Sons, Inc., New York, 1942.
7. Chestnut, H., and R. W. Mayer: "Servomechanisms and Regulating System Design," vol. I, John Wiley & Sons, Inc., New York, 1951.
8. Glasstone, S.: "Principles of Nuclear Reactor Engineering," D. Van Nostrand Company, Inc., Princeton, N.J., 1955.

CHAPTER 8

TESTING

Since a minimum mass, or minimum physical size, as well as a particular distribution of nuclear material, is required for criticality of a nuclear reactor, exact testing of a nuclear system on a reduced-scale basis is generally impossible. Even if a geometric-scale model could be made critical, the distribution of fissionable material required for criticality would result in neutron behavior and flux distribution quite different from that desired for the full-scale device. As a result, true nuclear static and dynamic characteristics must be determined by full-scale tests operating at design power. It is possible, however, to obtain much useful data from full geometric-scale nuclear tests at very low power levels, with a considerable reduction in the complexity of facilities required. In addition, tests to determine the engineering capabilities of a design can often be made on small scale models or portions of the proposed reactor structure by simulating the fission heating with ohmic heating of the appropriate components.

It is therefore logical to divide a testing program into two major phases. The first phase involves component development testing and the determination of low-power full-size nuclear characteristics; and the second is concerned with the static and flight testing of full-scale, full-power systems. In addition to a discussion of the problems associated with component development and full-scale testing, material is presented in this chapter on instrumentation. Also, since a major factor in any full-scale testing is nuclear radiation, certain features of the health hazards involved and the radiation safety procedures that must be considered are included.

8-1. Component Development Testing. Various aspects of the testing required to develop the components of a complete device are presented in this section. These include nonnuclear testing, radiation damage, the use of in-pile loops for component development, and the examination of nuclear characteristics from the preliminary-design-survey standpoint. Nuclear characteristics are investigated by means of critical assemblies and by the utilization of geometrical mockups operating at very low fission power.

Nonnuclear. The design of components of any complicated and high-performance device necessitates a considerable amount of experimentation. The extensive installations at the various contractors and governmental agencies concerned with chemical rocket-engine development are examples of the complexity of the facilities needed to satisfy testing requirements. The philosophy of design of components for a nuclear rocket system is very little different from that in the chemical rocket field. The design itself, however, is often more complex, since the components of a nuclear system must live and satisfactorily operate in a radiation environment. Aside from radiation-damage effects, which will be discussed later, the principal effect of the radiation field results from the deposition of energy within component structures, causing internal heating, expansion, and thermal stresses. It is possible to duplicate some of these conditions within a test component by use of electrical ohmic-heating techniques.

The use of electrical power to simulate the nuclear heat generated within component structures is a generally accepted technique in the reactor-development field. For simulation of conditions in nuclear rocket reactors, the chief difficulty lies in the power requirements for duplication of realistic conditions in structures of reasonable size.

For example, for tests of core components designed to operate in a reactor with a core power density of 100 Mw/ft³ (Sec. 4-4) a total power of 1 Mw permits tests only on a cube of core 2.6 in. on a side. The problem of electrical heating is made more difficult by the fact that most materials of interest for use in rocket-reactor construction are good electrical conductors, thus requiring high internal current flow in order to simulate high-power-density nuclear heating. Furthermore, for high-power testing (several megawatts of power) it is not feasible to use alternating current, for magnetic field coupling and induced secondary currents in structures surrounding the test sample give rise to structural loads, vibrations, and extraneous instrumentation signals which can destroy the test sample or obviate the test data. For these reasons high-power electrical-resistance heating experiments are best conducted with direct current. This is a situation that in turn requires heavy bus bars and extensive switching equipment in the power-distribution system. An example is shown in Fig. 8-1, which shows part of the power-distribution system for the Component Test Facility at the Los Alamos Scientific Laboratory. Induction heating, except under certain specialized conditions, does not offer any advantages over direct resistance heating.

Since the operating time of a rocket vehicle is quite short (order of minutes), it is not necessary to use power-generation equipment capable of indefinite operation; in actual practice, high-capacity storage batteries offer many advantages over other systems. Figure 8-2 shows a storage-battery installation capable of delivering 1 Mw at high current for about half an hour.

All things considered, electrical heating is a useful and versatile method of simulating nuclear heating for heat-transfer experiments, materials tests, and hot structural tests. Figure 8-3 shows a typical installation

FIG. 8-1. Power-distribution system, Component Test Facility, Los Alamos Scientific Laboratory.

of equipment used for component development at a power level of about 1 Mw at the Los Alamos Scientific Laboratory's Component Test Facility.

Nuclear Testing. At some point in the design of reactor components, it becomes necessary to determine the effect of the reactor neutron and gamma flux field on materials and components in and around the reactor and to investigate the nuclear behavior of the reactor itself. The methods by which these experimental investigations can be carried out are generally not simple or inexpensive. Nuclear mockups or critical assemblies and research-reactor irradiation facilities are a necessary requirement for carrying out such studies. The reactor facilities are needed to investigate, by means of in-pile tests, the effect of irradiation on the operation of certain subsystems and the material used in the design, while the critical-assembly facilities are utilized in determining the over-all neutronic behavior of the design.

FIG. 8-2. Storage-battery installation, Component Test Facility, Los Alamos Scientific Laboratory.

IN-PILE TESTING. The materials used in construction of any nuclear rocket reactor must be able to withstand, for short periods of time, extremely high radiation fluxes without damage. In addition, missile or reactor power-plant components located outside the reactor, as installed in a missile air frame, must also be radiation-proof or must be shielded from the leakage-radiation field during reactor operation. Since weight is a premium in any missile system, component shielding must be kept to a minimum. To minimize the shielding a prior knowledge of the maximum allowable radiation doses for which the components remain undamaged is required. To obtain these damage data the material is placed in the radiation field of an operating reactor for various periods of time and at various levels of neutron flux. After irradiation the samples are examined and the extent of damage is ascertained. Generally, it is the time-integrated total dose that determines the degree of radiation damage; thus some aspects of the radiation effects of rocket reactors which produce extremely high (by ordinary reactor standards) radiation fields for short times can be duplicated by component and materials testing in low-power reactors for long times. Many common engineering materials have been subjected to radiation-damage tests in various

Fig. 8-3. Test equipment, Component Test Facility, Los Alamos Scientific Laboratory.

research reactors and much of the data available from these tests is useful for preliminary-design purposes. A general picture of the behavior of some materials and equipment in radiation fields is shown in Fig. 8-4 and Table 8-1.

In addition to radiation-damage testing, it is often desirable to test the operation of a complete component assembly in a radiation field. Like materials-damage data, these tests are made by placing the component assembly of interest in the neutron- and gamma-radiation field of a research reactor. Since the assemblies are most often placed within the reactor core itself, the tests are called in-pile tests or in-pile loops. For nuclear rocket reactors a typical test might involve the determination of the escape of fission fragments from an internally fission-heated fuel element (by the test-reactor neutrons) as a function of temperature, time,

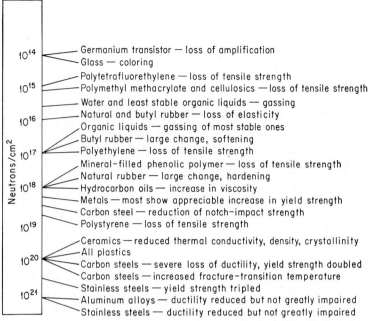

FIG. 8-4. Sensitivity of engineering properties to radiation. Irradiation dose is in epithermal neutrons. (*From O. Sisman and J. C. Wilson, Nucleonics, vol. 14, no. 9, September, 1956.*)

TABLE 8-1. IMPORTANCE OF VARIOUS FACTORS IN CAUSING RADIATION DAMAGE*

	Gamma radiation	Thermal neutrons	Epithermal neutrons	Fission fragments	Dose rate	Environment	Temperature	Stress	Initial state
Metals, nonfissile...	L	L†	H	H‡	?	M?	M	?	M
Ceramics..........	L	L†	H	H‡	?	?	M	?	M
Plastics and elastomers.........	H	L†	H	L§	H?	H	H	H	H
Fuels.............	L	H	H	H	?	?	H	?	H
Control and shield elements........	L	H	H	L§	?	?	M	?	H
Electrical components¶........	H	L†	H	L§	H	H	H	M	M
Liquids (except metals)..........	H	L†	H	L§	L	L	H	L	L

H, high; M, medium; L, low; ?, unknown.
* From O. Sisman and J. C. Wilson, *Nucleonics*, vol. 14, no. 9, pp. 58–62, September, 1956.
† For low-cross-section materials.
‡ When in contact with fuel.
§ Normally not in contact with fuel.
¶ Permanent change only, for all except electrical components.

and neutron flux level. For other types of reactors other problems are of interest. For example, the effect of radiation on the corrosion rate in a fuel-circulating loop of a liquid-fueled reactor can be studied by a circulating-fuel loop in an in-pile test. In Fig. 8-5 some of the features of the Materials Testing Reactor at Arco, Idaho, are shown. This large research reactor is used almost exclusively for in-pile test purposes.

FIG. 8-5. Materials Testing Reactor at the National Reactor Testing Station, Arco, Idaho. (*Phillips Petroleum Company.*)

It should be pointed out that, in order to extract the maximum information from these experiments, hot handling, disassembly, and analysis facilities must be available. Facilities of this sort are discussed in some detail on page 297.

CRITICAL ASSEMBLIES. While the calculational methods described in Chap. 6 provide the preliminary bases of design, they cannot take into account all the heterogeneities that exist in a reactor as a result of being designed capable of fabrication and assembly. Therefore, in addition to in-pile experimentation, criticality experiments are necessary to determine the over-all nuclear characteristics of the actual design.

These critical-assembly experiments are normally carried out in two steps. The initial assembly tests are of a survey nature, where reactor details are simulated in an approximate, flexible manner. At this time the gross effect of core and reflector materials and material distribution is determined while the assembly is critical, but at a very low power level (order of watts to at most a few kilowatts). In the second phase of critical testing, the equipment is more elaborate and the tests are more detailed. For instance the data obtained from these tests would include

Fig. 8-6. Los Alamos Scientific Laboratory bare plutonium critical assembly JEZEBEL. (a) Safe; (b) half-assembled; (c) critical.

the required investment and distribution of fissionable material, the distribution of neutron flux (and concurrently the heat generation or fission distribution), the room-temperature temperature coefficient of reactivity, and the effectiveness and location of control rods. Also, material-replacement measurements are often made to determine "importance functions" for the distribution of materials within the reactor. For nuclear rocket reactors, since the propellant is generally hydrogenous and thus a moderator, it is also necessary to investigate the effect the propellant has on the neutronics of the machine.

The type of equipment that is employed in conducting criticality

Fig. 8-7. Honeycomb critical-assembly machine. (a) Safe; (b) critical. (*Los Alamos Scientific Laboratory Photograph.*)

experiments will vary considerably. For experiments which are needed to verify certain theoretical calculations about critical masses and neutron-burst spectrums, a bare assembly is often used. One such device is the Los Alamos Scientific Laboratory's bare plutonium assembly JEZEBEL. Figure 8-6 shows this assembly in the safe, half-assembled, and critical conditions.

In the preliminary survey work for a reactor, the nuclear mockup must be kept flexible, so that changes in geometry can be readily made. At the Los Alamos Scientific Laboratory, this work is carried out with the aid of the critical-assembly machine shown in Fig. 8-7. The geometry of a proposed reactor is duplicated by inserting critical material and moderator in the honeycomb structure. The two halves of the assembly are then brought together, and the criticality of the stacking is determined. It should be noted that, in this type of assembly, it is almost impossible to reproduce the structural characteristics of proposed design.

Fig. 8-8. Critical assembly KIVA at the Los Alamos Scientific Laboratory.

Therefore, in order to determine the effect the actual structural details have on the over-all neutronics, a third type of critical assembly is utilized. These machines are geometrical models of the final device and are operated at a very low fission power level. As a result, they are often referred to as zero-power reactors. The experiments made with these zero-power devices provide detailed neutronic data about particular design configurations, information that cannot be obtained in any other way. Consequently, the experiments are an absolute necessity if optimum performance is to be achieved in the final operating reactor.

While the power levels during all phases of critical testing are low, they still must be high enough to support accurate measurements and, in some cases, to cause nuclear heating of the assembly. Consequently, the experiments must be carried out in either a shielded enclosure or a remote area. The facilities requirements for conducting these experiments must (1) assure a high degree of safety, (2) permit ease of assembly, (3) allow the maximum of data extraction, and (4) be capable of surviving minor nuclear accidents. Figures 8-8 and 8-9 show one of the critical-assembly buildings and its remotely located control room which are part of the critical-assembly facilities at the Los Alamos Scientific Laboratory.

FIG. 8-9. Remote-control room of the Los Alamos Scientific Laboratory critical-assembly facility.

8-2. Full-scale Testing. The full-scale testing required for proof development of a nuclear rocket propulsion system is similar to that required for large chemical rocket systems, and typically consists of an extensive static-firing program followed by a vehicle-flight-test phase. The areas of interest studied during each of these phases are somewhat different in nature. The value of static testing is principally that of obtaining the data necessary to establish the operational reliability of the propulsion system and proof of the propulsion-reactor design, while flight tests are for the purpose of integrating the various vehicle components into a complete missile system, operating under the desired design conditions in the proper environment.

The discussion presented herein of the problems associated with full-scale testing is thus divided into two sections: static and flight testing. But since the problems of testing large chemical rocket propulsion systems are covered in the available literature, the discussion will be primarily concerned with the features of large-scale rocket testing unique to the development of a nuclear-reactor-powered propulsion system.

Static Tests. The major concern unique to the static testing of a nuclear rocket engine arises from the nuclear radiation that exists within and near the device during test operation. Unlike the flight-test phase, where the unit remains in the vicinity of the launching stand for only a short time, static testing requires that equipment, instrumentation, and facilities withstand relatively long periods of irradiation. In addition, the facilities must be capable of reuse without constituting, because of neutron activation of test structures, a radiation hazard to test personnel. Since the purpose of these tests is to check the design criteria and to establish component and system capability at high power, the areas which must be investigated include rocket-motor performance, reactor structural stability, system control characteristics, and nuclear behavior of the reactor under high-power-density operation.

PERFORMANCE. The performance of the device as a rocket motor is probably the easiest design parameter to determine by test. Measurement of the thrust F and the propellant-mass flow rate w provides information for the determination of the effective specific impulse from the relation $I_{sp} = F/w$. If thrust measurements cannot be made directly, the effective specific impulse can be computed from Eq. (2-53), provided of course that the nozzle velocity and discharge coefficients and the average propellant molecular weight are known and that measurements are made of the propellant core-exit temperature and pressure, the propellant-weight flow rate, and the nozzle-exit pressure. Therefore, for verification of rocket-motor performance by test, the recorded data should include thrust, propellant-weight flow rate, gas temperature at core exit, and gas pressure at reactor core and nozzle exit.

REACTOR STRUCTURAL CAPABILITY. The determination of the structural behavior of the reactor during a high-power nuclear-heating test is a much more involved problem. Since the core structure will usually be the most marginally designed component, it is the portion of the reactor which should be investigated in detail. Unfortunately, it is also the region most difficult to study during operation. This is due to the fact that it is operating at the highest temperature and pressure loading and is in the highest radiation field. In addition, it appears extremely doubtful that temperature- and stress-strain-measuring instrumentation incorporated in a reactor core will give reliable information over the complete operating range. However, some detailed core structural measurements can be made during reduced-power and low-temperature testing runs. For "design point" structural data, measurements of the system pressures during high-power operation should provide some useful information. This approach is particularly applicable if the major core *structural* load is due to the pressure drop resulting from the propellant passing through the heat exchanger. This will generally be the case for the heat-exchanger reactors discussed in this text. While this procedure can verify the structural design, it does not provide much diagnostic information if failure occurs during the run. Nor does it furnish useful data about the thermal stresses that exist throughout the core during operation. As a consequence, every effort should be made to carry out extensive structural investigations during the component-development phase discussed in the previous section. For other components such as the pressure shell, neutron reflector, and rocket nozzle, the usual structural measurements can normally be made, as the operating temperatures of these components are much lower than that of the reactor core. However, the effect of radiation, as it distorts or influences these "standard" measurements, must still be considered. For structural purposes straingauge, pressure, and temperature measurements should be made at critical points of the device. In addition, although a heat-exchanger core is generally a highly damped device, vibrational instrumentation must be considerable for complete analysis of reactor structural stability.

CONTROL SYSTEM. It is during the static-test program that the dynamic characteristics of the reactor control system must be determined. This information is an absolute necessity to the control design of the flight version. Although the reactor-control-system design is based upon the analytical and simulation methods described in Chap. 7 and tested by operation during the zero-power experiments, its characteristics can only be verified in detail by full-scale testing, using the actual propulsion-system input signals. Here, for the first time, under conditions of varying propellant flow rates and temperatures, as well as effects of variation in temperature on the core nuclear properties, the response of the complete control system is obtained.

For high-power-density heat exchangers the peak core temperature determines the allowable maximum reactor performance; thus it is desirable to use this parameter for control purposes. However, a direct measurement of this temperature in many cases is not feasible, or is at best difficult, and it becomes desirable to use some other temperature closely coupled to the peak core temperature as a prime control signal. The temperature most closely coupled (in time) to the peak core-structure temperature is the propellant core-exit temperature. This temperature is relatively easy to measure directly, or it may be calculated by using the nozzle as a transducer. The other variables that must be measured and fed into the reactor-propulsion-system program-controller are the propellant flow rate, the core power level, and the control-rod position. The flow rate and the control-rod position are readily determined, since reasonably accurate flow meters and position indicators are available. The core-power-level measurement, however, is a much more complicated procedure, and is discussed in detail in Sec. 7-5.

In summary for the control-system testing and checkout, the principal variables which must be measured include the propellant flow rate and pressure, propellant core-exit temperature, core power level, and control-rod position.

NUCLEAR ASPECTS. Like the control system, only a full-scale test can provide the information needed to determine the nuclear behavior of the reactor core operating at design temperature and including the propellant effects. It is during this period of operation that the reactor should experience the desired neutron flux distribution at the proper temperature, along with the actual geometric changes that result from thermal expansion and structural loads. All of these influence that most important parameter discussed in Chaps. 6 and 7, the *temperature coefficient of reactivity*. The evaluation of this temperature coefficient is one of the most important objectives of the static-test program because it provides the basis on which the reactor control system and the in-flight thrust program of the flight-propulsion system are designed. Besides the temperature coefficient of reactivity, the effect of temperature on the local neutron thermal base and on the fission space distribution throughout the core must also be investigated. As previously discussed, in Chaps. 4 and 6, it is a stringent design requirement that the core of a heat-exchanger reactor have a uniform power distribution normal to the direction of flow of the propellant. Since the zero-power (critical-assembly) experiments are carried out under temperature and propellant-distribution conditions much different from those at high power, the power distribution will not be similar. Therefore, it is left to the full-scale nuclear-heating tests for verification of the theory, calculational procedures, and the fabrication techniques associated with the nuclear loadings and fissionable-material distribution. While some external measurements of the fission distribution can be made with neutron or gamma-ray instrumentation during a test run, nuclear measurements within the core itself are extremely difficult and do not appear feasible. This is partially due to the fact that many such measurements tend to compromise some part of the core design. If it is possible, however, to gain access to the core structure after the test has been completed, analysis of the fission products present or the rate of emission of beta or gamma radiation will yield a considerable amount of information, particularly information about the fission process and its distribution that existed during the period of test operation. Although the half-lives of the fission products vary from fractions of a second to millions of years, it has been found[1,2] that the rate of emission of beta particles and of gamma photons from these fission products can be related to the fission process by means of an empirical expression which is accurate to within better than a factor of 2. For periods from about ten seconds up to several weeks after fission has taken place, the relationships for the decay rate per fission are approximately

$$\frac{dN_\beta}{dt} = 3.8 \times 10^{-6}t^{-1.2} \qquad \text{particles/(sec)(fission) for beta} \qquad (8\text{-}1a)$$
radiation

$$\frac{dN_\gamma}{dt} = 1.9 = 10^{-6}t^{-1.2} \qquad \text{photons/(sec)(fission) for gamma} \qquad (8\text{-}1b)$$
radiation

where t is the time in days after the fission. These expressions can be related to the power level of the reactor if it is assumed that the mean energy of the beta particles is 0.4 Mev and that of the gamma-ray photons is 0.7 Mev. Then from Eqs. (8-1) the rate of emission of beta and gamma energy becomes

$$P_d'(t) = 2.7 \times 10^{-6}t^{-1.2} \qquad \text{Mev/(sec)(fission)} \qquad (8\text{-}2)$$

Now if the reactor has been operating at a constant power of P_r watts for a period of T days, the rate of emission of beta and gamma energy, at a time τ days after start-up, due to fissions occurring at the time T is from Eq. (8-2)

$$P_d'(\tau) \approx 2.7 \times 10^{-6}(\tau - T)^{-1.2} \qquad \text{Mev/(sec)(fission)} \qquad (8\text{-}3)$$

and since 3.1×10^{10} fissions per second or 2.68×10^{15} fissions per day is equivalent to 1 watt of power, the number of fissions occurring in the reactor operating at P_r watts during an interval of dT days is $2.68 \times 10^{15}P_r\,dT$. It follows, therefore, that the rate of emission of beta and gamma energy at a time τ days after start-up, due to the fissions in the interval dT, becomes

$$P_d'(\tau) \approx 7.3 \times 10^9 P_r(\tau - T)^{-1.2}\,dT \qquad \text{Mev/sec} \qquad (8\text{-}4)$$

If the reactor has been operating for a period of T_0 days since start-up, then the rate of emission of energy at time τ after start-up, from the fissions occurring during the period of reactor operation, becomes

$$P_d(\tau) \approx 7.3 \times 10^9 P_r \int_0^{T_0} (\tau - T)^{-1.2}\,dT$$
$$\approx 3.7 \times 10^{10}P_r[(\tau - T_0)^{-0.2} - \tau^{-0.2}] \qquad \text{Mev/sec} \qquad (8\text{-}5)$$

As 1 Mev $= 1.6 \times 10^{-13}$ watt-sec, the rate of emission of beta and gamma energy at time τ days after start-up for a reactor operated at a power of P_r watts for a period of T_0 days becomes

$$P_d(\tau) \approx 5.9 \times 10^{-3}P_r[(\tau - T_0)^{-0.2} - \tau^{-0.2}] \qquad \text{watts} \qquad (8\text{-}6)$$

It should be noted that the quantity $\tau - T_0$ is the time in days after shutdown and is sometimes called the "cooling time." Equation (8-6) is shown in graphical form in Fig. 8-10. It is evident that, by a postrun measurement of the level of beta- and gamma-ray energy emission from a core fuel element, the fission distribution within that element can be established. It is also possible to determine the distribution of fission products within a fuel element after a test run by means of radiochemical techniques. However, both methods must be used with caution, since there exists a high probability that some of the fission products will have

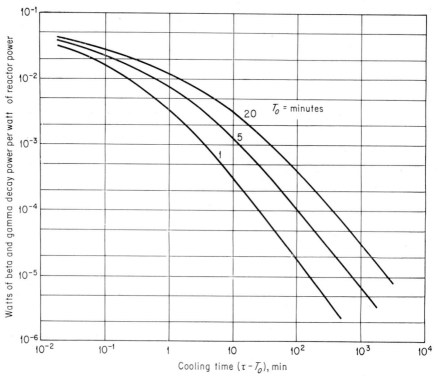

FIG. 8-10. Beta-particle and gamma-ray decay power after reactor shutdown.

escaped from the core into the propellant and exhausted to the atmosphere. It should be reiterated that any post-mortem examination of highly irradiated material requires extensive hot-handling and disassembly facilities.

Flight Tests. The flight testing of any rocket vehicle is the final phase of its design and development. The objective of this stage of the testing program is to ascertain the mutual influence of the various components and subassemblies on the system as a whole. The effect of environment not attainable during the static tests, such as aerodynamic forces, control loads, and high accelerations, must also be determined. While some of the problems associated with flight testing are similar to those of a static test, a number of others are distinctly different, with some being easier to solve and some more difficult. For instance, the question of site contamination, under normal operation, is not as severe a problem at the launching site. Here the missile remains on the stand for only a short period, while during a static test the complete run is carried out on the test pad. On the other hand, data transmission during a static test can be, by the use of direct cable leads, a comparatively simple procedure. But for a flight test, the only means of data transmission is that of telemetering. This is not always easy, especially if the time resolution desired is extremely short. Furthermore, telemetered signals between a nuclear rocket and the ground must pass through an ionized sheath surrounding the vehicle propulsion-system section which was caused by absorption (ionization) of reactor gammas in the air. This situation does not pose any insoluble problems. It does, however, put some restrictions on choice of telemeter carrier frequency and requires analysis of the signal attenuation to be expected in passing through the ionized sheath.

Since an adequate treatment of the various methods employed in instrumenting and flight-testing a complete missile is beyond the scope of this book,* the discussion will be limited to some of the facility-construction problems that are influenced by the nuclear aspects of the device being tested.

Facilities. The installations required for static and flight testing of chemical rocket engines and missiles are extensive and expensive. Figures 8-11 and 8-12 are examples of the facilities needed to proof-test present-day chemical rocket systems. Of primary concern is what happens to these facilities when they are required to operate in the radiation field associated with high-performance nuclear devices.

STATIC TEST STANDS. To assure safety in testing nuclear rocket motors a greater degree of remoteness of the various facility components from each other and from the surrounding communities is needed than that required for similar testing of chemical rockets. Protecting against a chemical explosion or fire is a much less difficult task than shielding against the gamma-ray or neutron flux field resulting from even a normally operating nuclear device. The problem becomes extreme if the requirement of minimizing the consequences of a possible nuclear accident is added. The easiest way to accomplish personnel protection without massive and expensive shielding is to separate the test stands and control rooms by large distances (1 to 2 miles). This of course adds further complications in the transmission of test-data signals, since in many cases

---

* For details regarding the current literature available on this subject, the reader is referred to the excellent bibliography given in G. P. Sutton, "Rocket Propulsion Elements," 2d ed., John Wiley & Sons, Inc., New York, 1956.

the longer cable runs necessitate expensive signal amplification. Figure 8-13 is a sketch which shows what might be required in the way of facility separation for a possible nuclear rocket-motor development testing installation.

Another consideration is the cost of test-stand construction. A chemical-engine test stand can have an extremely high utilization factor but a nuclear-rocket-engine stand becomes radioactive even under normal operation. Thus a considerable cooling-off period is required before the level of activity is reduced to the point that the stand can be revisited.

FIG. 8-11. Rocket-engine firings on static test stands. (*Rocketdyne, A Division of North American Aviation, Inc.*)

Therefore, not only should construction costs be minimized, but the materials used in stand fabrication must be carefully selected to minimize the level of residual radioactivity. In this regard, aluminum is by far the best of the common structural materials, since it has a relatively low neutron-activation cross section and the active isotope decays rapidly. Also to be considered is the effect of neutron and gamma heating of the test-stand materials, as excessive heating can produce distortion of the stand structure. In practice, separate cooling must be provided for the stand and for any surrounding radiation-absorbing materials (e.g., concrete blockhouses and instrumentation wiring). As discussed in Chap. 6, the amount of radiation heating, and thus the cooling requirement, is directly proportional to the density of the absorbing material. Here, again,

FIG. 8-12. Complete missile static-test stand at the United States Army Redstone Arsenal. (*Official United States Army photograph.*)

aluminum is superior to other common structural metals such as steel or nickel.

Any auxiliary equipment which is generally expensive should, if possible, be reusable. Therefore, the portions of this equipment that are located at or near the test pad must also be designed under the same neutron-activation and gamma-absorption criteria as the stand itself. Normally this will include such components as instrumentation, propel-

TABLE 8-2. INDUCED ACTIVITIES IN METALS PRESENT IN STRUCTURAL MATERIALS*

Element	Isotope mass no.	Natural abundance, %	σ_a, barns	Active species	Half-life	γ-ray energy, Mev
Aluminum	27	100	0.22	Al^{28}	2.3m	1.78
Titanium	50	53	0.04	Ti^{51}	72d	1.00
Chromium	50	4.4	16	Cr^{51}	27d	0.32
Manganese	55	100	13.3	Mn^{56}	2.6h	2.1
Iron	58	0.33	0.8	Fe^{59}	46d	1.3
Cobalt	59	100	37	Co^{60}	5.3y	1.3
Nickel	64	1.9	3.0	Ni^{65}	2.5h	0.93
Copper	63	69	4.3	Cu^{64}	12.8h	1.35
Zinc	64	48.9	0.5	Zn^{65}	250d	1.12
	68	18.5	0.1	Zn^{69}	13.8h	0.4
Zirconium	94	17.4	0.1	Zr^{95}	65d	0.92
Molybdenum	98	23.8	0.13	Mo^{99}	67h	0.84
Tantalum	181	100	21.3	Ta^{182}	113d	1.2
Tungsten	186	28.4	34	W^{187}	24h	0.76

* From S. Glasstone, "Principles of Nuclear Reactor Engineering," D. Van Nostrand Company, Inc., Princeton, N.J., 1955.

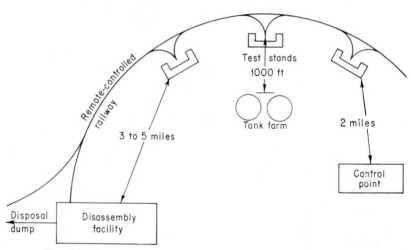

FIG. 8-13. Layout of a possible nuclear rocket static-test facility.

lant storage tanks, pumps, flow-control valves, and connecting piping. Table 8-2 gives the induced activities in some of the metals which are present in structural materials.

DISASSEMBLY FACILITIES. A major consequence of testing in a radiation field is that posttest examination of components must be done remotely. Such a post-mortem is essential for either the determination of fission distribution in the reactor core or a study of the possible causes of component failures. The facilities required to accomplish disassembly and hot handling, without personnel hazard, are structures basically consisting of massive concrete shields and extensive remote-handling equipment. Elaborate radiation-safety monitoring systems and controls must also be provided for operator protection during a disassembly or other hot-handling operation. This type of facility represents a considerable investment; therefore, the test-area layout and test scheduling

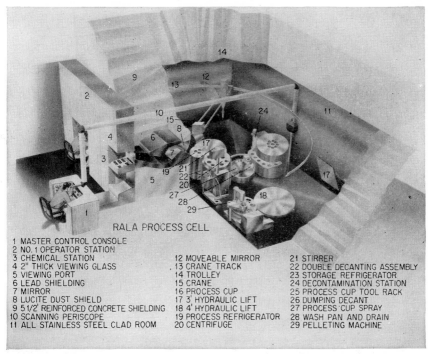

RALA PROCESS CELL

1 MASTER CONTROL CONSOLE
2 NO. 1 OPERATOR STATION
3 CHEMICAL STATION
4 2" THICK VIEWING GLASS
5 VIEWING PORT
6 LEAD SHIELDING
7 MIRROR
8 LUCITE DUST SHIELD
9 5 1/2' REINFORCED CONCRETE SHIELDING
10 SCANNING PERISCOPE
11 ALL STAINLESS STEEL CLAD ROOM

12 MOVEABLE MIRROR
13 CRANE TRACK
14 TROLLEY
15 CRANE
16 PROCESS CUP
17 3' HYDRAULIC LIFT
18 4' HYDRAULIC LIFT
19 PROCESS REFRIGERATOR
20 CENTRIFUGE

21 STIRRER
22 DOUBLE DECANTING ASSEMBLY
23 STORAGE REFRIGERATOR
24 DECONTAMINATION STATION
25 PROCESS CUP TOOL RACK
26 DUMPING DECANT
27 PROCESS CUP SPRAY
28 WASH PAN AND DRAIN
29 PELLETING MACHINE

FIG. 8-14. High-gamma-source preparation facility at the Los Alamos Scientific Laboratory.

must be based on the efficient and continued use of such facilities. Figure 8-14 shows an artist's sketch of the high-gamma-source preparation facility at the Los Alamos Scientific Laboratory, while Fig. 8-15 shows the remote-control console of this facility. Note the massiveness of the structure. Figure 8-16 shows the remote-handling equipment used in the high-level cell at the Knolls Atomic Power Laboratory.

FLIGHT-TEST LAUNCHING SITES. Isolation and separation requirements for flight-test installations are somewhat more severe than those previously discussed for static-test stands. The obvious reason for this is that the isolation must be sufficient to ensure human safety in case of

FIG. 8-15. Remote-control console of the high-gamma-source preparation facility.

FIG. 8-16. Operating face of the high-level cell at the Knolls Atomic Power Laboratory. (*General Electric Company.*)

the failure (crash) of a missile *shortly* after launching and (1) before enough fission products have accumulated to vaporize the reactor in the air but (2) after enough fissions have occurred to produce radioactivity which is potentially biologically dangerous even when dispersed locally.

The probability of a *nuclear* accident in any test is less for a launching site than for a static-firing site, because of the shorter nuclear-reactor operating time on and near the launching site as compared with the static-test case. However, the probability of reactor destruction as a result of failure of other system components is greater for flight than for static tests. This is fundamentally because a complete flight-test missile is an order of magnitude more complex (in terms of number of short-lived or unproved system components) than a system required for the ground static test of a propulsion unit. Thus, the *over-all* probability of reactor destruction in a flight test may be greater or less than that for a static test, depending on the stage of development of the components in the complete system. However, the consequences of *reactor* destruction are always less severe in flight testing, because flight-test failures which could harm (contaminate) the launching site must occur at or very shortly after the missile is launched and hence before the reactor contains very many fission products. On the other hand, a nuclear accident which could harm a static stand could occur at or after reactor shutdown, when the maximum number of active fission products has been produced.

In this connection, range-safety precautions in flight-testing nuclear missiles should not present any greater problems than now exist for chemical missiles. For as previously discussed and as shown in Fig. 8-10, a nuclear rocket motor which has operated at power for a short period of time emits a considerable amount of decay energy. Thus, a malfunction of the missile system, more than a few seconds after launching under nuclear power, will result in the vaporization of the reactor power plant by decay heat. If launching of a nuclear test missile is done with chemical rocket boosters, the reactor will always be vaporized while air-borne. For nuclear missiles, then, all that is needed for the destruction of the missile, if it exceeds the limits imposed by range safety, is to remove the reactor control rods completely or shut off the propellant supply, thereby causing the immediate destruction of the reactor by vaporization.

Instrumentation or data-gathering problems are more difficult in flight tests than in static firings, since direct-wire data transmission can be utilized for only the first few seconds (or first few hundred feet) of vehicle flight; after this time, communication with the vehicle must be by high-frequency signals. All such telemetering is complicated by the previously discussed ionized sheath which surrounds the reactor end of the vehicle.

Auxiliary facilities for flight-test installations include propellant storage and transfer equipment and a large amount of optical and electronic tracking and communications equipment.   The complexity of propellant-handling equipment depends largely upon the choice of propellant. Cryogenic propellants, such as liquid hydrogen or methane, will require expensive storage dewars and continuous-refrigeration equipment.   These high-investment items provide an incentive to design toward the utilization of a ready or noncryogenic propellant.

In summary, the facility requirements for full-scale nuclear rocket testing must include geographic remoteness of sites, separation of facility components, careful selection of test-stand materials, and extensive buildings and equipment for handling irradiated and radioactive material.

8-3. Instrumentation.   The instrumentation requirements for nuclear rocket-motor analysis during static and flight testing are extremely complex and severe, for all the nuclear instrumentation requirements of an operating reactor must be satisfied in addition to those required for normal chemical rocket motors.   The radiation activity resulting from even a short-time test run of a nuclear rocket motor can be high enough to deny human access to the test device.   This in turn makes the normal repair or replacement of faulty instrumentation difficult and sometimes impossible.   Thus, each measurement must be made as reliably as possible, and must have an adequate backup measurement to ensure the desired over-all test reliability.   The ever-present problem of gamma-heating and -radiation damage during test operation also contributes to an already difficult situation.   Though a difficult task, useful and accurate data can be obtained if careful consideration is given to the measurements needed and the proper selection, location, and shielding of the sensing elements.

The types of measurement needed fall into two categories, the first concerned primarily with the control of the system, the second providing information on the over-all performance of the particular design.   In Chap. 7 the instrumentation required for control purposes was discussed in some detail; therefore the discussion here is limited to the instrumentation employed in determining the performance behavior of the device. In testing for performance, one is interested in measuring certain parameters in critical areas and comparing the results with those used in the design.   For a nuclear rocket motor, the areas of interest are those concerned with the nuclear, structural, hydrodynamic, and thermal characteristics of the device under test, as well as with the over-all "black box" performance of the device.   Descriptions of instrumentation for non-nuclear testing in the chemical rocket field are adequately presented elsewhere,[3] so the discussion herein is limited to a brief presentation of some of the problems particular to the testing of nuclear-powered systems.

Structural Instrumentation. The instrumentation used in measuring stress-strain, vibration, and acceleration in the structural components of a nuclear rocket motor is similar to that commonly used in dynamic structural testing of power machinery. However, in the selection of the types of instrument for use in testing nuclear reactors, consideration must be given to the effects of a radiation-field environment on the accuracy and stability of the instrument itself. For example, designs based on the use of capacitors, phototubes, or photocells should be avoided, since these circuit elements are quite susceptible to radiation damage. Similarly, variable-capacitance gauges can give false readings because of ionization in the gas and structure surrounding the capacitive elements. The major problem in the analysis of data obtained from sound structural instrumentation lies in the probability of temperature errors. Not only must the varying temperature level of the component be compensated for, but the temperature effects due to gamma-ray absorption and neutron attenuation within the instrument itself must be considered. For example, excessive gamma heating of a strain-gauge wire can produce spurious component-deflection signals if the gamma heating has not been compensated for in the gauge installation.

Hydrodynamic Instrumentation. Although the control system requires measurement of the total flow rate, the primary feature of interest in proving (or disproving) the hydrodynamic characteristics of the design is the internal local flow distribution. By the use of pitot probes, which measure the total pressure head, and pitot-static probes, which give the velocity pressure head, sufficient data may be obtained for the determination of both the pressure and velocity distributions in the flow. One difficulty encountered in making such measurements is in being certain of the flow direction relative to the probe axis, since flow misalignment can introduce considerable errors in these measurements. Another is the poor response time associated with a lengthy capillary system typical of small-size pitot-probe installations. If high-response electrical pressure pickups are used, the installation problems become extreme because of the relatively large size of these pickups. The validity of the measurement is sometimes questionable also, because of the flow disturbances caused by the instrument itself. Generally, however, careful design and installation of probe type of survey instrumentation will yield reasonably accurate average data.

Thermal Instrumentation. The measurement of temperatures presents the most difficult problem in the component, static, and full-scale flight testing of a nuclear rocket engine. As has been pointed out (perhaps repetitiously), the prerequisite of a successful design is a high power density in the heat-exchanger core and a high specific impulse from the propellant. The achievement of both of these by the heat-exchange processes discussed in Chap. 4 requires very high core-structure operating temperatures. It is these extreme temperatures which are difficult to measure.

THERMOCOUPLES. For structural components, bare-metal thermocouples may be used. Their installation must be carefully done, however, in order to minimize the local errors caused by the presence of the thermocouple. Also the gamma and neutron heating, which may be different in the thermocouple material and the material being measured, can present some difficulties. At high local temperatures, the errors introduced by radiation from the thermocouple to the cooler surroundings must also be considered. Table 8-3 gives the ranges of temperature for

TABLE 8-3. CHARACTERISTICS OF HIGH-TEMPERATURE THERMOCOUPLES*

Thermocouple	Useful upper limit, °F	dE/dT in range specified, $\mu v/°F$
Chromel-constantan......................	1400	42 (32–1400°F)
Iron-constantan..........................	1400	32 (32–1400°F)
Chromel-alumel..........................	2200	23 (32–2200°F)
Platinum–90% platinum, 10% rhodium.......	2650	6.3 (1200–2650°F)
Iridium–50% iridium, 50% rhodium.........	3700	2.9 (2000–3700°F)

* E. F. Flock and A. I. Dahl, The Measurement of Gas Temperature by Immersion Type Instruments, *J. Am. Rocket Soc.*, vol. 23, no. 3, pp. 155–164, May–June, 1953.

reliable operation of thermocouples of various materials. Under certain circumstances metallic thermocouples[4] can be used for measurement of temperatures in excess of 3000°F. With the exception of elements in the platinum group, all metals are excluded from oxidizing atmospheres, and in a strongly reducing environment only tungsten, molybdenum, and rhenium show the requisite chemical inertness. In an incompatible environment, the metal thermocouple needs the protection of a hermetic, refractory enclosure and a neutral gas. This added complexity makes installation more difficult, and in many cases increases the thermal inertia of the couple so that rapid response is difficult to achieve.

OPTICAL AND RADIATON PYROMETRY. For measurement of temperatures above the thermocouple range, it is usual practice to utilize the radiant energy of a hot body. In the optical pyrometer a comparison of the brightness of a hot body is made with the brightness of a lamp filament. The observer adjusts the current in the filament until a match is secured between the brightness of the filament and that of the image. The magnitude of the filament current at the instant the match of brightness is obtained is a measure of the temperature of the source. This presupposes the use of an accurately calibrated filament source whose temperature is known as a function of heating current. Standard calibrated filament sources are available for such purposes. The major source of error in this type of measurement is in lack of knowledge about the emissivity of the surface being measured. The emissivity of a body, as the term is used in pyrometric literature, can be affected by its material, surface condition, and particular configuration. Consequently, considerable calibration work must be undertaken to ensure accurate meas-

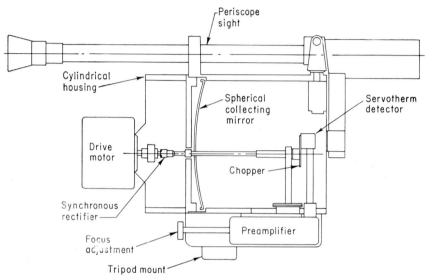

Fig. 8-17. Schematic diagram of the Servotherm radiation pyrometer. (*Servo Corporation of America.*)

urements in any specific installation. While the optical pyrometer has been built around the frequency-response characteristics of the human eye, particularly its remarkable ability to detect small differences in the brightness of illuminated areas placed side by side, it has not been adapted to automatic recording and control of high temperatures. The major reason for this is that no photoelectric or other means has been developed for matching the brightnesses of two adjacent or overlapping fields, independently of their relative areas, as well as can be done by eye. For these purposes, however, the total-radiation pyrometer is suitable. The word "total" is used with reservations, since no practicable pyrometer measures the energy emitted at all wavelengths by a hot body. Figure 8-17 shows a schematic diagram of a currently available total-radiation pyrometer. Like the optical pyrometer, the errors introduced by uncertainty in the emissivity of the surface being sighted on must be considered. For a more complete discussion of the theory and characteristics of both optical and total-radiation pyrometers, the reader is referred to the literature cited in the references. In addition to the above difficulties of "normal" use, the designer must also consider problems associated with nuclear testing, such as discoloration of optical components due to radiation absorption or interaction, gamma-ray heating, and ionization in thermopile or photocell elements.

GAS TEMPERATURES. At low temperatures and flow velocities, thermocouple measurements of gas temperatures are comparatively routine, but if the flow velocity is extreme, the uncertainty in the "temperature recovery factor" (Chap. 4) can introduce considerable error in the measurements. For measurement of temperatures in excess of the thermocouple limits, variations of the radiation techniques described above are possible. Other methods, based on the pressure-temperature relationships in the flow of a compressible fluid through a sonic orifice, have been developed and operate satisfactorily under controlled conditions. They are not, however, presently used in normal diagnostic instrumentation of rocket motors. A review of the present status and application limits of gas-measuring instrumentation is given in Ref. 5 and should prove particularly useful to the rocket-motor designer.

Thrust Instrumentation. Many different rocket-motor-thrust-measuring devices are in accepted use. Thrust jacks of the hydraulic or pneumatic type are usually used in obtaining a direct low-frequency-response thrust measurement. For measuring instantaneous thrust, high-response strain gauges or pressure gauges (measurement of pressure fluctuations in a hydraulic load cell) are frequently employed. Most of these methods require a slight motion in the direction of the thrust, and care must be taken to account for errors introduced by external restraints, such as bearing friction, instrumentation leads, and propellant inlet or auxiliary coolant piping. To eliminate these factors it is often preferable to use a null system which is based on a balance of forces around a fixed geometric position. Since the designer generally has considerable freedom in the location of thrust-measuring units, proper positioning and adequate shielding can usually be provided to reduce the nuclear problems of radiation damage, internal heating, and spurious-signal generation.

8-4. Health Hazards and Radiation Safety. To this point, the discussion of problems resulting from testing in a nuclear-radiation field has been limited to those of design and installation of the device and its equipment. Of equal, if not greater, importance is the problem of health and safety of the personnel taking part in the testing program. While in the field of health physics the *general* problems of protection against radiation are investigated, only those aspects of the radiation hazards that might be expected to result from the testing of a nuclear rocket motor will be presented in this section. The biological effects of radiation and the expected dosages during testing are discussed, as well as the techniques and instrumentation used in radiation monitoring.

Biological Effects. In general it is believed that most of the effects of radiation are of the so-called *threshold type*, which means that injury occurs after the total dose received has exceeded a particular amount. Various circumstances can influence the nature and extent of injuries due to radiation. For sources external to the body, the only ones of interest in this section, the biological damage depends on whether the exposure is *acute* or *chronic*. *Acute exposure* results from the receipt of a relatively large radiation dose within a short time interval, while *chronic exposure* results from frequent, repeated exposure to relatively low radiation dose-rate intensities. For the same total (time-integrated) radiation dosage, chronic exposure will generally have less serious consequences than acute exposure.

Another factor which influences the extent of injury from an external exposure is the area or volume of the body which is exposed. Often used in this connection is a quantity which is defined as the product of the dose and the mass of the body receiving that dose and referred to as the integral dose. For instance, an acute exposure of a small portion of the body may have permanent effects on that portion but leave the general health of the individual unimpaired, while the same exposure received over the whole body and reaching certain vital areas could prove fatal. This is due to the fact that different portions of the body show different sensitivities to radiation. The most radiosensitive regions are the bone marrow, reproductive organs, gastrointestinal tract, and the lymphoid tissue. The skin, lungs, and liver are of intermediate sensitivity, while the muscles and full-grown bones are the least sensitive.

The biological effects of nuclear radiation can be largely attributed to ionization which causes the destruction of various molecules that play an important part in the functioning of living cells. Particularly, it is the specific ionization, the number of ion pairs produced per centimeter of path, which has the most effect. In general, the greater the specific ionization, the greater the damage for a given energy absorption. The specific ionization resulting from the interaction of charged particles such as alpha particles, beta rays, or protons with tissue is greater than that resulting from interaction with neutrons or gamma quanta. However, because of the short range of alphas and betas, these particles do not present as severe a radiation hazard from *external* sources as do neutrons and gamma rays, which are able to penetrate within the body. Gamma-ray energy is absorbed by photon-electron interactions with atoms of tissue; thus gammas produce ionization directly. Neutrons generally do not produce ionization directly but can cause considerable damage because of the production of protons or gamma rays by neutron capture in hydrogen and nitrogen nuclei. From the nuclear rocket-testing standpoint, the leakage radiation of neutrons and gamma rays presents the greatest health hazard.

Radiation Dose Units. It would be desirable to have a unit of dosage proportional to the biological damage produced but measurable in terms of relatively simple physical quantities. Because the nonlinear character of biological radiation makes it almost impossible to fulfill this double requirement, the units now in use are a compromise and include:

ROENTGEN (R). Defined as "that quantity of X or gamma radiation such that the associated corpuscular emission per 0.001293 gram of air produces, in air, ions carrying 1 electrostatic unit (1 esu) of quantity of electricity of either sign." The mass of air given in the definition represents 1 cm³ of dry air at standard temperature and pressure (STP). It should be noted that the roentgen applies only to X and gamma radiation in air, and the radiation dose expressed in roentgens does not depend on the time during which it is received. In practice, the dosage rate is given in terms of roentgens per hour (r/hr) or milliroentgens per hour (mr/hr), with the integrated dose in roentgens being the product of the dose rate times the exposure period. Frequently the dose rate is used as a measure of the radiation intensity or flux in a certain region. This is biologically justifiable only for gamma rays of a specified energy. The radiation intensity is the rate at which the energy flows past a unit area at a given location, but the dosage rate in roentgens per unit time is a measure of the rate at which energy is absorbed in air at that point. Thus the dose rate will be determined by the absorption coefficient of air, and this varies with the energy of the radiation.

ROENTGEN PER HOUR AT ONE METER (RHM). Defined as "the quantity of a specified gamma ray source that produces a dosage rate of 1 r/hr in air at a distance of one meter." This unit is used primarily for the calibration of radiation-monitoring instrumentation.

ROENTGEN EQUIVALENT PHYSICAL (REP). This unit was originally defined as the dose of any nuclear or ionizing radiation that results in the absorption of 87 ergs per gram of tissue. In recent years, the rep has been used to denote a dose of 97 ergs absorbed per gram of tissue.

RADIATION ABSORPTION DOSE (RAD). Defined as "the absorbed dose of any nuclear radiation which is accompanied by the liberation of 100 ergs of energy per gram of absorbing material." Besides being of different magnitude, the rad differs from the rep in that it does not prescribe the absorption material. However, for soft tissue the rep and the rad differ by only a few per cent, so that they may be considered as equal. Further, the name rad does not imply a relationship to the roentgen as does the rep.

RELATIVE BIOLOGICAL EFFECTIVENESS (RBE). For various reasons it is convenient to compare biological effectiveness of ionizing radiation with that of X rays of 200-kev energy. On this basis the RBE is defined as

$$RBE = \frac{\text{physical dose of 200-kv X rays to produce effect of interest}}{\text{physical dose of comparison radiation to produce same effect}}$$

ROENTGEN EQUIVALENT MAN (rem). This unit was introduced in an attempt to provide a better criterion of biological injury when applied to different radiations and is defined as

$$\text{Dose in rems} = RBE \times \text{dose in rads}$$

MAXIMUM PERMISSIBLE EXPOSURE (MPE). For personnel who might be exposed to radiation, such as during a nuclear rocket testing program, the International Commission on Radiological Protection recommends that the MPE be set at a dose level as given in Table 8-4.

TABLE 8-4. MAXIMUM PERMISSIBLE EXPOSURE TO EXTERNAL SOURCES
OF RADIATION

Radiation	mr/week	mrem/week	mrep/week	mrads/week (in tissue)
X and gamma rays........	300	300	300	300
Beta particles............	...	500	500	500
Thermal neutrons.........	...	300	100	100
Fast neutrons............	...	300	30	30

Expected Doses. The complex nature of radiation damage does not permit the derivation of general radiation-dose-rate equations which are accurate for any situation. However, from the material given in Sec. 6-4, it is possible to obtain general equations which are accurate within a factor of about 10 or less. Although this seems at first glance to be a large inaccuracy, inspection of the graphs of the dose rate as a function of separation distance shows that this factor is absorbed by a variation of a few hundred feet in separation distance for the large separations desired in nuclear rocket testing. Greater accuracy in dose-rate prediction requires a thorough analysis of each specific situation of interest.

By use of the basic equations developed in Sec. 6-4, the dose rate in sea-level air, at any distance r from a symmetrically shielded nuclear reactor, is approximately given by

$$A_m \frac{D_\gamma}{P_r} = (3.36 \times 10^{10})(1 + 5.5 \times 10^{-5}r) \frac{\exp(-5.5 \times 10^{-5}r)}{r^2}$$

$$\text{rep/Mwhr or rads/Mwhr} \quad (8\text{-}7)$$

$$B_m \frac{D_{nf}}{P_r} = 2.20 \times 10^{11} \frac{\exp{(-3 \times 10^{-5}r)}}{r^2}$$

$$\text{rep/Mwhr or rads/Mwhr} \quad (8\text{-}8)$$

$$C_m \frac{D_{nth}}{P_r} = 4.05 \times 10^6 \frac{\exp{[-1.6 \times 10^{-4}(r - 3000)]}}{r}$$

$$\text{rep/Mwhr or rads/Mwhr} \quad (8\text{-}9)$$

where r is measured in centimeters, P_r is the reactor power in megawatts, and D is in roentgens equivalent physical per hour or rads per hour. The terms A_m, B_m, and C_m are attenuation factors for gammas, fast

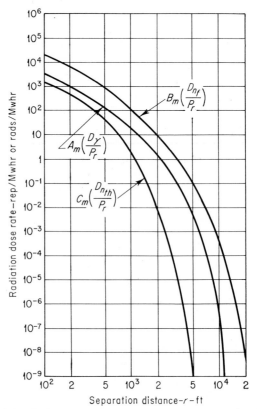

Fig. 8-18. Radiation dose rates as a function of separation distance.

neutrons, and thermal neutrons, respectively, and are always greater than 1. All of these factors are defined more fully in Sec. 6-4. Equation (8-9), for thermal-neutron dose, is valid only for $r > 3,000$ cm.

These dose-rate equations are plotted in Fig. 8-18 for various reactor-receiver separation distances. Note that the dose rates fall off very rapidly beyond a separation distance of about 1 mile, so that almost any power rocket reactor can be operated from a distance of about 2 miles without personnel hazard during operation.

The control-room doses will always be less for flight tests than for static tests because the reactor is not at the launching point for as long a period of operation. For this reason shield design based on static-firing requirements is always conservative (and therefore safe) for flight-testing purposes.

Radiation Safety. Adequate material shielding or large separation distances from the radiation source are the most positive means for radiation protection of personnel during the normal operation of a nuclear device. As a rule, however, for nuclear rocket testing it is impractical to provide sufficient shielding for complete protection. Even if it were practical, it would be undesirable to do so, since the reduced separation distances used in such a facility layout might be inadequate for complete safety in case of a nuclear accident. Therefore, the most generally useful procedure is to employ large separation distances and local shielding of personnel, with extensive use of radiation-monitoring equipment. By these means, the local level of radiation is minimized and access to unshielded areas is prohibited until the activity is reduced to allowable dose rates. The characteristics of radiation-shield materials and equations used in shielding calculations are covered in Chap. 6 and will not be repeated here. Consequently, the discussion which follows is concerned only with the techniques and instrumentation used in radiation monitoring, the other half of the radiation-safety picture.

ALPHA MONITORING. The alpha particle has a large mass and a double charge, both of which limit its travel in matter. For nuclear-reactor testing, this means that alpha control consists of the prevention of ingestion, inhalation, and spread of alpha contamination. The property which makes alphas so easily shielded makes the construction of detecting instruments and the use of these detectors very difficult. When properly adjusted, a proportional counter with a separate thin-walled probe can detect alphas in the presence of other types of radiation. Routine alpha monitoring, while requiring tedious and meticulous survey work, usually results in only a qualitative determination of alpha contamination.

BETA-GAMMA MONITORING. Here the problem is mainly the detection of a penetrating type of radiation. Most survey work is done with a Geiger-Mueller tube type of instrument. These instruments are calibrated by use of a radium source and will give an indication of beta radiation only when the tube is unshielded. Ion-chamber instrumentation, when modified with thin walls to permit the entry of beta particles, will in general give a more accurate response to beta radiation. When monitoring for beta or gamma radiation, rapid coverage can be made by checking at a distance of 2 to 6 in. from the object in question. X radiation below 100 kvp (kilovolts peak) is not as penetrating and should be checked with an unshielded Geiger-Mueller tube or with a thin-walled ion chamber. For recording individual exposures, some form of film badge is normally employed.

NEUTRON MONITORING. Proportional counters, similar to those used for alpha particles, containing boron-10 enriched trifluoride can be used to detect slow neutrons by the alpha particles resulting from the "fission" of B^{10} in the neutron-excited state. If the walls are kept thick enough

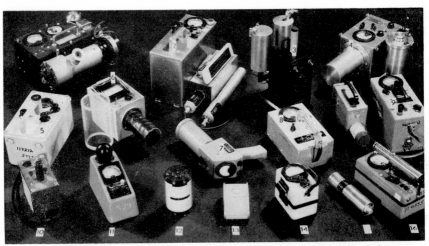

FIG. 8-19. Radiation-detection meters used at the Los Alamos Scientific Laboratory.

to exclude external alpha particles and the counting circuit is adjusted to be insensitive to beta and gamma radiation, the instrument will respond only to thermal neutrons.

Fast neutrons are detected with a proportional instrument which responds to the large pulses caused by recoil protons that are produced by the passage of fast neutrons through a thin layer of paraffin. This instrument, which may be used for both detection and measurement, will detect neutrons in the 0.1- to 10-Mev energy range. Individual exposures are recorded either by a boron-lined pocket chamber or by the excessive density shown under the cadmium filter on a beta-gamma film badge.

In summary, Fig. 8-19 shows many of the radiation-detection meters used at the Los Alamos Scientific Laboratory; their description and comments on their characteristics are given in Table 8-5.

TABLE 8-5. CHARACTERISTICS OF RADIATION-DETECTION METERS*

Item from Fig. 8-19	Type of meter	Radiation detected	Nominal range	Characteristics and limitations
1	Ion chamber	Beta and gamma	0–10⁵ $\mu c/m^3$	Tritium "Sniffer"—air drawn through chamber by small blower; sensitive to gamma radiation or any ion source (lighted match)
2	Proportional counter	Alpha	0–20,000 cpm	"Pee-Wee"—probe has steel grid over 0.25-mil Mylar window; microphonic, easily damaged, requires frequent calibration (Tuballoy source on case), affected by moisture
3	Ion chamber	Neutron	. . . .	Cambridge Instrument Model BM 1770—uses quartz-fiber electrometer
4	Ion chamber	Fast neutron	1.75 mr/hr 100 n/(cm²)(sec) 1,750 mr/hr 10⁵ n/(cm²)(sec)	"Neut"—Nuclear Model 2714; twin range and interchangeable chambers
5	Ion chamber	Gamma	0–50,000 mr/hr	AN/PDR-39; long warm-up period; zero adjust requires turning of range switch
6	Ion chamber	Beta and gamma	100–50,000 mr/hr	"LASL Model 100"—Mylar-covered probe with $\frac{1}{4}$-in.-thick Lucite beta shield; requires calibration chart; beta response assumed reliable
7	Ion chamber	Beta and gamma	0–5,000 mr/hr	"Cutie Pie"—end of chamber has thin window, beta shield, somewhat directional in response
8	Ion chamber	Alpha, beta, and gamma	0–5,000 mr/hr	"Juno"—sliding alpha and beta shields; slow warm-up; calibration not reliable for three types of radiation; not recommended for general laboratory alpha monitoring
9	Proportional counter	Fast neutron	0–500 mrep/hr	"Rudolph"—tissue-equivalent chamber for 0.2- to 10-Mev neutrons; four ranges
10	Ion chamber	Beta and gamma	0–1,000 mr/hr	"Met-Lab" model shown; Landsverk "Electroscope"; drift between light flashes measure of radiation; recommended for ICC shipment measurements

TABLE 8-5. CHARACTERISTICS OF RADIATION-DETECTION METERS* (*Continued*)

Item from Fig. 8-19	Type of meter	Radiation detected	Nominal range	Characteristics and limitations
11	Ion chamber	Gamma	0–200 mr	"Proteximeter"—portable integrating meter; simple operating instructions on bottom
12	Ion chamber	Gamma	0–20 mr	General Electric Model 4Sn11A2; self-contained, no tubes, batteries, or external power supply; self-charging
13	Ion chamber	Gamma	0.1–100 r/hr	"Pocket Alarm" Beckman Model MX-7B; alarm sounds at preset integrated exposure
14	Ion chamber	Gamma	0.5–500,000 mr/hr	Jordan "Radector"—two ranges, logarithmic response, mr/hr or r/hr; new models have beta window and built-in calibration source; small energy dependence above 75 kv
15	Scintillator detector	Gamma	. . . .	Nuclear Research Model SC-2a, detector head only; phosphor (usually NaI crystal) and photomultiplier tube
16	Geiger-Mueller	Beta and gamma	0–20 mr/hr 80,000 cpm	"Thyac"—vibrator high-voltage supply; mechanical difficulties make it somewhat unreliable

* From *Los Alamos Scientific Laboratory Rept.* LA-1835, September, 1954, and G. T. Hine and G. L. Brownell (eds.), "Radiation Dosimetry," Academic Press, Inc., New York, 1956.

REFERENCES

1. Way, K., and E. Wigner: The Rate of Decay of Fission Products, *Phys. Rev.*, vol. 73, no. 11, p. 1318, June, 1948.
2. Glasstone, S.: "Principles of Nuclear Reactor Engineering," D. Van Nostrand Company, Inc., Princeton, N.J., 1955.
3. Sutton, G.: "Rocket Propulsion Elements," 2d ed., John Wiley & Sons, Inc., New York, 1956.
4. Campbell, I. E., (ed.): "High Temperature Technology," John Wiley & Sons, Inc., New York, 1956.
5. Flock, E. F., and A. I. Dahl: The Measurement of Gas Temperature by Immersion Type Instruments, *J. Am. Rocket Soc.*, vol. 23, no. 3, pp. 155–164, May–June, 1953.
6. Barker, R. F., (ed.): General Handbook for Radiation Monitoring, *LA*-1835, Los Alamos Scientific Laboratory, September, 1954.

CHAPTER 9

ADVANCED AND EXOTIC SYSTEMS

The preceding chapters of this book have dealt at some length with the technical regimes or areas of interest pertinent to the use of fissionable material as a substitute for conventional "combustible" heat sources for rocket propulsion. However, the energy available in a pound of fissionable material is approximately 10^7 times larger than the energy available by chemical reaction from a pound of high explosive or from a pound of any other combustible mixture. It is thus obvious that burning fissionable material as though it were a combustible chemical fuel is not the most efficient way to use it, if efficiency is here reckoned on a weight basis.

The nuclear-reactor technology which has built up since 1945 has all been oriented toward use of fissionable fuel as a replacement for coal or hydrocarbon fuels. This is principally a result of the fact that conventional heat-engine practices are well developed, such engines having been in use on the order of 100 years, and that most of the interest in reactor development has been directed toward making sure but modest improvements in conventional power-generating techniques rather than in looking for completely new methods of utilizing this new source of energy. The atom has been adapted to the boiler, so to speak, rather than the other way around. Nevertheless, even in the heat-engine field it appears possible to devise methods of producing highly energetic bundles of material on a short-time (i.e., pulsed) basis for use in vehicle propulsion.

The performance of both chemical and nuclear heat-engine rocket motors, of the type discussed in the body of this text, is fundamentally limited by the energy of the molecular bond. For chemical rockets this limitation appears primarily as a limitation on the peak gas temperatures it is possible to achieve by combustion processes. For nuclear-heated rocket motors, the limitation arises by attainment of the molecular structural failure points of the various materials of interest. Unfortunately the best structural materials are limited to temperatures of about 5000 to 6000°R (Chap. 5) or about 0.25 ev. Fission-energy processes are not limited to this value because the energy of the fission process appears directly as kinetic energy of the two fission fragments, each with an energy of 60 to 100 Mev, or at a kinetic temperature of the order of 10^{12} °R. The energy appearing as a result of other nuclear processes, such as fusion, beta decay, and alpha emission, can also give rise to extremely energetic (several million electron volts) particles. Clearly, nuclear energy offers a tremendous potential advantage over chemical energy, which can never exceed a few volts per particle.

This chapter discusses some of the ways in which it may be possible to make "direct" use of nuclear energy for propulsion and thus achieve some of the 10^7 potential-energy advantage of nuclear over chemical processes. Also presented are some considerations of the use of nuclear-powered "conventional" heat-engine equipment to produce highly energetic particles on a pulsed or steady-state basis.

9-1. Fusion Energy. While it is well known that fusion can be produced between several different nuclides, attention will be concentrated here on the reaction between the higher isotopes of hydrogen: deuterium, D, and tritium, T. Two principal reactions are known. These are

$$D + D \rightarrow T + p + 4 \text{ Mev} \tag{9-1a}$$

and
$$D + D \rightarrow He^3 + n + 3.2 \text{ Mev} \tag{9-1b}$$

The tritium produced as shown by Eq. (9-1a) will react with other deuterium nuclei principally by

$$T + D \rightarrow He^4 + n + 17.6 \text{ Mev} \tag{9-2}$$

while the helium produced in the neutron branch of the reaction [Eq. (9-1b)] will react with excess deuterium to give

$$He^3 + D \rightarrow He^4 + p + 18.3 \text{ Mev} \tag{9-3}$$

For reference, the fusion cross sections for these reactions are shown in Fig. 9-1 as a function of particle energy.

The D-D reaction proceeds to yield protons or neutrons with a "branching ratio" of roughly

$$\frac{N_p}{N_n} = 1.04 \tag{9-4}$$

Thus we see that the neutron-producing reaction is about as probable as the proton-producing reaction.

The particle energies, hence "temperatures," resulting from these fusion reactions are enormous compared to those resulting from even the most energetic chemical reactions. If it were possible to expel the products of the reactions described by Eqs. (9-1) to (9-3) rearward from a rocket vehicle, the effective specific impulse of the "propellant" would be about 3×10^6 lb-sec/lb, some 10^4 times higher than conventional present-day chemical rocket capabilities! The catch is to make the reaction go in a controllable manner with a minimum of equipment.

From an inspection of the fusion cross sections shown in Fig. 9-1 it is clear that the reactions will not proceed until particle energies of the order of 10 kev are reached in the reacting mass. This energy corresponds to a kinetic temperature of about 10^8 °R; clearly gaseous fusion reactions cannot be contained by solid walls! Since the gases are totally ionized at these temperatures, it is possible, in theory, to contain (or constrain) them by use of electric and magnetic fields of appropriate gradients. However, no satisfactory solution to the containment prob-

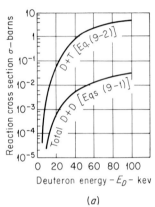
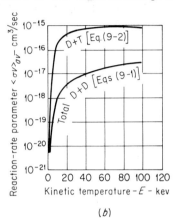

(a) (b)

FIG. 9-1. (a) Fusion cross sections as a function of relative particle energy. (b) Reaction-rate parameter for a Maxwellian particle distribution at a given kinetic temperature. (*Richard F. Post, Controlled Fusion Research: An Application of the Physics of High Temperature Plasmas, Rev. Mod. Phys., vol. 28, no. 3, pp. 338–362, July, 1956.*)

lem has yet been announced. Another formidable difficulty is that connected with the initiation of a fusion reaction in a mass of gas, initially at room temperature, which must be heated to some 10^8 °R. Solution of this problem in the weapons field, as evidenced by the successful development of thermonuclear bombs, does not ensure its solution for the controlled release of fusion energy. Vigorous programs for the development of devices to permit the controlled release of fusion energy are presently under way in the United States, Russia, and in Great Britain, France, and other countries. A report outlining some of the American work in the field has been given by Post,[2] while Kurchatov[3] has summarized some of the Russian experience.

It is evident that thermonuclear processes yield sufficient energy per unit of reacting mass to assure rocket-vehicle performance presently undreamed of. It is also evident that fruitful speculation on the possibilities for thermonuclear propulsion must await the successful achievement of controlled release of fusion energy.

9-2. Decay Energy. Since the discovery of radium, many other nuclei which spontaneously decay or disintegrate, releasing highly energetic particles in the process, have been found. The thorough study of nuclear phenomena which has paced the development of applied nuclear energy has disclosed hundreds of natural or artificially produced radioisotopes, many of which are now being used throughout the medical, industrial, and scientific fields.

Radioisotopes are produced by the fission of uranium nuclei (or other fissionable fuels) or can be manufactured by irradiation of stable elements in nuclear reactors. The distribution of primary fission products from the thermal fission of U^{235}, U^{233}, and Pu^{239} is given in Fig. 9-2, which shows that formation of a wide variety of radioisotopes is a natural result of the fission process. Reference to the Chart of the Nuclides in the Appendix discloses that most of these isotopes are β and γ emitters, yielding relatively high-energy electrons or energetic photons. The prime difficulty in considering the use of such fission-product isotopes is that they do not appear singly, but are formed, according to the distribution shown in Fig. 9-2, as part of a large group of "mixed" fission products. Chemical-separation processes are necessary to isolate any one desired fission product from the mixture. On the other hand radioisotope production by irradiation of a stable element results in the formation of

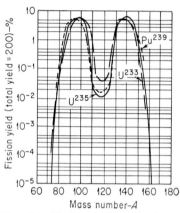

FIG. 9-2. Fission-product yields for thermal-neutron fission for several materials. (*From K. Way and N. Dismurke, Fission Product Yields, ORNL*-280 *and AECD*-2817, 1949.)

the desired isotope mixed only with the parent target element. No chemical-separation plants are required as for the extraction of single fission products; however, it is necessary to utilize reactors especially designed for irradiation usage. By this method it is possible to produce α-emitting isotopes as well as β and γ emitters.

Energetic photons are highly penetrating and must pass through large amounts of material in order to lose their energy. Alpha particles and high-energy (1-Mev) electrons have mass, are charged, and lose their energy quickly by ionization processes in passage through matter. As a consequence, γ emitters are not as useful for radioisotope heat sources as are α and β emitters. A glance through the Chart of the Nuclides shows that the decay energy for β emitters averages about 1 Mev, while α emitters yield about 4 Mev apiece. Two radioisotopes and about one excess neutron result from each fission process. If the excess neutron is used to produce another radioisotope, by irradiation, then three radioactive nuclei are potentially available from each fission. Assuming (optimistically) the production of two β emitters (fission products) and one α emitter (irradiated element), there will be about 6 Mev of decay energy available per fission. Since the initial kinetic energy of the fission fragments is about 160 Mev, only some 4 per cent of the total energy of the fission process theoretically can be converted for use as decay energy. Practical considerations reduce this to less than 0.2 per cent for most cases.[4]

Heat Sources. Choice of isotopes with appropriate half-lives permits consideration of radioisotope heat sources over a wide range of specific power output (i.e., megawatts per pound). Table 9-1 shows the possibilities for some potentially useful radioisotopes.

Decay energy in this form can be used to replace a reactor heat source heating a working fluid or propellant to high temperature to produce thrust as described in Chap. 2. The chief disadvantage of radioisotopes used as heat sources is that no control over the rate of energy production is possible; thus it is necessary to provide an auxiliary cooling system in order to prevent destruction (melting or vaporization) of the heat source while not in use. Another disadvantage is the present limited world-production capability for radioisotope sources of either type.[4] This is a consequence of the low energy-conversion ratio, discussed previously, when using the fission process to produce active isotopes. Typical heat-exchanger rocket reactors require power outputs of the order of 10,000 Mw (perhaps higher). At a conversion efficiency as high as 1 per cent this requires some 10^6 Mw of installed reactor capacity to produce the isotope heat source for one rocket motor, on a basis of continuous readiness. This power output is about 20 times the present power-plant capacity of the United States. These difficulties render radioisotope heat sources of little interest for rocket propulsion as considered herein as compared with controllable fission reactors. However, examination of the data in Table 9-1 shows that some radioisotopes which can be produced without excessive fission requirements may be useful as lightweight sources of very low (by rocket-motor standards) power.

Direct Momentum. It has often been proposed[5,6] that the momentum of the energetic particles be used directly to produce thrust and propel vehicles. Unfortunately these particles are emitted isotropically and, barring the discovery of some lightweight method of collimating them, will therefore deposit at least half of the total decay energy *within* the vehicle, if half is assumed to go rearward from the vehicle. This latter assumption implies a thin layer (to reduce self-absorption) of radioisotope "painted" on one side of the flat base of the vehicle to be propelled. For such a device, calculations[7] of the momentum and energy exchange show

TABLE 9 1. CHARACTERISTICS OF RADIOISOTOPES AS HEAT SOURCES

Artificially Produced Radioisotopes

Parent		Daughter		Resultant decay heat source		
Element	Natural concentration, %	Isotope	Half-life, yr	Material[a] required for irradiation,[b] lb/10³ Mwyr	Thermal power available at initial use[c]	
					kw/lb	kw/10³ Mwyr
Tm^{169}.........	100	Tm^{170}	0.36	140	10	1,400
Cs^{133}.........	100	Cs^{134}	2.31	80	6.9	550
Tl^{203}.........	29.5	Tl^{204}	2.69	820	0.17	140
Ca^{44}.........	2.1	Ca^{45}	0.42	295,000	10^{-3}	295

Chemically Separated Fission Products

Fission product	Weight factor[d]	Production rate,[e] lb/10³ Mwyr	Thermal power available			
			At initial use[f]		After 1 yr use	
			kw-lb	kw/10³ Mwyr	kw/lb	kw/10³ Mwyr
Mixed.......	...	880	0.58	510	0.14	120
Sr^{90}–Y^{90}......	1.5	25	0.32	8	0.34	8
Ru^{106}–Rh^{106} ..	2	40	4.2	19	1.8	7
Cs^{137}–Ba^{137}...	3	93	0.15	14	0.15	14
Ce^{144}–Pr^{144}...	3	84	2.4	200	0.95	80

[a] Material weights include natural parent material and artificially produced daughter isotopes.

[b] Production is assumed to take place in large thermal reactors (e.g., Hanford type) and to require irradiation for two half-lives to achieve near-saturated activity.

[c] Initial use assumed at end of irradiation period in production reactors (see footnote b).

[d] Defined as the ratio of total mass yield (through fission production and decay of percursors) of chemically similar isotopes to the yield of the primary fission product of interest, for the production conditions given in footnote f.

[e] Includes mass of all chemically similar isotopes (see footnote d).

[f] Fission products assumed to be produced in large reactors with a fuel cycle (in-reactor) time of 180 days. Fission-product separation assumed to be by chemical processes. Initial use assumed at 90 days after removal from production reactors.

that about 100 Mw must be dissipated by the vehicle for every pound of thrust produced by use of α emitters. For β emitters the heat dissipation must be some 3,500 Mw per pound of thrust. Assuming energy loss only by radiation (operation in space), and a maximum allowable vehicle base temperature of 5000°F, the radiating surface area required is about one square foot per megawatt of power-dissipation load. This scheme clearly is not a practical one and is not further considered.

In conclusion it appears that radioisotopes can be considered for use in rocket propulsion only as heat sources, but that the twin disadvantages of insufficient production capability and lack of controllability render them of little real interest for this application.

9-3. Fission Energy. The more prosaic application of fission energy has been considered in the body of this text. This use of fission energy as released in conventional heat-exchanger-type reactors is not considered in this chapter. Rather, various ways of utilizing fission energy directly or to produce extremely energetic particles are discussed. Also presented is an analysis of a conceptual fission reactor which is capable of operation at gas temperatures much above those possible in the heat-exchanger reactor.

Direct Momentum. The kinetic energy of most fission fragments falls between 60 and 100 Mev. As previously discussed for use of α and β emitters, active fissionable material could be spread in a thin film on the rear of the vehicle. Assuming it possible to produce fissions in this thin film, half of the energy would go rearward and half forward into the vehicle as before. Recoil of the fission fragments would propel the vehicle. The ratio of energy to momentum is about the same for fission fragments and α particles, and some 80 Mw of heat must be dissipated by the vehicle for each pound of thrust produced. Obviously, the objections given for direct use of radioisotopes also apply here and lead to the conclusion that this scheme should not be further considered.

Fission-fragment Heating. Fragments of a fissioned nucleus appear initially as highly charged ions (e.g., stripped of about 20 electrons) which lose their kinetic energy by ionization of the material through which they pass while slowing down. It would thus seem desirable to cause fissions in such a way that the fragment slowing down takes place directly in the propellant gas rather than in structure which becomes heated and then heats the propellant by molecular collisions on the structure surfaces. In the limit such action can be achieved homogeneously in gaseous reactors or "fizzlers" discussed in the following section. However, even structured reactors of the heat-exchanger type can take partial advantage of direct fragment heating by employment of thin films of fissionable fuel on the structure surfaces.[8] In such a system up to 47 per cent of the available energy of the fission process (excluding neutrinos) theoretically can be deposited directly in the propellant gas, resulting in up to 40 per cent greater specific impulse from the propellant, for the same limiting structural-material temperature.   About 7 per cent of the available fission energy is carried by prompt gammas and neutrons which will lose most of their energy in the solid structure rather than the gas.

One method of achieving operation at a constant limiting structure temperature involves the use of two-pass flow over the reactor-core fuel elements.   For such flow, heat is transferred to the propellant by con-

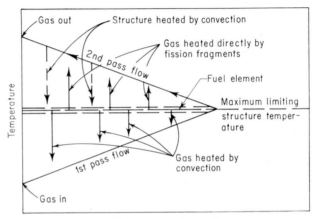

Distance along flow path

Fig. 9-3. Temperature profile for fission-fragment heating in two-pass flow.

vection in the first pass and by direct fission-fragment heating in the second pass.*   The fissionable fuel is assumed to be in a thin film on the second-pass side of the flow path.   A typical temperature profile for this arrangement is shown in Fig. 9-3.   Practical difficulties in the design of core structure for such operation arise from consideration of the range of fission fragments.   In order to maximize the energy directly deposited in the gas, the fissionable fuel film must be thin enough to allow most of the "outward bound" fragments to escape through the film, and the path length through the gas must be long enough to permit absorption of most of the fragment energy.   Thus there must be a large fuel-film surface area in the core in order to satisfy minimum critical-mass requirements, and the various surfaces must be separated from each other by distances equivalent to one or two mean free paths for slowing down of fission fragments at the conditions prevailing in the gas.   It is obvious that these two requirements lead to large-volume cores, since high specific surface area results from finely divided structure which, in turn, leads to

* Following a suggestion by W. C. Cooley, private communication, 1955.

large volumes if large hydraulic diameters are employed between fuel elements. Quantitative assessment of the potentialities of this system requires knowledge of the range of fission fragments in various gases and in films of fuel-bearing material, as well as values of critical mass for reactors of interest. The fraction of energy lost as a function of range (in dimensionless form) for fission fragments penetrating any material is shown in Fig. 9-4, based upon experimental evidence indicating that the

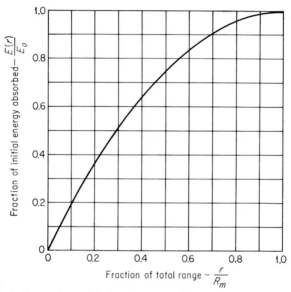

FIG. 9-4. Energy loss of fission fragments in passage through matter.

rate of energy loss decreases roughly linearly with decreasing residual range.[9] Note that 85 per cent of the total energy is lost in only 60 per cent of the range. The range in air at standard conditions $R_a{}^o$ is between 1.9 and 2.5 cm. Approximate range in other gases or at different conditions can be obtained from[10]

$$\frac{R_m}{R_a} = \frac{\rho_a}{\rho_m} \sqrt{\frac{A_m}{A_a}} \tag{9-5}$$

and
$$\frac{R_a}{R_a{}^o} = \frac{T}{500P} \tag{9-6}$$

where subscript a refers to air and m to the material of interest. Densities are denoted by ρ, A is the *atomic* weight ($A_a = 14.5$),* T is the temperature of interest in °R, and P is the system pressure in atmospheres.

* As used here, "atomic weight" means the average number of nucleons per *atom* in the absorbing medium.

As an example, the range in hydrogen ($A_m = 1$) at 5000°R and 100 atm is about $R_m \approx (2)(2\%)$ $\sqrt{1/14.5}$ $(^{5000}\!\!/_{500})(^{1}\!\!/_{100}) = 0.76$ cm. A similar calculation shows that the range in high-density materials such as U, UC$_2$, or UO$_2$ is roughly 10^{-3} cm or less. Assuming a parallel-plate core structure with plates spaced at the range of 0.76 cm calculated above, the specific surface area available for fuel coating (one side only) within the core is about 1.3 cm^2 per cubic centimeter of core volume. Since the fuel thickness must be less than one-tenth of the fragment range in the fuel to avoid excessive heating in the fuel layer (Fig. 9-4), the specific fuel volume is less than 1.3×10^{-4} cm^3 of fuel per cubic centimeter of core for the conditions under consideration. This amounts to an average fuel density of only 0.08 lb of U^{235} per cubic foot of core. Since this is about half as large as the lowest critical fuel concentration reported in the open literature for a well-moderated (D$_2$O) reactor[11] and is comparable to that calculated for very clean, gaseous, reflector-moderated cores,[12] it is extremely doubtful that such a system could be made critical. Halving the plate spacing doubles the available fuel volume as does doubling the fuel-layer thickness; however, both these changes increase the structure heating and reduce the energy available for direct gas heating by about 20 to 25 per cent of the available fission energy. Assuming changes of geometry and/or fuel thickness to raise the fuel density to 0.15 lb of U^{235} per cubic foot of core and a critical mass of about 75 lb or so (roughly typical for large moderated reactors), the required core volume would be on the order of 500 ft^3. For a plate thickness of 0.05 in., such a core would have a bulk density of the order of 25 to 60 lb/ft^3 and would thus be quite heavy and consequently of little interest for rocket propulsion in view of the relatively small (maximum of 40 per cent) specific-impulse advantage available over the more "conventional" convective-heat-exchanger type of reactor. Possible variations in detailed design will not invalidate this conclusion when the complications of providing internal neutron moderators are also taken into account.

Gaseous Reactors or "Fizzlers." The possibility of heating an expendable material (propellant) to extremely high temperatures by utilizing an intimate mixture of fissionable fuel and diluent in a nuclear reactor has been mentioned in the preceding section. Such reactors will obviously be gaseous in the heat-exchange (core) volume, and can be conveniently referred to as "fizzlers," since they present a certain resemblance to a fizzling uncontrolled fissioning system. This idea is not a new one, having been proposed as early as 1949.[13] A schematic outline of a possible steady-state continuous-flow reactor of this type is shown in Fig. 9-5.

Since temperatures of interest are those which lead to performance much superior to that of conventional rockets and since conventional rockets operate at gas temperatures comparable to the boiling points of many common structural materials, it is clear that steady-state fizzlers must operate at temperatures above the vaporization temperatures of materials of interest. For this reason all steady-state reactors operating on the principle previously mentioned can be analyzed as gaseous reactors, whether the diluent and fissionable fuel are initially mixed in the solid or liquid state within the reactor chamber, analogously to a solid-propellant rocket, or the diluent and fuel (in solid, liquid, or gaseous form) are injected into a reaction chamber, as in conventional liquid-fueled rocket motors.

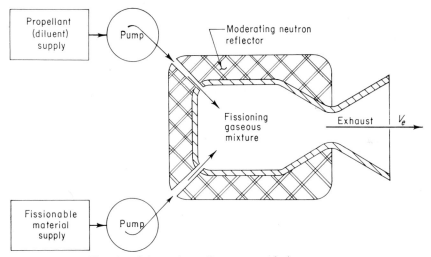

FIG. 9-5. Schematic outline, gaseous-fission reactor.

The performance of any jet power plant can be well characterized by the specific impulse of the working fluid used. High specific impulse means high thrust per unit working-fluid-weight flow rate, thus high total impulse with low fluid expenditure. This is doubly important in fizzlers, since expulsion of fission-fragment-heated diluent will inevitably carry some of the fissionable fuel out the nozzle as well.

The specific impulse of the fuel plus diluent (if any) mixture is given by

$$I_{sp} = \frac{v_e}{g_c} = \frac{F}{w_{tot}} \tag{9-7}$$

where v_e = mixture exhaust velocity
F = thrust
w_{tot} = mixture weight flow rate

For adiabatic expansion to zero pressure (infinite nozzle-area ratio) the maximum exhaust velocity is

$$v_e = \sqrt{\frac{2g_c\gamma}{\gamma - 1} \frac{P_c}{\rho_{tot}}} \tag{9-8}$$

where P_c = mixture-chamber pressure

ρ_{tot} = mixture density within reactor core

γ = ratio of specific heats for gaseous mixture

Combining Eqs. (9-7) and (9-8), the specific impulse is related to the system pressure by

$$P_c = \rho_{tot} \frac{g_c(\gamma - 1)}{2\gamma} (I_{sp})^2 \tag{9-9}$$

Substituting from Eq. (9-7) for one of the I_{sp} terms, Eq. (9-9) becomes

$$P_c = \frac{g_c(\gamma - 1)}{2\gamma} \rho_{tot} I_{sp} \frac{F}{W_{tot}} \tag{9-10}$$

Multiplying top and bottom by the system operating time t_b leads to a relation between total impulse, pressure, specific impulse, and total fuel plus diluent usage. This is

$$P_c = \frac{g_c(\gamma - 1)}{2\gamma} I_{sp} I_{tot} \frac{\rho_{tot}}{W_{tot}} \tag{9-11}$$

where total impulse is $I_{tot} = Ft_b$ and W_{tot} is total weight of all expelled material expended over the time t_b. The term W_{tot}/ρ_{tot} is obviously the total volume of all the mixture if it were all at the chamber temperature and pressure.

For a system in which no separation of fissionable fuel and diluent takes place within the reactor, the fuel will leave the reactor along with the diluent, and the total volume (arbitrarily at core conditions) of each mixture component will equal the total volume of the complete mixture; hence

$$\frac{\rho_{tot}}{W_{tot}} = \frac{\rho_{dil}}{W_{dil}} = \frac{\rho_{fuel}}{W_{fuel}} \tag{9-12}$$

However, if fuel and diluent separation can be achieved, by centrifugal forces due to core rotation, for example, or by other means, the expelled mixture volume (at core pressure and temperature conditions) is related to the expelled component volumes by

$$\frac{\rho_{tot}}{W_{tot}} = \frac{\rho_{dil}}{W_{dil}} = S \frac{\rho_{fuel}}{W_{fuel}} \tag{9-13}$$

where S is the weight-separation ratio, defined as the ratio of fuel mass actually expelled from the system to that expelled if no separation takes place. Using this, Eq. (9-11) becomes

$$P_c = \frac{g_c(\gamma - 1)}{2\gamma} I_{sp} I_{tot} S \frac{\rho_{fuel}}{W_{fuel}} \tag{9-14}$$

The only nuclear requirement on Eq. (9-14) is that ρ_{fuel} be sufficient to ensure reactor criticality. As previously discussed, all systems of interest will be gaseous at core-operating conditions; thus knowledge of the critical fissionable-material densities in gaseous-reactor systems is necessary for further analysis of the problem. A recent study[12] of the conditions for criticality in such systems shows that fuel densities less than 0.05 lb/ft³ can be achieved for U^{235}, U^{233}, or Pu^{239} as fuel. Curves of the required critical fuel density for a clean (unpoisoned) system using U^{235} are shown in Fig. 9-6, for three different reflector materials, as a function of core radius (see also Fig. 6-9). Since the neutron temperature in this type of reactor is determined primarily by the reflector-moderator temperatures, which must be kept comparatively low to avoid melting or vaporization, the critical-mass estimates of the reference report (based upon room-temperature cross sections) are probably correct to a first approximation over a very wide range of gaseous-core temperatures. However the sensitivity of reactor criticality to neutron poisons (such as structural metals) in the reflector is likely to be rather high. Making an allowance for the use of some structural materials around the core, a fuel density of $\rho_{fuel} = 0.10$ lb/ft³ is probably a reasonable lower limit for a gaseous reactor of moderate size.

Since temperatures of interest are presumed to be higher than in conventional chemical rocket motors, the core gases can be assumed monatomic, again to a first approximation, with a characteristic specific-heat ratio of $\gamma = 5/3$. Using these two values and $g_c = 32.2$ (lb mass/lb force)(ft/sec²) and converting to pressure in pounds per square inch, the pressure–impulse–fuel-weight relation is reduced to

$$P_c = 4.5 \times 10^{-3} I_{sp} I_{tot} \frac{S}{W_{fuel}} \tag{9-15}$$

Consideration of several examples clearly illustrates the practical difficulties confronting steady-state fizzlers of useful performance capability:

1. Assume no separation of fuel and diluent takes place within the reactor, so that $S = 1$. Assume that it is desired to achieve specific impulse comparable to but not greater than that obtained in ordinary modern chemical rocket engines; hence $I_{sp} = 300$ lb-sec/lb. Then for a vehicle which requires 100,000 lb thrust for about 150 sec (roughly typical of very large missiles) the system pressure is related to the total fissionable fuel expenditure by

$$P_c = \frac{2 \times 10^7}{W_{fuel}} \qquad \text{lb/in.}^2 \tag{9-16}$$

For these conditions, then, a system pressure of 1,000 lb/in.² (high by conventional standards) will result in the use (loss) of 20,000 lb of fissionable material. This is clearly an impractical figure. On the other hand, for an assumed maximum fuel expenditure of W_{fuel} = 300 lb the system pressure must be 67,000 lb/in.², which is equally impractical.

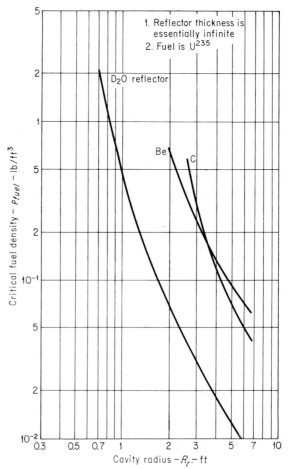

Fig. 9-6. Critical fuel density in cavity reactors. [*G. Safonov, The Criticality and Some Potentialities of Cavity Reactors (Abridged), RM-1835, RAND Corporation, Santa Monica, Calif., July 17, 1955.*]

2. Approaching the problem from another viewpoint, assume a maximum allowable fuel expense of W_{fuel} = 300 lb and a specific impulse of 3,000 lb-sec/lb, tenfold better than conventional chemical rockets. Then, for the vehicle total impulse previously postulated (1.5 × 10⁷

lb-sec), the system pressure is related to the separation ratio by

$$P_c = 6.7 \times 10^5 S \tag{9-17}$$

For a system pressure of 1,000 lb/in.^{2} the fuel-separation ratio must thus be 1.5×10^{-3}, requiring a 670:1 fuel-mass separation. It is conceivable that such could be achieved by rapid rotation of the core gases or perhaps by use of electric or magnetic fields, although it is not clear that separation ratios of the required magnitude could be practically attained by either method.

In conclusion, steady-state fizzlers can be considered practical only if separation ratios of the order of 10^{-3} can be achieved.

9-4. Reactor Systems. If the goal of a high-performance propulsion unit is assumed capable of satisfaction by achievement of very high temperature without consideration of vehicle acceleration (i.e., total propellant flow or system power) capability, then it is possible to consider systems which can produce small amounts of energetic material, often at the expense of use of much heavy equipment. Such high-performance systems are obviously of use in free-fall conditions in space where no artificial acceleration requirements (such as overcoming the earth's field) exist.

Thermomechanical Cycles. One general class of such devices can be called the thermomechanical cycles. Typical systems make use of nuclear-powered conventional thermodynamic cycles to heat successively smaller fractions of the starting gas to higher and higher temperatures, concentrating diffuse initial potential energy (e.g., gas at high temperature and/or high pressure) supplied by nuclear processes in a small fraction of the working fluid which is then expelled to provide momentum exchange and thrust on the vehicle. Of course, each step in an exchange cycle requires rejection of "waste" heat with a consequent lowering of over-all efficiency. However, efficiency per se is of no importance because the energy available from fission reactors is, practically speaking, limitless. What is important is the power requirement (i.e., time rate of energy expenditure), since the weights of power-handling components such as turbines and heat exchangers are generally rather directly related to their power capacities. In order to minimize component weight it is thus desirable to operate at high efficiency.

One example of a possible thermomechanical cycle is shown schematically in Fig. 9-7. This is presented to illustrate the sort of cyclic device of interest herein and should not be misconstrued as an optimum conceptual design. Here a reactor furnishes energy to drive a pump (pump 1) which in turn supplies a liquid propellant to be vaporized and heated under high pressure in the reactor. The hot high-pressure gas is then delivered to a gas storage tank or plenum chamber. One end of a shock tube is fed through valve 1 from the storage tank while the other end is fitted internally with a Kantrowitz-type diffuser[14] and an axial orifice exit through valve 2.   In one operating cycle, pump 1 takes propellant from the tanks, pressurizes it, pumps it through the reactor, where it is heated to high temperature (5000°R), and delivers it to the storage tanks.   At this point in the cycle the shock tube is still filled with low-pressure gas remaining from the preceding cycle.   Valve 1 is rapidly opened, causing a strong shock wave to move up the shock tube from the

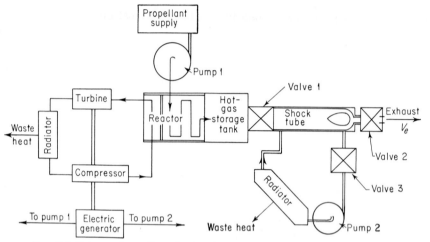

Fig. 9-7. Schematic outline, shock-tube thermomechanical-cycle system.

storage tank, compressing and heating the gas within the tube.   The peak compression occurs at and downstream of the diffuser, which pierces the shock wave and turns it to form a converging cylindrical wave[14] at the tube exit.   Valve 1 is then closed and valve 2 is opened to allow the core of the cylindrically shock-bounded gas to escape at high velocity. When the temperature of the exiting gas drops by a factor of, say, 3 or 4 from the peak temperature achieved, valve 2 is closed again and valve 3 is opened to cool down the remaining gas in the shock tube by radiation to space in order to reduce the residual pressure without excessive loss of propellant gas.   This cycle is continuously repeated to yield bundles of high-temperature gas which leave the system at high velocity and with high specific impulse, thus providing a propellant-conservative and hence high-performance propulsion system.

Typical peak temperatures possible in pulsed thermomechanical heating systems of this and other types may be as high as 10^5 °R.

Electrical Heating.   Another general class of high-performance system is that in which the propellant gas is heated directly by electrical means, causing ionization and recombination in the gas stream.   The electrical power required can be produced by a more-or-less conventional nuclear-electric generating system using a reactor-powered turbine-generator set, or by other more direct nuclear-electric conversion methods, when and if these are developed. The most straightforward use of electrical energy is by resistance heating, with resultant gas compression under certain conditions. In principle the upper temperature limit for such a process is well over 10^6 °R; indeed this method of heating is being pursued in an attempt to achieve controlled thermonuclear reactions.[2,3] A practical

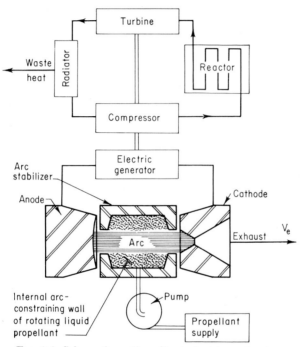

FIG. 9-8. Schematic outline, direct electric arc heater.

limitation on resistance heating of relatively large masses of gas arises from radiative heat losses to the walls of the container in which the gas is heated. Considering this factor, a "practical" operating temperature for a nonreacting (in the thermonuclear sense) plasma might be about 10^5 °R. Experimental work on high-temperature stabilized arcs has been done in recent years in Russia[15] and Germany,[16] resulting in the achievement of arc-plasma temperatures as high as 93,000°R. Application of this work to propulsion is immediately obvious. One possible concept of a nuclear-electric, heated-arc system is shown in Fig. 9-8. Here electrical power is supplied to an arc which is maintained within a flowing, centrifugally stabilized cylinder of liquid propellant. Propellant vaporized from the liquid cylinder feeds the arc plasma and is exhausted from the plasma core through a cooled orifice in the cathode. Waste heat from the reactor-turbine-generator cycle is radiated to space.

Unlike the thermomechanical cycle described previously, this direct electric heating method is continuous and can provide constant thrust with propellant specific impulse at least some 15 times higher than the best attainable today in conventional chemical rockets. However, by analogy with the analysis in the following section, it appears doubtful that any direct electric heating system using conventional electrical generating equipment will be capable of producing thrust in excess of its own weight, and thus such systems seem most suited for use in free fall.

Accelerators. Another type of energy-conversion system capable of producing extremely energetic, directed particles is one involving the use of electric or magnetic fields to accelerate ions or charged particles to very high velocities. This use of particle accelerators often has been discussed as a potential method of supplying thrust for the propulsion of free-fall vehicles.[17-20] Because the idea has been put forth so often, it is worthwhile to examine the potentialities of particle accelerators as thrust producers in some detail and to correlate their performance with the other components of a complete nuclear-reactor-powered self-contained system as required for free-space operation. In considering such a scheme attention is given to the possibility of system optimization by proper choice of particle mass, charge, and accelerating voltage. The analysis presented closely follows that given recently in the open literature.*

Consider an arbitrary particle of mass M proton masses with a charge of Q electronic charges. It is easy to show[21] that the space-charge-limited current density within a time-invariant accelerating field E_b (in parallel-plate geometry) is given by

$$j = \frac{\epsilon_0}{2.25} \sqrt{2 \frac{e}{m_p} \frac{Q}{M} E_b} \frac{E_b}{d^2} \tag{9-18}$$

where ϵ_0 = permittivity of free space
e = electronic charge
m_p = mass of one proton
d = length of path within the uniform accelerating field
The thrust due to operation of this accelerator is proportional to the momentum change imparted to the charged-particle stream and is given (as previously) by

$$T = \frac{w v_e}{g_c} \tag{9-19}$$

for initial particle velocity small compared to final velocity. Here w

* By permission from *J. Brit. Interplanet. Soc.*, vol. 15, no. 6, pp. 297–304, December, 1956.

is particle-weight flow rate, v_e is accelerator exit velocity, and g_c is the force-to-mass conversion factor. The particle velocity at exit from the accelerating field is given by

$$v_e = \sqrt{2 \frac{e}{m_p} \frac{Q}{M} E_b} \tag{9-20}$$

Electric current is simply the flow of electric charge per unit time, and since each charge is associated with a mass, the current is directly related to the particle-weight flow rate. One ampere is defined as a flow of 6.28×10^{18} electronic charges per second; thus the weight flow rate is related to the current by

$$w = 6.28 \times 10^{18} \frac{M m_p}{Q} i \tag{9-21}$$

where i is the total current and is given by

$$i = jS^2 \tag{9-22}$$

where S^2 is the cross-sectional area of the accelerating field.

By combination of Eqs. (9-18) through (9-22) the thrust per unit cross section of accelerator tube (or accelerating field) can be shown to be

$$\frac{T}{S^2} = 5.58 \times 10^{18} \frac{e\epsilon_0}{g_c} \left(\frac{E_b}{d}\right)^2 \tag{9-23}$$

It is noted that the accelerator thrust per unit area as limited by space charge is completely independent of the particle mass, charge, or charge-mass ratio and depends only upon the gradient of the accelerating field. Thus from this standpoint (neglecting relativistic effects) electrons are as satisfactory as propellants as are mercury ions or charged iron filings. Although the space-charge-limited current is a direct function of the charge-mass ratio [Eq. (9-18)], the heavier charged particles have a lower mobility and hence a longer residence time in the region of effective space charge, thus nullifying the effect of greater mass flow per unit current.

However, the particle charge-mass ratio is important in determining the power consumption of an accelerator thrust system. The total electrical power is iE_b and is found from Eqs. (9-18) and (9-22) as

$$P_e = \frac{\epsilon_0}{2.25} \left(\frac{E_b}{d}\right)^2 S^2 \sqrt{2 \frac{e}{m_p} \frac{Q}{M} E_b} \tag{9-24}$$

The power consumption per unit thrust is of more interest. This is determined from Eqs. (9-23) and (9-24) to be

$$\frac{P_e}{T} = 1.13 \times 10^{-19} g_c \sqrt{\frac{Q}{M} \frac{E_b}{e m_p}} \tag{9-25}$$

Ordinary engineering units are not customarily used in accelerator design and analysis. A consistent set of units traditionally employed in this field is the mks (meter-kilogram-second) system. The physical constants appropriate to this unit system and required for evaluation of the foregoing equations are: $\epsilon_0 = 10^{-9}/36\pi$, $g_c = 9.80$ (kg mass/kg force) m/sec², $e = 1.60 \times 10^{-19}$ coulomb, and $m_p = 1.66 \times 10^{-27}$ kg. Application of these values to Eqs. (9-23) and (9-25) yields

$$\frac{T}{S^2} = 8.06 \times 10^{-13} \left(\frac{E_b}{d}\right)^2 \qquad \text{kg/m}^2 \tag{9-26}$$

and

$$\frac{P_e}{T} = 6.79 \times 10^{-2} \left(\frac{Q}{M}\right)^{\frac{1}{2}} E_b^{\frac{1}{2}} \qquad \text{Mw/kg} \tag{9-27}$$

From Eq. (9-26) it is obvious that voltage gradients of the order of 10^6 to 10^7 volts/m are required if noticeable thrust is to be produced from accelerators of reasonable size.

For estimation of system flight performance it is desirable to know the effective particle exhaust velocity, as given by Eq. (9-20), reduced by use of the above physical constants. Thus

$$v_e = 1.39 \times 10^4 \left(\frac{Q}{M}\right)^{\frac{1}{2}} E_b^{\frac{1}{2}} \qquad \text{m/sec} \tag{9-28}$$

Figure 9-9 shows the variation of P_e/T and v_e with the product $(Q/M)E_b$.

In order to gain an understanding of the effect of variation of the power system and accelerator characteristics on over-all vehicle performance, it is necessary to determine the relations between vehicle weight, thrust, and gross specific impulse and particle mass, charge, and accelerating voltage.

Assume a vehicle and propulsion system as outlined in Fig. 9-10. Here the propulsion-system weight is the sum of the propellant weight m_q, tankage weight m_t, accelerator weight m_a, thermal-energy-source weight m_s, electrical generating equipment weight m_e, and waste heat dump weight m_r. The vehicle gross weight m_0 is the sum of the propulsion-system weight and dead-load weight m_d. The dead-load weight is defined to include crew compartment, cargo or payload, any guidance or other equipment, and any vehicle structure not included in the propulsion-system weight.

The weight of accelerator, energy source, electrical generating equipment, and heat dumps is assumed proportional to the electrical power requirements, as

$$m_a + m_s + m_e + m_r = K_1 P_e \tag{9-29}$$

where the over-all specific weight K_1 is the sum of the individual specific weights of each component of the power plant.

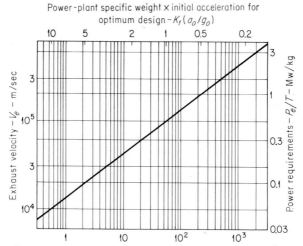

FIG. 9-9. Particle-accelerator characteristics.

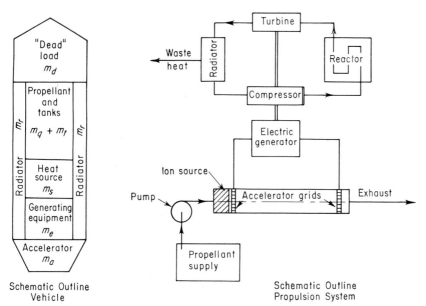

FIG. 9-10. Vehicle and particle-accelerator propulsion system.

Tankage weight is assumed to be a fraction K_2 of the weight of propellant carried; thus

$$m_t = K_2 m_q \tag{9-30}$$

Combining Eqs. (9-29) and (9-30) with the definition of gross weight, the total vehicle weight is given by

$$m_0 = m_d + m_q(1 + K_2) + K_1 P_e \tag{9-31}$$

Since the total impulse imparted to the vehicle is the product of the thrust T and the operating time t_b, assuming constant thrust, the over-all gross specific impulse of the complete vehicle is given by

$$I_{oa} = \frac{T t_b}{m_0} \tag{9-32}$$

By use of Eqs. (9-19) and (9-31) the over-all specific impulse can be expressed as

$$I_{oa} = \frac{m_q v_e / g_c}{m_d + m_q(1 + K_2) + K_1 P_e} \tag{9-33}$$

The electrical power output can be obtained from the rate of kinetic-energy addition to the propellant, and is

$$P_e = 4.90 \times 10^{-6} \frac{m_q}{t_b} \frac{v_e^2}{g_c} \qquad \text{Mw} \tag{9-34}$$

By use of the relation $m_d/m_q = (m_d/m_0)(m_0/m_q)$ and the familiar mass-ratio equation $m_0/(m_0 - m_q) = e^\xi$, where $\xi = \Delta v/v_e$, the dead-load weight can be expressed by

$$m_d = m_q \frac{m_d}{m_0} \Phi_\xi \tag{9-35}$$

where $\Phi_\xi = e^\xi/(e^\xi - 1)$. For reference the function Φ_ξ is shown graphically vs. $\Delta v/v_e$ in Fig. 9-11.

Combining Eqs. (9-34) and (9-35) with Eq. (9-33), the over-all specific impulse is given in terms of vehicle performance factors, particle exhaust velocity, and accelerator operating time as

$$I_{oa} = \frac{\lambda g_c}{v_e} + \left(4.90 \times 10^{-6} \frac{K_1 v_e}{t_b}\right)^{-1} \tag{9-36}$$

where $\lambda = 1 + K_2 + (m_d/m_0)\Phi_\xi$. It is easy to show that the over-all specific impulse reaches a maximum at a value of v_e given by

$$v_e^2 = 2.03 \times 10^5 \frac{\lambda g_c}{K_1} t_b \qquad \text{(m/sec)}^2 \tag{9-37}$$

The maximum over-all specific impulse is then

$$I_{moa} = 225 \sqrt{\frac{t_b}{\lambda g_c K_1}} \qquad \text{kg-sec/kg} \tag{9-38}$$

Note that this optimum specific impulse depends only upon the system operating time for any given vehicle performance requirements and structural specific-weight capabilities. As a matter of reference it should be noted that the conventional propellant specific impulse is given by

$$I_{sp} = 2\lambda I_{moa} \tag{9-39}$$

The value for optimum exhaust velocity given by Eq. (9-37), coupled

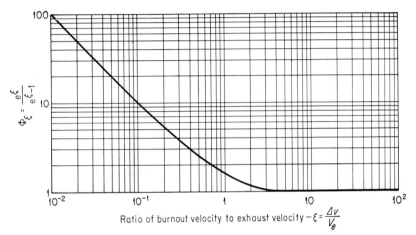

FIG. 9-11. Function Φ_ξ vs. ξ.

with Eq. (9-28), yields a relation between particle charge-mass ratio, accelerating voltage, and system operating time as

$$\begin{aligned}
\frac{Q}{M} E_b &= 1.05 \times 10^{-3} \frac{\lambda g_c}{K_1} t_b \\
&= 2.07 \times 10^{-8} (\lambda g_c I_{moa})^2 \\
&= 5.17 \times 10^{-9} (g_c I_{sp})^2 \tag{9-40}
\end{aligned}$$

The thrust-weight ratio is of interest because it will serve as a measure of the applicability of a particle-accelerator thrust system for use within a gravitational force field. This is equal to the vehicle acceleration in free fall and is given by

$$\begin{aligned}
\frac{T}{m_0} &= \frac{a_0}{g_0} \\
&= \frac{I_{moa}}{t_b} \\
&= \frac{225}{\sqrt{\lambda g_c K_1 t_b}} \\
&= \frac{5.07 \times 10^4}{\lambda g_c K_1 I_{moa}} \\
&= \frac{1.014 \times 10^5}{g_c K_1 I_{sp}} \tag{9-41}
\end{aligned}$$

where g_0 is the acceleration of gravity at sea level, 9.80 m/sec². The thrust-weight ratio will be large only for short operating times or for low values of maximum specific impulse. For a given set of vehicle parameters high specific impulse requires long operating time and low acceleration; hence such propulsive systems are clearly most useful in relatively field-free conditions in space.

Using Eq. (9-41), Eqs. (9-27), (9-28), and (9-40) can be rewritten in much simpler form involving only the power-plant specific-weight parameter and the initial vehicle acceleration. These equations are presented here for ready reference.

$$\frac{Q}{M} E_b = \frac{53.3}{(K_1 a_0 / g_0)^2} \tag{9-42}$$

$$\frac{P_e}{T} = \frac{0.494}{K_1 a_0 / g_0} \quad \text{Mw/kg} \tag{9-43}$$

$$v_e = \frac{1.01 \times 10^5}{K_1 a_0 / g_0} \quad \text{m/sec} \tag{9-44}$$

From the point of view of the vehicle designer it is evidently very desirable to increase the specific power output of the electrical plant as much as possible. Accordingly it is pertinent to examine briefly the weight characteristics of each of the components concerned.

Since heat rejection in space can only be practically accomplished by thermal radiation, the radiator weight is of importance. For operation at 600°C, with an emissivity of 1.0, roughly 300 ft² of radiating surface is required per thermal megawatt radiated. Assuming a weight of 2 kg/ft², including working fluid, the radiator specific weight is given by

$$\frac{m_r}{P_e} = \frac{600(1 - \eta_{oa})}{\eta_{oa}} \quad \text{kg/electrical Mw} \tag{9-45}$$

where η_{oa} is the over-all thermal-electrical conversion efficiency of the power plant. Of course, operation at higher temperature would reduce the area required and therefore the weight per unit power; however, the over-all cycle efficiency when using a temperature-limited heat source will go down as the sink temperature is raised. Determination of optimum sink temperature indicates that minimum system weight results from operation with the sink temperature between 0.75 and 0.8 of the source temperature. Thorough analysis of the entire radiation-heat-sink problem has been presented in the open literature[22] and should be consulted for further information.

The size and hence weight of a fission-reactor heat source is limited only by the heat-transfer capabilities of the fissioning volume (reactor core). Heat-flux densities up to 1 thermal Mw/ft³ are easily attainable with liquid-metal coolants and moderate temperature-driving potentials.[23] Heat-generation and -removal rates higher than this value have been achieved with the MTR (Materials Testing Reactor) at Arco, Idaho.[24] Assuming a mean reactor density of about 100 kg/ft³ of core volume, typical of large power reactors such as the X-10 graphite pile,[25] the reactor weight is then crudely given by

$$\frac{m_{s_1}}{P_e} = \frac{100}{\eta_{oa}} \quad \text{kg/electrical Mw} \tag{9-46}$$

This figure neglects the fact that a minimum reactor size will be required for nuclear criticality, regardless of power level; however, for use of the above specific weight this consideration becomes of second-order importance for power outputs greater than about 20 to 40 thermal Mw.

For various reasons related to the operation of the heat engine it may be desirable to isolate the reactor from the rest of the power-plant circuitry. To do so requires that a secondary heat exchanger be provided to transfer heat from the reactor coolant to an independent heat-engine working fluid. Gas-to-gas exchangers capable of transferring up to 2 kw/kg have been developed for many years.[26] It is evident that this performance could be doubled in a liquid-to-gas heat exchanger in which the liquid-side resistance to heat transfer is very low compared to that on the gas side. Heat-transfer performance greater than this has been achieved in liquid metal–to–air exchangers.[27] Thus for heat transfer to gas as a heat-engine working fluid the secondary heat-exchanger weight is taken to be

$$\frac{m_{s_2}}{P_e} = \frac{250}{\eta_{oa}} \quad \text{kg/electrical Mw} \tag{9-47}$$

Available high-performance conventional electrical generators[28] have a specific weight of about

$$\frac{m_{e_1}}{P_e} = 1,000 \text{ kg/electrical Mw} \tag{9-48}$$

As recently suggested,[29] it may be possible to produce electrical power much more cheaply than this, weightwise, by use of electrostatic generators. Unfortunately, performance figures for such devices must await their development, hence cannot be included here.

For a pressurized closed-gas-cycle heat-engine system, using inert gas such as He or N_2 as the working fluid, it should be possible to build a high-performance turbine-compressor with a specific weight of the order of

$$\frac{m_{e_2}}{P_e} = 500 \text{ kg/electrical Mw} \tag{9-49}$$

Such a system would be similar to the Ackeret-Keller regenerative units[30] in use for some years. The desirability of regeneration can be determined only by a weight analysis made by balancing radiator weight against regenerator weight. At first glance the regenerator seems an inefficient (weightwise) device, being a gas-to-gas heat exchanger. It appears doubtful that increased cycle efficiency would be sufficient to pay its freight in space.

The lightest of the propulsion-system components should be the particle accelerator, basically consisting of a charged-particle source and an accelerating-grid structure supported on a dimensionally stable framework. Though admittedly a guess, accelerator weight could be as low as

$$\frac{m_a}{P_e} = 100 \text{ kg/electrical Mw} \qquad (9\text{-}50)$$

Assuming this value and an over-all efficiency of 25 per cent, the specific weight of the complete propulsion system, less propellant and tankage, is estimated as

$$K_1 = 4{,}800 \text{ kg/electrical Mw} \qquad (9\text{-}51)$$

for use of conservative design and standard or near-standard equipment. At best, a factor-of-10 improvement might be hoped for from refined development of individual components.

As an example of the possibilities with even the rather conservative approach used above, consider a vehicle in which it is desired that the propellant specific impulse be 10,000 kg-sec/kg, about thirty times the best attainable by chemical rockets today. For $K_1 = 4{,}800$ kg/electrical Mw, Eq. (9-41) can be used to show that $a_0 = 2.17 \times 10^{-4} g_0$. Though small this acceleration is not trivial. The gravitational acceleration of the sun's field at the orbital distance of the earth is only $6.04 \times 10^{-4} g_0$! Specifying an over-all specific impulse of 3,000 sec, the thrust-unit operating time is found to be 1.38×10^7 sec, or about 5.3 months. The value of λ is determined from Eq. (9-39) to be $\lambda = 1.667$. Assuming $m_0 = 10^5$ kg, then $T = 21.7$ kg. Now for $(Q/M)E_b = 50$ from Eq. (9-40) or (9-42), Eq. (9-27) or (9-43) shows that $P_e/T = 0.48$ Mw/kg, so that $P_e = 10.4$ electrical Mw. Since $K_1 = 4{,}800$, the weight of equipment necessary to produce the electrical power is 5×10^4 kg. For an accelerator voltage gradient of $E_b/d = 10^7$ volts/m, Eq. (9-26) yields $T/S^2 = 80.6$ kg/m^2, so that $S^2 = 0.25$ m^2. This corresponds to a circular accelerator grid about 0.56 m, or 1.85 ft, in diameter. The propellant-weight flow rate is computed from Eq. (9-19) and found to be $w = 2.17 \times 10^{-3}$ kg/sec. The total propellant weight is thus 3×10^4 kg. Now for a tank 10 per cent as massive as its contained propellant, $K_2 = 0.1$; thus

$$\frac{m_d}{m_0} \Phi_\xi = 0.567$$

For $K_2 = 0.1$ the tank weight is $m_t = 3 \times 10^3$ kg. Summing up all the weights it is found by subtraction that $m_d = 1.7 \times 10^4$ kg; thus $m_d/m_0 = 0.170$ and Φ_ξ must be 3.33. Therefore $e^\xi = 1.43$ and

$$\xi = \frac{\Delta v}{v_e} = 0.358$$

Since $v_e = 9.80 \times 10^4$ m/sec (by definition of $I_{sp} = 10,000$ kg-sec/kg), then $\Delta v = 3.50 \times 10^4$ m/sec, or 21.8 miles/sec. The total impulse over the entire motor operating time has the enormous value of 3×10^8 kg-sec. This is over 200 times the total impulse required by a V-2 rocket missile for normal flight.

Note that, for the same specific impulse values, a reduction in K_1 results in a corresponding linear reduction in system operating time and increase in vehicle acceleration. For a power-plant specific weight of 1 kg/electrical Mw, a vehicle acceleration of g_0 is theoretically attainable.

9-5. In Conclusion. The reader has undoubtedly noted that this last chapter, concerning the possible future, has leaned heavily on the potential uses of plasmas and ionized gases and the interaction of electric and magnetic fields with charged matter. This emphasis is not entirely wishful thinking, but rather reflects the growing importance of that field of physical research and development now labeled *magnetohydrodynamics* or *magnetogasdynamics*.

Big steps in engineering development have always come from the successful fusion of previously unrelated technical regimes. We stand today on the threshold of the marriage of electromagnetic field theory with the fields of compressible-fluid flow and nuclear-reaction phenomena. It is not beyond the bounds of possibility that the production of electrical power directly from nuclear processes will, in time, be a fruit of this union of thought; and, as we have seen, lightweight electrical power sources may well hold the key to man's attempt to explore his immediate universe, the solar system—and beyond.

REFERENCES

1. Sänger, E.: Stationäre Kernverbrennung in Raketan, *Astronautica Acta*, vol. 1, fasc. 2, sec. VI, pp. 86–87, 1955.
2. Post, Richard F.: Controlled Fusion Research: An Application of the Physics of High Temperature Plasmas, *Rev. Mod. Phys.*, vol. 28, no. 3, pp. 338–362, July, 1956.
3. Russian Thermonuclear Experiments, text of speech given by Igor V. Kurchatov at Harwell, England, on April 26, 1956, reported in *Nucleonics*, vol. 14, no. 6, pp. 36–43, 123, June, 1956.
4. Vitro Engineering Division: Review of Fission Product Heat Sources for Power Generation in the 1–5 Kw Range, Vitro Corp. of America. Published Nov. 5, 1954, as U.S. AEC document *KLX*-1735, Office of Technical Services, U.S. Department of Commerce.

5. Shepherd, L. R., and A. V. Cleaver: The Atomic Rocket—1, *J. Brit. Interplanet. Soc.*, vol. 7, no. 5, pp. 190–191, September, 1948.

6. Seifert, H. S., and M. M. Mills: Problems in the Application of Nuclear Energy to Rocket Propulsion, p. 2, *Jet Propulsion Laboratory Memo.* 3-4, Jan. 23, 1947; abstracted in *Phys. Rev.*, vol. 71, p. 279, 1947.

7. Serber, Robert: The Use of Atomic Power for Rockets, pp. 1–3, *Project RAND, RAD-2*, July 5, 1946.

8. Shepherd, L. R., and A. V. Cleaver: The Atomic Rocket—2 and —3, *J. Brit. Interplanet. Soc.*, vol. 7, no. 6, pp. 237, 240, November, 1948; vol. 8, no. 1, p. 30, January, 1949.

9. Goodman, Clark (ed.): "The Science and Engineering of Nuclear Power," vol. I, pp. 65–66, fig. 1-33, Addison-Wesley Publishing Company, Reading, Mass.

10. Ref. 9, p. 60.

11. "The Reactor Handbook," vol. I ("Physics"), chap. 1.5, p. 491, table 1.5.10, *AECD*-3645, March, 1955.

12. Safonov, G.: The Criticality and Some Potentialities of Cavity Reactors (Abridged), *RM*-1835, RAND Corporation, Santa Monica, Calif., July 17, 1955.

13. Shepherd, L. R., and A. V. Cleaver: The Atomic Rocket—3, *J. Brit. Interplanet. Soc.*, vol. 8, no. 1, pp. 23–24, 30–37, January, 1949.

14. Perry, Robert W., and Arthur Kantrowitz: The Production and Stability of Converging Shock Waves, *J. Appl. Phys.*, vol. 22, no. 7, pp. 878–886, July, 1951.

15. Praining, O.: The Attainment of High Temperatures (up to 55,000°K) under Laboratory Conditions, *Uspekhi Fiz. Nauk*, vol. 55, no. 4, pp. 595–608, 1955.

16. New Propulsion Devices, reported in Technical Review Section of *J. Brit. Interplanet. Soc.*, vol. 15, no. 4, pp. 214–215, July–August, 1956.

17. Oberth, H.: "Wege zur Raumschiffahrt," R. Oldenbourg-Verlag, Munich, 1929.

18. Shepherd, L. R., and A. V. Cleaver: The Atomic Rocket—4, *J. Brit. Interplanet. Soc.*, vol. 8, no. 2, pp. 59–70, March, 1949.

19. Spitzer, L., Jr.: Interplanetary Travel between Satellite Orbits, *J. Brit. Interplanet. Soc.*, vol. 10, no. 6, p. 249, November, 1951.

20. Bussard, R. W.: A Nuclear-Electric Propulsion System, *J. Brit. Interplanet. Soc.*, vol. 15, no. 6, pp. 297–304, November, 1956.

21. Ryder, J. D.: "Electronic Engineering Principles," 5th printing, chap. 5, Prentice-Hall, Inc., Englewood Cliffs, N.J., 1950.

22. Cross, C. A.: The Fundamental Basis of Power Generation in a Satellite Vehicle, *J. Brit. Interplanet. Soc.*, vol. 11, no. 3, pp. 117–125, May, 1952.

23. Jackson, C. D. (ed.): "Liquid Metals Handbook, Sodium-NaK Supplement," p. 277, table IV-2, *TID*-5277, U.S. AEC, July, 1955.

24. Ref. 11, p. 766, table A.2.5.

25. Ref. 11, p. 764, table A.2.3.

26. Goodman, Clark (ed.): "The Science and Engineering of Nuclear Power," vol. II, p. 193, fig. 11-8, Addison-Wesley Publishing Company, Reading, Mass. (Escher Wyss heat-exchanger data.)

27. Ref. 23, pp. 422–424, fig. VI-16.

28. Kalikow, I.: Nothing Is Really Ever Finally Solved, *Gen. Elec. Rev.*, vol. 57, no. 6, pp. 48–51, November, 1954.

29. Brosan, G. S.: An Electrical Machine for Use in Extra-terrestrial Environment, *J. Brit. Interplanet. Soc.*, vol. 14, no. 5, pp. 270–274, September, 1955.

30. Keller, C.: Closed Cycle Gas Turbine, Escher Wyss—AK Development, 1945–1950, *Trans. ASME*, vol. 72, pp. 835–850, August, 1950.

APPENDIX

Multiply	By	To obtain
Length:		
centimeters	0.03281	feet
centimeters	0.3937	inches
feet	30.48	centimeters
inches	2.540	centimeters
microns	10^{-4}	centimeters
angstroms	10^{-8}	centimeters
Volume:		
cubic centimeters	3.532×10^{-5}	cubic feet
cubic centimeters	0.06102	cubic inches
cubic feet	2.832×10^{4}	cubic centimeters
cubic feet	7.481	gallons
cubic feet	28.32	liters
cubic inches	16.39	cubic centimeters
gallons	0.1337	cubic feet
gallons	3.785	liters
liters	0.03532	cubic feet
liters	0.2642	gallons
Mass:		
grams	2.205×10^{-3}	pounds
kilograms	2.205	pounds
pounds	453.5	grams
pounds	0.4535	kilograms
slugs (standard gravity conditions)	32.17	pounds
slugs (standard gravity conditions)	9.807	kilograms
Density:		
grams per cubic centimeter	0.03613	pounds per cubic inch
grams per cubic centimeter	62.43	pounds per cubic foot
pounds per cubic inch	27.68	grams per cubic centimeter
Pressure:		
atmospheres	14.70	pounds per square inch
atmospheres	1.0132×10^{6}	dynes per square centimeter

TABLE A-1. CONVERSION FACTORS (*Continued*)

Multiply	By	To obtain
atmospheres..................	29.92	inches of mercury
atmospheres..................	760.0	millimeters of mercury
dynes per square centimeter....	2.953×10^{-5}	inches of mercury
dynes per square centimeter....	7.501×10^{-4}	millimeters of mercury
pounds per square inch........	2.036	inches of mercury
pounds per square inch........	51.715	millimeters of mercury
bars.......................	10^6	dynes per square centimeter
Force:		
dynes.....................	1.020×10^{-6}	kilograms
dynes.....................	2.248×10^{-6}	pounds
kilograms..................	9.807×10^5	dynes
kilograms..................	2.205	pounds
pounds....................	4.448×10^5	dynes
Heat and energy:		
Btu.......................	251.8	calories
Btu.......................	3.930×10^{-4}	horsepower-hours
Btu.......................	0.2931	watthours
Btu.......................	2.931×10^{-4}	kilowatthours
Btu.......................	2.931×10^{-7}	megawatthours
calories...................	3.968×10^{-3}	Btu
electron volts..............	1.603×10^{-12}	ergs
electron volts..............	1.603×10^{-19}	watt-seconds
horsepower-hours............	2,544	Btu
watthours..................	3.413	Btu
kilowatthours...............	3.413×10^3	Btu
megawatthours..............	3.413×10^6	Btu
million electron volts........	1.603×10^{-6}	ergs
million electron volts........	1.603×10^{-13}	watt-seconds
million electron volts........	1.520×10^{-16}	Btu
Power:		
Btu per second.............	1.055×10^{-3}	megawatts
Btu per hour...............	2.931×10^{-7}	megawatts
Btu per hour...............	2.931×10^{-4}	kilowatts
Btu per hour...............	0.2931	watts
Btu per hour...............	3.930×10^{-4}	horsepower
horsepower................	2,554	Btu per hour
horsepower..	0.7457	kilowatts
kilowatts..................	3,413	Btu per hour
kilowatts..................	1.341	horsepower
megawatts.................	947	Btu per second
watts.....................	3.413	Btu per hour
Specific heat:		
Btu per pound per degree Fahrenheit..................	1.000	calories per gram per degree centigrade

TABLE A-1. CONVERSION FACTORS (*Continued*)

Multiply	By	To obtain
Thermal conductivity:		
Btu per hour per square foot per (degree Fahrenheit per foot)	12.0	Btu per hour per square foot per (degree Fahrenheit per inch)
Btu per hour per square foot per (degree Fahrenheit per inch)	0.0833	Btu per hour per square foot per (degree Fahrenheit per foot)
Btu per hour per square foot per (degree Fahrenheit per foot)	4.134×10^{-3}	gram-calories per second per square centimeter per (degree centigrade per centimeter)
Btu per hour per square foot per (degree Fahrenheit per foot)	1.731×10^{-2}	watts per square centimeter per (degree centigrade per centimeter)
gram-calories per second per square centimeter per (degree centigrade per centimeter)	241.9	Btu per hour per square foot per (degree Fahrenheit per foot)
watts per square centimeter per (degree centigrade per centimeter)	57.79	Btu per hour per square foot per (degree Fahrenheit per foot)
Viscosity:		
centipoises	1.0×10^{-2}	poises
poises	1.0	grams per second per centimeter
centipoises	2.09×10^{-5}	pounds force–second per square foot
centipoises	2.42	pounds mass per hour per foot
pounds force–second per square foot	47.8×10^{3}	centipoises
Temperature:		
degrees Kelvin	1.8	degrees Rankine
degrees centigrade	1.8	degrees Fahrenheit $-$ 32
degrees centigrade + 273.2	1.0	degrees Kelvin
degrees Fahrenheit + 459.7	1.0	degrees Rankine
Heat-transfer coefficient:		
Btu per hour per square foot per degree Fahrenheit	1.355×10^{-4}	gram-calories per second per square centimeter per degree centigrade
Btu per hour per square foot per degree Fahrenheit	5.678×10^{-4}	watts per square centimeter per degree centigrade
gram-calories per second per square centimeter per degree centigrade	4.187	watts per square centimeter per degree centigrade
gram-calories per second per square centimeter per degree centigrade	7.373×10^{3}	Btu per hour per square foot per degree Fahrenheit
watts per square centimeter per degree centigrade	1.761×10^{3}	Btu per hour per square foot per degree Fahrenheit

TABLE A-2. PHYSICAL CONSTANTS

Universal gas constant

R_u = 8.314 abs joules/(°K)(g mole)

    = 1.987 cal/(°K)(g mole)

    = 1,545.33 ft-lb/(lb mole)(°R)

    = 1.986 Btu/(lb mole)(°R)

Gravitational conversion factor

g_c = 32.2 (lb mass/lb force)ft/sec²

Acceleration due to gravity at sea level

g_0 = 32.2 ft/sec²

    = 980.7 cm/sec²

Mechanical equivalent of heat

J = 778.2 ft-lb/Btu

Boltzmann's constant

k = 1.3804 × 10^{-16} erg/°K

    = 8.61 × 10^{-5} ev/°K

Velocity of light

c = 2.998 × 10^{10} cm/sec

    = 9.835 × 10^8 ft/sec

Avogadro number

N_0 = 6.02 × 10^{23} nuclei/g atom

Stefan-Boltzmann constant

σ = 5.67 × 10^{-5} erg/(cm²)(°K)⁴(sec)

    = 0.171 × 10^{-8} Btu/(ft²)(°R)⁴(hr)

Planck's constant

h = 6.625 × 10^{-27} erg-sec

Fig. A-1. Chart of the Nuclides*
List of the Elements

Name	Symbol	Atomic number Z	Name	Symbol	Atomic number Z
Actinium	Ac	89	Mendelevium	Mv	101
Aluminum	Al	13	Mercury, hydrargyrum	Hg	80
Americium	Am	95	Molybdenum	Mo	42
Antimony, stibium	Sb	51	Neodymium	Nd	60
Argon	A	18	Neon	Ne	10
Arsenic	As	33	Neptunium	Np	93
Astatine	At	85	Nickel	Ni	28
Barium	Ba	56	Niobium, columbium	Nb	41
Berkelium	Bk	97	Nitrogen	N	7
Beryllium	Be	4	Osmium	Os	76
Bismuth	Bi	83	Oxygen	O	8
Boron	B	5	Palladium	Pd	46
Bromine	Br	35	Phosphorus	P	15
Cadmium	Cd	48	Platinum	Pt	78
Calcium	Ca	20	Plutonium	Pu	94
Californium	Cf	98	Polonium	Po	84
Carbon	C	6	Potassium, kalium	K	19
Cerium	Ce	58	Praseodymium	Pr	59
Cesium	Cs	55	Promethium	Pm	61
Chlorine	Cl	17	Protactinium	Pa	91
Chromium	Cr	24	Radium	Ra	88
Cobalt	Co	27	Radon	Rn	86
Columbium (see niobium)			Rhenium	Re	75
Copper	Cu	29	Rhodium	Rh	45
Curium	Cm	96	Rubidium	Rb	37
Dysprosium	Dy	66	Ruthenium	Ru	44
Einsteinium	E	99	Samarium	Sm, Sa	62
Erbium	Er	68	Scandium	Sc	21
Europium	Eu	63	Selenium	Se	34
Fermium	Fm	100	Silicon	Si	14
Fluorine	F	9	Silver, argentum	Ag	47
Francium	Fr	87	Sodium, natrium	Na	11
Gadolinium	Gd	64	Strontium	Sr	38
Gallium	Ga	31	Sulfur	S	16
Germanium	Ge	32	Tantalum	Ta	73
Gold, aurum	Au	79	Technetium	Tc	43
Hafnium	Hf	72	Tellurium	Te	52
Helium	He	2	Terbium	Tb	65
Holmium	Ho	67	Thallium	Tl	81
Hydrogen	H	1	Thorium	Th	90
Indium	In	49	Thulium	Tm	69
Iodine	I	53	Tin, stannum	Sn	50
Iridium	Ir	77	Titanium	Ti	22
Iron, ferrum	Fe	26	Tungsten	W	74
Krypton	Kr	36	Uranium	U	92
Lanthanum	La	57	Vanadium	V	23
Lead, plumbum	Pb	82	Xenon	Xe	54
Lithium	Li	3	Ytterbium	Yb	70
Lutetium	Lu	71	Yttrium	Y	39
Magnesium	Mg	12	Zinc	Zn	30
Manganese	Mn	25	Zirconium	Zr	40

* By Knolls Atomic Power Laboratory, operated by the General Electric Company for the United States Atomic Energy Commission. Originally prepared by G. Friedlander and M. Perlman, revised by J. R. Stehn and E. F. Clancy of the Knolls Atomic Power Laboratory. The above table is a list of the chemical elements; page 346 gives the key and information on the use of the chart; and pages 347 to 359 constitute the chart proper.

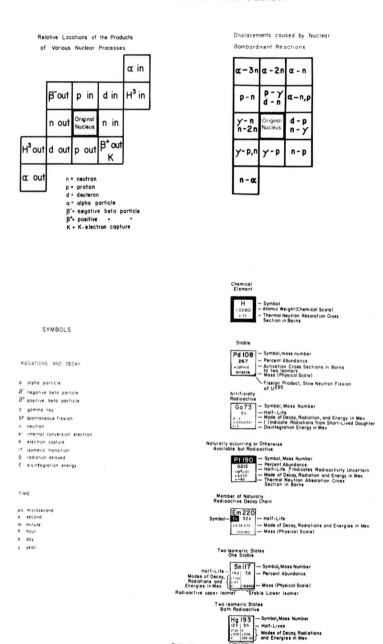

FIG. A-1. Chart of the Nuclides (*continued*).

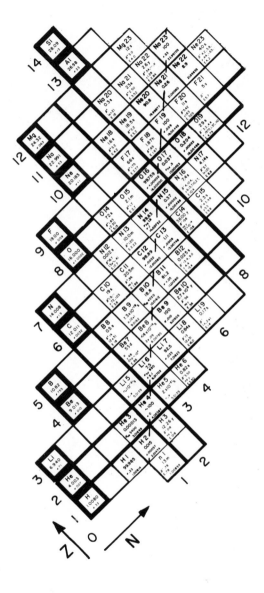

FIG. A-1. Chart of the Nuclides (*continued*).

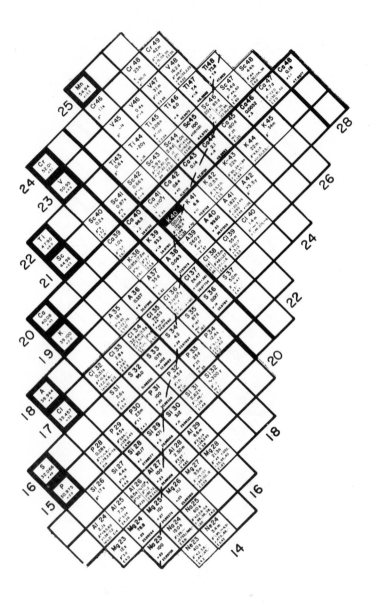

FIG. A-1. Chart of the Nuclides (*continued*).

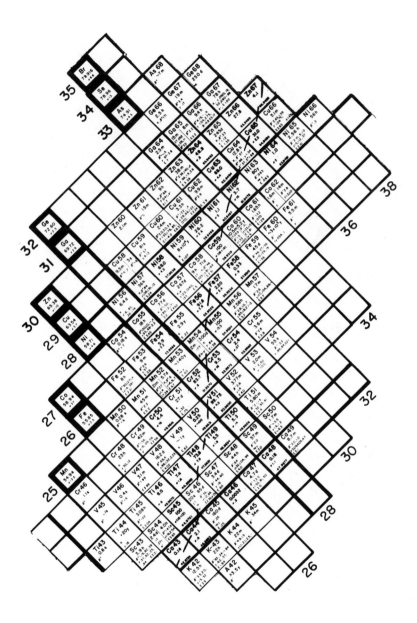

FIG. A-1. Chart of the Nuclides (*continued*).

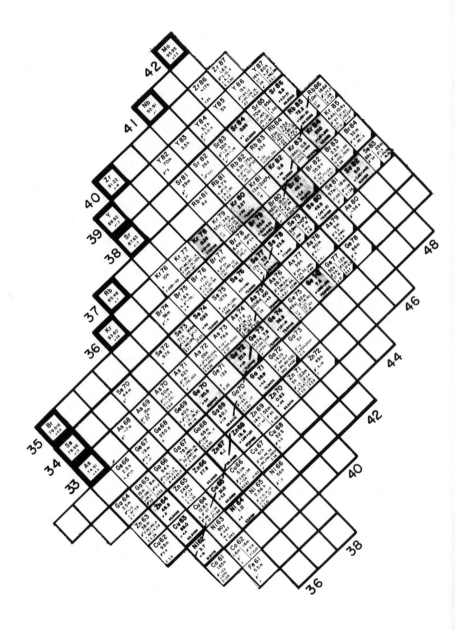

Fig. A-1. Chart of the Nuclides (*continued*).

FIG. A-1. Chart of the Nuclides (*continued*).

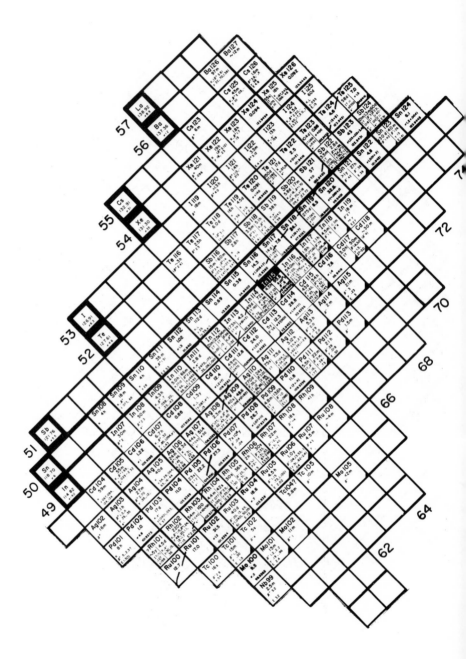

FIG. A-1. Chart of the Nuclides (*continued*).

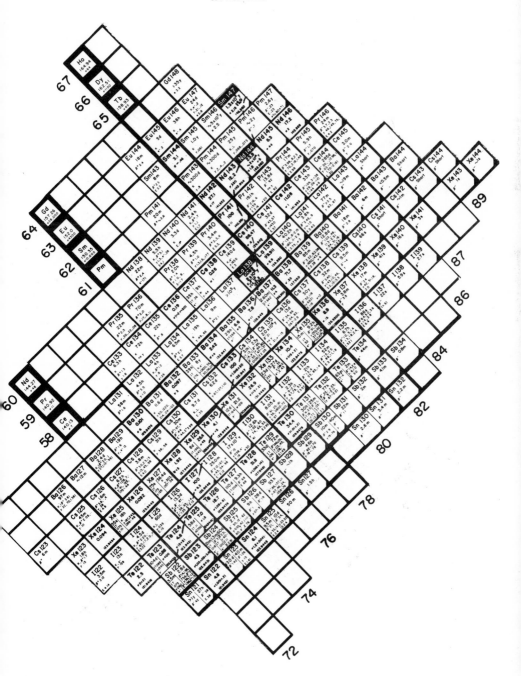

Fig. A-1. Chart of the Nuclides (*continued*).

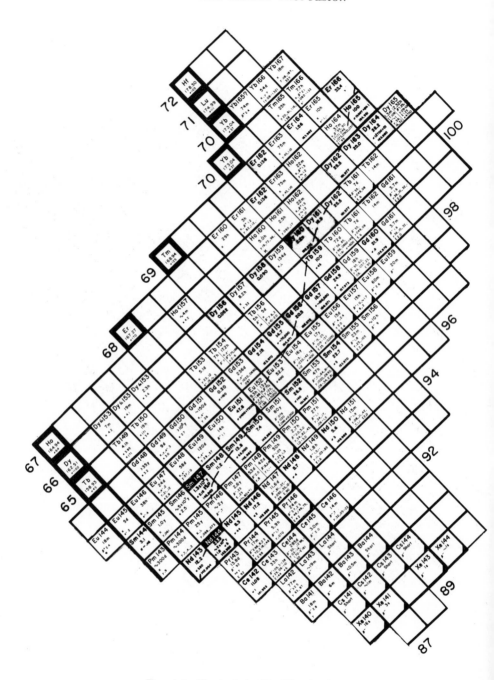

Fig. A-1. Chart of the Nuclides (*continued*).

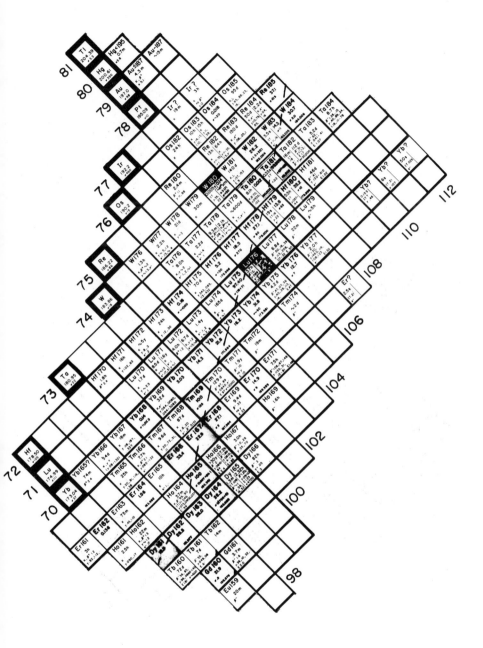

FIG. A-1. Chart of the Nuclides (*continued*).

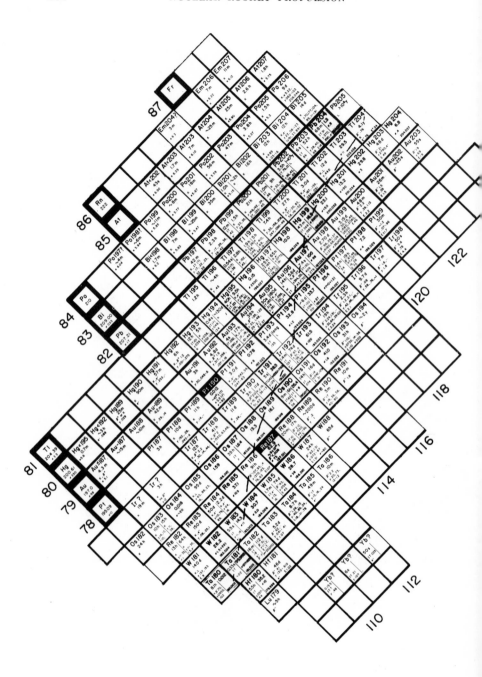

FIG. A-1. Chart of the Nuclides (*continued*).

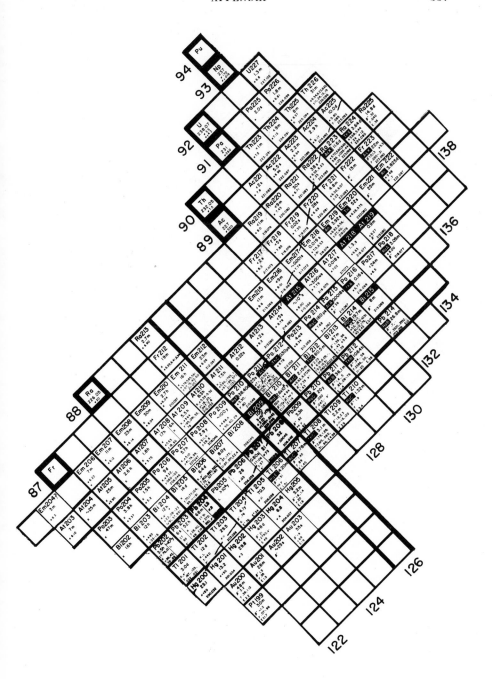

Fig. A-1. Chart of the Nuclides (*continued*).

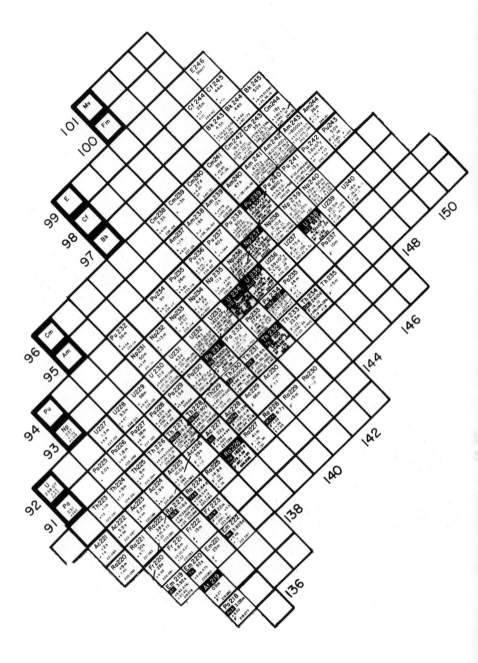

FIG. A-1. Chart of the Nuclides (*continued*).

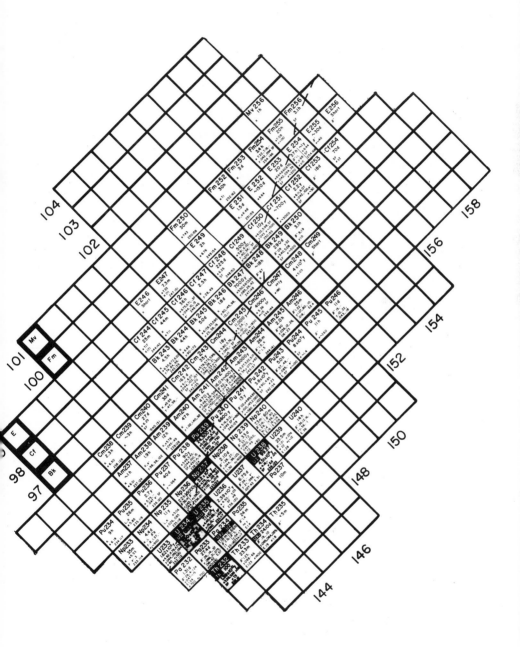

Fig. A-1. Chart of the Nuclides (*continued*).

INDEX

Absorption, energy coefficients of, 226, 227
  of gamma rays, 223–230, 233
    build-up factor, 224, 225
    mass coefficients of, 226–228
  of neutrons, 191, 230–232
Acceleration, launch, optimum, 11, 12, 46, 82, 83
Accelerators (see Particle accelerator)
Adiabatic wall temperature, 47, 49, 87, 88
Advanced systems, fission power for, 319
    direct momentum, 319
    fission-fragment heating, 319–322
    gaseous reactors, 322–327
    nuclear-electric plants, 328–330
    particle accelerators, 330–339
    thermomechanical cycles, 327, 328
  fusion power for, 314
  performance of, 312, 338, 339
  radioisotope-decay power for, 316–319
Aerodynamic drag, 9
Aerodynamic heating, 46–50, 89
Aerodynamic lift, 9, 10
Age theory (see Fermi age theory)
Age-to-thermal in moderators, 201, 202
Air scattering, 234
  attenuation factors, effective, 233
    gammas, 235, 236
    neutrons, 237–241
      fast, 237–239
      thermal, 241
Alcohol, 27–29, 32
  ethyl, 26–28, 34, 39, 41, 42
  methyl, properties of, 27, 28, 34, 39, 41, 42
Alpha emitters, 316, 317
Aluminum, nuclear properties of, 227, 228, 296
  physical properties of, 154
  radiation effects on, 187
    ductility, 187
  scattering cross sections of, 231
Ammonia, 24–34, 36, 39, 41, 42, 56, 150
  heat-transfer coefficient of, 49
  moderating properties of, 157
  nuclear properties of, 158
  nuclear-vehicle performance with, 65, 68, 70, 71, 76, 77, 80
Amplifiers, operational, 261–264

Analog computer, 260–263
  computing circuits, 262
  (See also Simulation)
Analog methods, 115, 116
Atmosphere, density of, 11, 12
  effect on missile performance, 9–13
Atomic number of elements, 347
Atomic weight of materials (see Nuclear properties; Physical properties)
Attenuation factors, air scattering (see Air scattering)
  shadow shielding, 234–236
Attenuation length for gamma rays, 226
Avogadro number, 346

Ballistic flight, 14
  ground range, 14–16
    as function of burnout velocity, 15
Batteries for electrical heating, 278–280
Beryllium, as moderating material, 149, 156
  nuclear properties of, 158, 201, 227, 228
  physical properties of, 150
  radiation effects on, 184
    ductility, 187
  scattering cross section of, 231
Beryllium oxide, as moderating material, 149, 156
  nuclear properties of, 158, 201
  physical properties of, 150
  radiation effects on, 185
Beta radiation, decay energy from fission products, 291, 292, 316
  emitters (see Radioisotopes)
Biological effects of radiation, 305, 306
  dose rates (see Dose rates)
  dose units, 306, 307
  exposure, 305
  specific ionization, 305
Boltzmann's constant, 346
Bootstrapping, 245
Borides, metallic, as fuel-element material, 148
Boron, absorption cross section of, 161
  as control-rod material, 151
  nuclear characteristics of, 156, 159, 161
  physical properties of, 152
  thermal-neutron absorption of, 161

361

Boron carbide, as control-rod material, 151
  physical properties of, 152
  radiation effects on, 186
Boundary-layer equations, 89–92
Branching ratio of fusion reactions, 314
Buckling, definition of, 200
Buckling equations for bare reactors, 201
Build-up factor, 224
  for gamma-ray absorption, 225
  for various materials, 225
Burnout velocities, of chemical vehicles, 72, 73, 75–77
  of multistage vehicles, 75
  of nuclear vehicles, 68–70, 76
  and particle accelerators, 335

Cadmium, absorption cross section of, 161
  as control-rod material, 151, 152
  and liquid, 152
  nuclear characteristics of, 159, 161
  physical properties of, 152
  radiation effects on, 186
Carbides, metallic, 145, 148, 155
Carbon (see Graphite)
Cavity reactor, 210–212
  critical conditions of, 211
  fuel densities in, 326
Center-of-mass coordinate system, 190
Charge-to-mass ratio of charged particle, 331, 333
Chemical vehicle, 65, 70, 72–75
  burnout velocities of, 72, 73, 75–77
  performance parameters of, 74
Choking in compressible flow, 134
Chromium, some nuclear properties of, 296
Closed-loop system, 255
Coatings, protective, against corrosion, 178
Cobalt, some nuclear properties of, 296
Collision (see Scattering)
Comparative analysis of vehicles, 60, 61, 76, 77
Compensated ion chamber, 275, 276
Components, of control system, 245–247
  of rocket power plant, weight of, 45, 50–60, 63
  testing of (see Testing)
Compton scattering, of gamma rays, 223, 224, 226
  interaction coefficients of materials, 228
Conduction, 106–116
  by analog methods, electrical, 115
    hydraulic, 115, 116
    magnetic, 115, 116
  Fourier equation of, 107, 114
  general equation of, 106
  nonsteady-state, in slab, 109
  by numerical methods, relaxation, steady-state, 110–113
    unsteady-state, 113, 114

Conduction, steady-state, in concentric spherical shell, 108
  in cylinder, 108, 109
  in slab, 108
Conductivity (see Thermal conductivity)
Continuity equation, 89, 91, 125
Contraction coefficient, for plenum effects, 124
Control-element material, nuclear properties of, 151, 159, 161, 162
  physical properties of, 152
  radiation effects on, 186
  requirements of, 140
  temperature in, 140
Control system, block diagram of, 246
  components of, 245–247
  dynamics equations, 248, 249
  instrumentation (see Control-system instrumentation)
  operation, 268–272
  performance, 245–247
  simulation, 260–267
  stability of, 257–260
  testing of, 289, 290
Control-system analysis, feedback concept, 254–257
  mathematical methods for, 247–260
  for stability, 257–260
Control-system instrumentation, block diagram of, 274
  compensated ion chamber, 275, 276
  fission chambers, 275
  proportional counters, 274, 275
  range of coverage, 273
Control-system operation, power range, 271
  shutdown, 271, 272
  start-up, 268
Controllers, 245–247
Convective heat transfer, coefficients of, 47–49, 58, 86–88, 96, 105
  experimental correlation of, 100–102
  by forced convection, 91, 92
  by free convection, 92
  in laminar flow, 92, 101, 103
  in packed spheres, 102, 103
  in porous flow, 96–98
  in turbulent flow, 93–96, 100, 101, 104
Conversion factors, 341–343
Coolant flow, distribution of, 163, 164
Cooling time, 291, 292
Coordinate system, of bare reactors, 200
  center-of-mass, 190
  laboratory, 190
Copper, some nuclear properties of, 296
Core geometry, heterogeneous, 220, 221
  homogeneous, 200, 201, 208–211, 219, 220
  interaction effects in, 162–164
  packed-sphere, 118
  solid-rod, 117, 118
  stacked-plate, 116, 117
  tube. 117

Corrosion, of graphite, 179
  of metals, 179
  protection against, by coatings, 178–181
    by neutral propellants, 180
Creep, rate of, 174, 175
  thermal stresses and, 165, 173–178
Creep properties, of graphite, 144, 177
  of molybdenum, 147
  of tantalum, 147
Critical assemblies, 283–287
  devices for, Honeycomb, 285, 286
    Jezebel, 284, 285
  test facilities for, 286, 287
Critical mixtures, material densities
    used, 210
  U^{235}, and Be, 209
    and C, 211
    and BeO, 210
    and C, 211
    and D_2O, 208
    and H_2O, 208
Critical reactor, cavity type, 211, 326
  material constituency in, 199
    (See also Critical mixtures)
  size of bare geometry for, 199
    minimum volume, 201
Criticality, conditions of, 191, 192
  equations for, 199, 200
Cross sections, absorption, 155, 159–161
  of some moderators, 158, 201
  fission, 160
  fusion, 315
  macroscopic, 155, 158
  Maxwellian averaged, 160
  microscopic, 155, 158, 160
  for monoenergetic neutrons, 160
  scattering, 158, 231
Cyclohexane, properties of, 150, 158

Dead load, 2, 60
Decay energy, from fission products,
    316, 317
  of radioisotopes, 318
Decay power, of beta radiation, 291
  of gamma radiation, 291
  after shutdown, 291, 292
Delayed neutrons, 190, 214–216, 270
  precursors of, 212, 214–216
  in reactor control, 190, 264, 270
  in reactor kinetics, 214–216
  time-dependent equation of, 214, 249,
    264
Density of materials (see Nuclear prop-
    erties; Physical properties)
Detection meters (see Instrumentation)
Diffusion equation, 196
  approximate methods of analysis, 198
  limitations of, 196, 197
  multigroup analysis of, 203, 204
  time-dependent, 214
Diffusion length, 200
  for matrix assemblies, 203
  of moderators, 201

Diffusivity, eddy, 94
  thermal, 107
Dissipation function, 90
Dissociation equations, 35–38
Dollar unit, 271
Dose rates, from fast neutrons, 237–239,
    308
  symmetrical source, 238
  from gamma source, symmetrical, 233,
    236, 237, 307, 308
  permissible exposure, 307
  and separation distance, 308
  from shadow shielding, 235, 242
  from thermal neutrons, 240–242, 308
Dose units, 306, 307
Drag, aerodynamic, of vehicle, 9

e-folding period, 214, 270
Eddy diffusivity, 94
Effective multiplication factor, 199, 269
Electrical heating, in component testing,
    278, 279
  by nuclear-electric system, 328–330
Electrostatic unit (esu), 306
Elements, list of, 347
Energy-absorption coefficients, 226
  of various materials, 227
Energy equation, 90, 91, 125
Equilibrium constants, 35–37
Equivalent diameter, 101, 123, 124
Erosion, of graphite, 178
  of metals, 178
Escape velocity, 16, 17
Ethyl alcohol, 26–28, 34, 39, 41, 42
Europium, absorption cross section of,
    161
  as control-rod material, 151, 152
  nuclear characteristics of, 159, 161
Excess multiplication factor, 249, 269
Excess reactivity, 212, 213
Exhaust velocities, of accelerated parti-
    cles, 332, 333
  ideal, 18–20
  of propellants, 41
  of real nozzles, 25
Experimental correlation, of heat trans-
    fer, 100–104
  laminar flow, 101–103
  packed spheres, 102, 103
  turbulent flow, 100, 101, 104
Exposure, to radiation, acute, 305
    chronic, 305
  permissible value of, 307
    (See also Dose rates)

Fast neutrons, 198, 204
Fatigue by thermal stress, 166, 167
Feedback, concept of, 254–257
Feedback system, 256, 257
Fermi age theory, 198, 199, 202
  time-dependent modifications, 214
Fission chambers, 275

Fission cross sections, 160
Fission density, distribution of, 164, 192
  in heterogeneous cores, 220, 221
  in homogeneous cores, 219, 220
Fission fragments, energy of, 221, 319
  energy loss, 321
  heating by, 319, 320
Fission process, 190–193
  decay energy from, 316–319
  direct momentum from, 319
  energy released in, 221
  time-dependent, 212–214
  (See also Reactor kinetics)
Fission products, chemically separated, 318
  as heat source, 318
  from thermal neutron fission, 316
  thermal power available from, 318
Fizzlers, 322
Flight tests, 292, 293
  test facilities for, 297, 299, 300
Flow stability, choking, 134
  in laminar-turbulent region, 128–132
  criteria for, 132, 133
  in porous flow, 132, 133
  in two-phase flow, 134, 135
Fluid friction, coefficients of, Kármán-
    Nikuradse relation, 123
  in laminar flow, 103, 123
  in porous flow, 98, 99
  in turbulent flow, 104, 123
  with heat addition, 124–127
Fluorine, chemical vehicle performance
    with, 72–77
Flux distribution (see Neutron flux)
Forces on vehicle, in earth's field, 8
  in free space, 7
Frequency response, 257
Friction (see Fluid friction)
Fuel element, material for, nuclear
    characteristics of, 139, 153, 156
  nuclear properties of, 153, 155, 156
  physical properties of, 142–149
  radiation effects on, 182, 183
  requirements of, 138, 139
  thermal conductivity of, 145
  thermal stresses in, 138, 145, 164, 165
Fuel loading, 193
Full-scale testing, flight, 292, 293
  for performance data, 288
  static, 288
  for structural capability, 288
Fusion cross sections, 315
Fusion energy, 314, 315
Fusion reactions, 314
  rates, 315

Gadolinium, absorption cross section of, 161
  as control-rod material, 151, 152
  nuclear characteristics of, 159, 161

Gadolinium oxide, as control-rod
    material, 152
  physical properties of, 152
Gamma ray, absorption of, 223, 226, 230
  activity of, induced in metals, 296
  air-scattering effects, 233–235
    with shadow shielding, 234, 235
  attenuation of, 224, 226, 233, 236
  Compton scattering of, 223, 224, 226
  decay energy of, from fission products,
      221, 222, 291
  power, 291, 292
  dose rates, 233, 236, 237, 307, 308
  emitters (see Radioisotopes)
  energy released in fission, 221, 291
  leakage of, 233
  shielding for, 234–237
  source strength of, 226
Gamma-ray flux, from infinite cylinder
    source, 225, 229
  leakage of, 233
  from planar source, 224, 229
  from spherical source, 225, 229
  spreading factor, 228
  for various geometries, 229
Gamma-ray heating, in structural
    materials, 152
  and thermal stress, 153, 164
Gas constant, universal, 344
Gaseous reactors, examples of, 323,
    325–327
  fizzlers, 322
  specific impulse of, 323
  system pressure, 324, 325
  weight-separation ratio, 324
Gases, molecular weight of, 39
  properties of, 30–35
  thermal conductivity of, 32
  viscosity of, 31
Graphite, corrosion of, 34, 35, 179
  creep properties of, 144, 176, 177
  as fuel-element material, 143, 156
  as moderator, 149, 156
  nuclear properties of, 155, 158, 227,
      228
  physical properties of, 145, 150
  radiation effects on, 182–184
  scattering cross section of, 158, 231
  tensile strength of, 143, 145
  thermal conductivity of, 142
    effect of neutron dose on, 184
Grashof number, 101, 102
Gravitation force, to mass-conversion
    factor, 88, 346
  variation of, with height, 11

Hafnium, physical properties of, 152
  radiation effects on, 186
Hagen-Poiseuille relation, 92, 93, 128
Harmonics, spherical, solution to trans-
    port equation, 195
Health hazards (see Biological effects of
    radiation)

Heat, of dissociation, 30
  mechanical equivalent of, value of, 88, 346
  of vaporization, 28
Heat capacity, 28, 33, 34
Heat transfer (see Conduction; Convective heat transfer)
Heavy water (D_2O), as moderator, 149, 156, 157
  nuclear properties of, 158, 201
  physical properties of, 150
  radiation effects on, 185
Heterogeneous cores, fission density distribution in, 220, 221
Homogeneous cores, bare reactors, 199–201
  critical mixtures of spheres, 208–211
  fission density distribution in, 219, 220
Honeycomb, critical assembly device, 285, 286
Hydraulic diameter (see Equivalent diameter)
Hydrazine, chemical vehicle performance with, 72–77
  properties of, 28, 29, 34, 39, 41, 42
Hydrides, metallic, as moderators, 151, 157
Hydrocarbons, as moderators, 157
  as propellants, 29, 33, 34
  (See also Methane; Octane; Propane)
Hydrogen, chemical vehicle performance with, 72–77
  corrosion by, 34, 35, 178–181
  dissociation parameter of, 40
  heat-transfer coefficient of, 48
  as moderator, 156, 157
  nuclear vehicle performance with, 68, 69, 71, 76, 79
  as propellant, 28–35, 39, 41, 42
  scattering cross section of, 231

Inconel, physical properties of, 154
Induced activities in metals, 296
In-pile tests, 280, 281, 283
Instrumentation, hydrodynamic, 301
  monitoring, 309, 310
  radiation-detection meters, 310–312
  structural, 301
  thermal, gas temperatures, 304
    pyrometry, optical, 302, 303
      radiation, 303, 304
    thermocouples, 302
  thrust, 304
  (See also Control-system instrumentation)
Interaction coefficients, for gamma photons, 226, 227
  of various materials, 228
Interaction effects, in core geometry, 162–164
  of flow scheme, 163, 164
  in material selection, 162, 163
Ion pairs, production of, 223, 305

Iron, nuclear properties of, 225, 296
  scattering cross section of, 231

Jezebel, critical assembly device, 284, 285

Kármán-Nikuradse relation, 123
Kinetics (see Reactor kinetics)

Laboratory coordinate system, 190
Laminar flow, experimental correlation of heat transfer, 101, 103
  friction coefficients in, 103, 123
  Hagen-Poiseuille relation in, 92, 93, 128
  recovery factor in, 89
  stability of, 131
Laplace equation, 107
Laplace transform, 250–254
  pairs, 253
Leakage, of gamma-ray flux, 233
  of neutrons, 195
    fast, 237
    thermal, 239, 240
Lift, aerodynamic, of vehicle, 9, 10
Light velocity, value of, in vacuum, 346
Linear systems, 247
Liquid propellants, critical pressures of, 28
  critical temperatures of, 28
  densities of, 26
  molecular weight of, 28
  properties of, 26–28
  thermal conductivity of, 28
  vapor pressures of, 27
  viscosity of, 28
Log-mean temperature difference, 58, 106

Mach number, 87, 125
Macroscopic cross sections, 155, 158
Magnetohydrodynamics, 339
Manganese, nuclear properties of, 296
Mass-absorption coefficients, 226–228
Mass-ratio equation, atmosphere effects on, 10
  complete, 11
  of vehicle, in earth's field, 8
    in free space, 7
    for multistages, 13
Materials, for control elements (see Control element)
  for fuel elements (see Fuel element)
  induced activities in, 296
  for moderators (see Moderators)
  radiation effects, factors causing, 181–187, 282
    sensitivity to, 282
  structural (see Structural material)
Materials-testing reactor (MTR), 283

Maximum permissible exposure (MPE), 307
Mechanical equivalent of heat, value of, 88, 346
Methane, properties of, 27, 28, 30–34, 39, 41, 42
Methyl alcohol, properties of, 27, 28, 34, 39, 41, 42
Microscopic cross sections, 155, 158, 160
Migration area, 202
Migration length, 202
   of some moderators, 201
Missile system generalized, 2, 3
Moderating ratio, 158, 159
Moderators, materials, liquids, 149
   nuclear characteristics of, 156, 157, 159
   nuclear properties of, 156–159, 201
   physical properties of, 149–151
   radiation effects on, 183–186
   requirements of, 139, 140
   tensile strength of, 150
   thermal conductivity of, 150
   thermal stresses in, 140, 149, 150
Molecular weight, of gases, 39
   of liquid propellants, 28
   (See also Nuclear properties; Physical properties)
Molybdenum, as fuel-element material, 146, 296
   nuclear properties of, 155
   physical properties of, 145
   radiation effects on, 187
   ductility, 187
   stress-time curves of, 147
   tensile strength of, 146
Momentum, direct from fission fragments, 319
   from particle accelerators, 330
   from radioisotopes, 317–319
Momentum equation, of fluid flow, 89, 91, 125
   of vehicle, in earth's field, 8
   in free space, 7
Monitoring, instrumentation, 310–312
   neutrons, 310
   of radiation, alpha particles, 309
   beta and gamma rays, 309
Monte Carlo method, for gamma absorption, 223
   for solution of diffusion equation, 193, 194
   with time dependence, 213
Multigroup method, material densities used in, 210
   multiregion, 205, 206
   solution to age-diffusion equation by, 204–211
   two-energy-group analysis, 198, 204–206
Multiplication factor, effective, 199, 200, 269
   and prompt critical, 214, 270
   excess, 249, 269
   infinite, 199, 200

Multistage vehicles, burnout velocities of, 75
   maximum performance of, 13, 14

Navier-Stokes equation, 89
Neutron absorption, 191, 230
Neutron cross sections (see Cross sections)
Neutron dose rates (see Dose rates)
Neutron energy, loss of, 197, 231, 232
   released in fission, 221
Neutron-energy groups, 198, 204
   shielding, for fast neutrons, 237–239
   for thermal neutrons, 239–242
Neutron flux, distribution of, 195–198, 205
   equations for bare geometries, 201
   by two-group method, 205
   time-dependent, 214–216
Neutron-flux leakage, of fast neutrons, 237
   of thermal neutrons, 239, 240
Neutron level, 192, 269, 270
Neutrons, delayed (see Delayed neutrons)
   generation of, 192
   leakage of, 195, 237, 239
   lifetime of, 214, 249, 269, 270
   monoenergetic, cross sections for, 160
   radiation damage by, 182–187
   resonance escape probability, 215
   scattering of (see Scattering)
   slowing-down equation, 197
   thermal base energy of, 204
Nickel, nuclear properties of, 227, 228, 296
Niobium, as fuel-element material, 142, 148
   nuclear properties of, 155, 156
   physical properties of, 145
   tensile strength of, 146
Niobium carbide, 145, 148, 155
   as protective coating, 178
Niobium nitride, 148
Nitrides, metallic, as fuel-element material, 148
Noncircular-flow passages, equivalent diameter of, 101, 123, 124
Nonlinear systems, 250
Nonnuclear testing, 278, 279
   by electrical heating, 278
Nozzle, area ratio, 21
   discharge coefficient, 23
   efficiency of, 19
   exhaust velocity of, ideal, 18, 20
   maximum, 19, 41
   real, 25
   isentropic expansion in, 18
   losses, 22, 23
   reduced velocity of, 23
   throat area, 21
   weight of, 59, 60

Nuclear properties, of control-rod material, 151, 159, 161, 162
  of fuel-element material, 153, 155, 156
  of moderator material, 156–159, 201
  of structural material, 162
Nuclear rocket (*see* Nuclear vehicle)
Nuclear testing, with critical assemblies, 283–287
  with in-pile tests, 280–283
Nuclear vehicle, burnout velocities of, 68–70, 76
  comparative analysis of, 76, 77
  component weight coefficients, 63
  control (*see* Control system)
  performance, with ammonia, 68, 70, 71, 80
    generalized, 64–67
    with hydrogen, 68, 69, 71, 79
    parameters, 71
  testing (*see* Testing)
Nuclides, chart of, 345–360
Numerical methods in conduction problems (*see* Conduction)
Nusselt number, 87, 100
Nyquist method of stability analysis, 259

Octane, properties of, 26–28
1/*v* law, 217
Open-loop system, 254, 255
Operational amplifiers for computers, 261–264
Optical pyrometry, 302, 303
Orbital velocity, 16, 17
  time of revolution, 17
Organic liquids, radiation effects on, 185, 186
Oxygen, chemical vehicle performance with, 72–77
  heat-transfer coefficient of, 48

Packed spheres, 118
Pair production, 223, 305
Particle accelerator, momentum from, 330
  performance of, 338, 339
  power requirements of, 331, 333
  propulsion system, 333
  specific weight, 332–335
  vehicle, 333
  velocity of particles, 331, 333, 335
Performance, comparative, 65, 76, 77
  of generalized nuclear vehicle, 61–67
  of particle accelerator, 338, 339
  (*See also* Chemical vehicle; Nuclear vehicle)
Period, range, 269
  instrumentation, 273
  of reactor, 214, 270
Physical constants, 344

Physical properties, of control-rod materials, 151, 152
  of fuel-element materials, 142–149
  of liquid propellants, 26–28
  of moderator materials, 149–151
  of structural materials, 152–154
Piping, weight of, 54
Planck's constant, 346
Plasma, 329
Plenum, contraction coefficient for, 124
  effects on flow, 123, 124
Poiseuille's law, 122
  (*See also* Hagen-Poiseuille relation)
Poisson's ratio (*see* Physical properties)
Porous flow, heat transfer, 96–98
  inertial coefficients of, 99
  resistance of, 98
  stability of, 132–134
  viscous coefficients of, 99
Power, to heat propellant, 24
  pumping, 55, 132, 248
  specific, 79, 80
    consumption by propellant, 42
    optimization of, 79, 80
  turbine, 55, 248
Power density of core, 77–80, 119–121
  and thermal stress, 171
Power output of core, 58
Prandtl number, 87
Precursors, delayed-neutron, in reactor kinetics, 212–214, 216
  time-dependent equation of, 214, 249, 264
Pressure, pump discharge, 52, 57, 248
  stagnation, 126
  system, optimized, 80, 81
  tank, 51
Pressure drop of flow, with heat addition, 124–127
  plenum effects, 123, 124
  Poiseuille's law for, 122
  in tubes, 92, 122, 123
Pressure shell, weight of, 57, 59
Prompt critical, 214, 270
Propane, properties of, 26–28, 34, 39, 41, 42
Propellant, criteria for, 24, 25
  exhaust velocities of, 41
  losses of, 46
  vaporization in tanks, 46, 49, 50
  volume, 51
  weight of, 46, 49–52
  (*See also* Gases; Liquid propellants)
Proportional counters, 274
Pump, discharge pressure, 52–55, 57, 248
  equipment, 52
  power required, 55, 248
    for porous flow, 132
  specific speed of, 53
  weight of, 52, 55, 56

Rad unit, 306
Radiation, biological effects (*see* Biological effects of radiation)

Radiation damage (*see* Radiation effects)
Radiation-detection meters, 310–312
Radiation dose units, defined, 306, 307
  expected, 307, 308
  (*See also* Dose rates)
Radiation effects, in control-element
    material, 186
  and damage, cause of, 181, 182
    factors in, 282
  in fuel elements, 182–184
  in metals, 296
  in moderators, 183–186
  in organic liquids, 185, 186
  sensitivity of engineering properties
    to, 282
  in structural materials, 186, 187
  in water and D_2O, 185
Radiation monitoring, 309, 310
Radiation pyrometry, 303, 304
Radiation safety, 309
Radioisotopes, α, β, and γ emitters, 316,
    317
  artificially produced, 318
  chart of nuclides, 345–360
  decay energy of, 318
  from fission, 316, 318
  as heat sources, 317, 318
  momentum from, 317–319
Rate phenomena, 38
Reaction rates, of chemical recombina-
    tion, 38, 39
  of nuclear fusion, 315
Reactivity, coefficient of, 216, 217
  effect on, of geometry, 218
    of material density, 217
    of propellant, 218
    of temperature, 217, 290
  definition of, 269
  excess, 212, 213
  influences on, 213
  magnitude of effects, 213, 214
Reactor calculations, results of, 207–212
  (*See also* Critical mixtures)
Reactor computation codes, availability
    of, 207
Reactor core, geometries of, 116–118,
    219–221
  power of, density, 58, 119
    output, 58, 78
    specific, 77–80
    weight of, 58
Reactor design, for flight test, 166
  for ground test, 166
  and thermal stresses, 164–167
Reactor kinetics, delayed-neutron effects,
    214
  equations of, 214–216, 264
  diffusion equation, 214, 215
  Fermi age modification, 215
  reactivity coefficients, 216–219
  simulation of, 264–267
Reactor period, 270
  e-folding time, 214, 270

Reactor statics, criticality, 192, 199–201
  fission reaction, 190–193
  mathematical methods, 193–207
    age-diffusion theory, 198–207
    Boltzmann transport equation, 195
    Monte Carlo, 193, 194
  results of calculations, 207–212
  (*See also* Critical mixtures)
Recovery factor, defined, 88
  in laminar flow, 89
  in turbulent flow, 89
Reflector, requirements, 57, 139, 140,
    149, 151
  (*See also* Moderators)
  savings, 202
  weight, 58
Relative biological effectiveness (RBE),
    307
Relaxation methods in conduction,
    110–113
Rem unit defined, 307
Remote-control operation, 287, 296–298
Rep unit defined, 306
Resonance escape probability, 215
Reynolds analogy, 93–96, 104, 126
Reynolds number, 87, 103
  critical, 93
  modified, 102
Rhenium, as fuel-element material,
    142, 148
  nuclear properties of, 155
  physical properties of, 145
  tensile strength of, 146
Rhm unit defined, 306
Rocket motor weight, 57–60
Roentgen unit, 306
Root-locus method of stability analysis,
    259
Routh's criterion for stability, 258

Satellites, orbital characteristics of, 14,
    16, 17
Scattering, air (*see* Air scattering)
  Compton, of gammas, 223, 224, 226
    interaction coefficients, 228
  of neutrons, elastic, 190, 191
    forward, 156, 191
    inelastic, 191
    up in energy, 218
Scattering cross sections, 158, 231
Shear stress in fluids, 92–96, 103
Shielding, material absorption equation,
    233
  shadow, attenuation factors of, 234–236
    dose rates from, 235, 242
    for fast neutrons, 237–239
    for gamma rays, 234–237
    for thermal neutrons, 239–242
Shutdown decay power, 291, 292
Simulation, of control system, 260–267
  with electronic analog computer,
    260–264
  of reactor kinetics, 264–267

Slowing down of neutrons, approxima-
    tions in, 198
  equation for, 197
  in hydrogen, 198
Slowing-down length, 202
  of moderators, 201
Slowing-down power of moderators,
    198, 199
Solid rods, 117, 118
Source range, 268
  instrumentation for, 273, 274
Specific heats, of gases, at constant
    temperature, 33
  effective heat capacity, with dis-
      sociation, 41
  mean, 34
  synthetic ratio of, 41
  of liquid propellants, 28
Specific impulse, actual, 24
  from fission, 320
  from fusion, 314
  of gaseous reactor systems, 323–325
  ideal, 21
  of particle-accelerator systems, 334,
    335
Specific ionization, 305
Specific speed of pump, 53
Specific weight, of nuclear-electric
    generators, 338
  of particle accelerators, 332, 338
  of pump, 52, 55, 56
  of reactors, 337
  of turbine compressors, 338
Stability, control-system analysis for,
    257–260
  flow (see Flow stability)
Stacked plates, 116, 117
Stagnation pressure, 126
Stagnation temperature, 88, 125
Stanton number, 101, 104
State equation, 90, 91, 125
Steel, stainless, physical properties of,
    154
  radiation effects on, 187
  ductility, 187
Stefan-Boltzmann constant, 346
Strain (see Thermal strain)
Strength (see Tensile strength)
Stress (see Thermal stress)
Structural materials, for components, 141
  gamma heating in, 141, 152
  nuclear properties of, 162
  physical properties of, 152–154
  radiation effects on, 186, 187
  thermal conductivity of, 154
  thermal stresses in, 152–154
Structural weight, 51, 57–60
Systems, advanced and exotic (see
    Advanced systems)
  control, 244–247
  missile, 2
Systems analysis, 45
  limitations of, 82, 84
  optimization by, 77–83

Tank, propellant, overpressure in, 51
  volume of, 51
  weight of, 51–53
Tantalum, as fuel-element material, 142,
    148
  hydride embrittlement of, 179
  nuclear properties of, 155, 156, 296
  physical properties of, 145
  stress-time curves of, 147
  tensile strength of, 146
Tantalum carbide, 145, 148, 155
  as protective coating, 178
Tantalum nitride, 148
Temperature, adiabatic wall, 47, 49, 87
  in control element, 140
  effect of, on reactivity, 217, 290
  stagnation, 88, 125
Temperature coefficient of reactivity,
    217, 290
Temperature difference, log-mean, 58,
    106
Temperature distribution and thermal
    stresses, 167
Temperature measurement (see Instru-
    mentation)
Tensile strength, of graphite, 143, 145
  of metals, 145, 146, 154
  of moderators, 150
Test facilities, for critical assemblies, 286,
    287
  for flight tests, 297, 299, 300
    range safety, 299
  for gamma-source preparation, 297
  instrumentation, 299
  for remote handling, 296, 297
  requirements for, 287, 300
  static test stands, for chemical systems,
      294, 295
    for nuclear systems, 293–296
Testing, of components, 277–287
  nonnuclear, 278, 279
  nuclear, 279–287, 290
  of control system, 289, 290
  facilities for (see Test facilities)
  flight tests, 292, 293
  full-scale, 288, 289
  instrumentation (see Instrumentation)
Thermal conductivity, of control-rod ma-
    terials, 152
  of fuel-element materials, 145
  of gases, 32
  of graphite, 142
    effect of radiation on, 184
  of liquid propellants, 28
  of moderator materials, 150
  of structural materials, 154
Thermal diffusivity, 107
Thermal neutrons (see Neutron energy
    groups)
Thermal strain, elastic, 167–173
  inelastic, 173–178
Thermal stress, and core power density,
    171
  and creep, 165, 173–178

Thermal stress, equations for, 167–177
  fatigue by, 166, 167
  in flat plates, 170–173
  in fuel elements, 138, 145, 164, 165
  general, 164–167
  in moderators, 140, 149, 150
  and reactor design, 164–167
  reduction in allowables, 166, 167
  in rods, 168, 169, 172
  in spheres, 168, 169, 172
  in structural materials, 152–154
  and temperature distribution, 167
  transient, 175, 176
  in tubes, 168–173
Thermal-utilization factor, 203
Thermocouples, high-temperature, 302
Thermomechanical cycles, 327, 328
  shock-tube, 328
Thermonuclear process, 314, 315
Thrust, actual, 24
  equation, for, 10
  ideal, 21
  of particle accelerators, 330, 331
    thrust-to-weight ratio, 335
  variable, 8
Thrust structure, weight of, 57, 60
Titanium, nuclear properties of, 296
  physical properties of, 154
Transfer function, 253
Transport equation, Boltzmann, 195–198
  diffusion approximation, 196–198
Tubes, core generating of, 117
  thermal stresses in, 168–173
Tungsten, as fuel-element material, 142, 144
  nuclear properties of, 155, 156, 296
  physical properties of, 145
  tensile strength of, 146
Tungsten carbides, 145, 148, 155
Tungsten nitrides, 148
Turbine, power of, 55, 56, 248
  weight of, 54
Turbulent flow, experimental correlation
  of heat transfer, 93–96, 100, 101, 104
  friction coefficients in, 96, 104, 123
  heat-transfer coefficient in, 96, 100, 101, 104
  recovery factor in, 89
  stability of, 128–133
Two-phase flow, 134, 135

U^{235}, in cavity reactors, 211
  critical mixtures of, 208–211
  energy released in fission of, 221

V-2 rocket, 45, 47
$1/v$ law, 217
Valves, weight of, 54
Vapor pressure of liquid propellants, 27
Vehicle performance, in earth's field, 7, 8
  in free space, 6, 7
  optimization of, 77–83
  (See also Chemical vehicle; Multistage
    vehicles; Nuclear vehicle)
Velocity, burnout (see Burnout velocities)
  escape, 16, 17
  exhaust (see Exhaust velocities)
  of light, value of, in vacuum, 346
Viscosity, eddy, 94
  of gases, 31
  of liquid propellants, 28
Void fraction, of packed spheres, 118
  of stacked plates, 117

Water (H$_2$O), heat-transfer coefficients
  for, 48
  as moderator, 149, 157
  nuclear properties of, 201, 225
  physical properties of, 26–28, 33, 34
  as propellant, 27, 31
  radiation effects on, 185
Weight, atomic, of materials (see Nuclear
    properties; Physical properties)
  coefficient of, 63
  of components, 45
  of nozzle, 59, 60
  of particle accelerator, 332–335
  of piping, 54
  of pressure shell, 57, 59
  of propellant, 46, 49–52
  of pumping equipment, 54, 56
  of pumps, 52, 55, 56
  of reactor core, 58
  of reflector, 58
  of rocket motor, 57–60
  of structure, 51, 57–60
    thrust, 60
  of tanks, 51–53
  of turbine, 54
  of valves, 54
Wigner effect, 181

Zinc, nuclear properties of, 296
Zirconium, nuclear properties of, 296
Zirconium carbide, 145, 148, 155
  as protective coating, 178
Zirconium hydride, hydrogen density in, 151
  nuclear properties of, 157, 158
  specific gravity of, 150
Zirconium nitride, 148